NEUROBIOLOGICAL ASPECTS
OF PSYCHOPATHOLOGY

Officers of the

AMERICAN PSYCHOPATHOLOGICAL ASSOCIATION

for 1967-1968

Benjamin Pasamanick, M.D., *President* ...... New York, New York

Joel Elkes, M.D., *President-Elect* .... Baltimore, Maryland

Barbara Fish, M.D., *Vice-President* .... New York, New York

Fritz A. Freyhan, M.D., *Secretary* .... New York, New York

Murray Glusman, M.D., *Treasurer* .... New York, New York

Milton Greenblatt, M.D., *Councillor* .... Boston, Massachusetts

Bernard C. Glueck, Jr., M.D., *Councillor* ...... Hartford, Connecticut

Committee on Program

Joseph Zubin, Ph.D. .... New York, New York

Charles Shagass, M.D. .... Philadelphia, Pennsylvania

NEUROBIOLOGICAL ASPECTS OF PSYCHOPATHOLOGY

Edited by **JOSEPH ZUBIN, Ph.D.**
Department of Mental Hygiene, State of New York; Department of Psychology, Columbia University, New York City

and **CHARLES SHAGASS, M.D.**
Eastern Pennsylvania Psychiatric Institute, Philadelphia, Pennsylvania

THE PROCEEDINGS OF THE FIFTY-EIGHTH ANNUAL MEETING OF THE AMERICAN PSYCHOPATHOLOGICAL ASSOCIATION, HELD IN NEW YORK CITY, FEBRUARY, 1968.

GRUNE & STRATTON

NEW YORK • LONDON • 1969

SAMUEL W. HAMILTON AWARDS

Name		Symposium
Clarence P. Oberndorf, M.D.	1952	Depression
John C. Whitehorn, M.D.	1953	Psychiatry and the Law
David M. Levy, M.D.	1954	Psychopathology of Childhood
Stanley Cobb, M.D.	1955	Experimental Psychopathology
Sandor Rado, M.D.	1956	Psychopathology of Communication
Karl M. Bowman, M.D.	1957	Problems of Addiction and Habituation
Bernard Glueck, Sr., M.D.	1958	Trends in Psychoanalysis
Sir Aubrey Lewis, M.D.	1959	Comparative Epidemiology in the Mental Disorders
Franz J. Kallmann, M.D.	1960	Psychopathology of Aging
Nolan D. C. Lewis, M.D.	1961	Future of Psychiatry
Franz Alexander, M.D.	1962	Evaluation of Therapy
Heinrich Klüver, Ph.D.	1963	Psychopathology of Perception
Paul H. Hoch, M.D.	1964	Psychopathology of Schizophrenia
Curt P. Richter, Ph.D.	1965	Comparative Psychopathology
George A. Jervis, M.D., Ph.D.	1966	Psychopathology of Mental Development

PAUL H. HOCH AWARDS

Name		Symposium
Barbara Wootton, Lady Wootton of Abinger	1967	Social Psychiatry
Joseph Zubin, Ph.D.	1968	Neurobiological Aspects of Psychopathology

HENRY M. AND LILLIAN STRATTON AWARDS

Name		Symposium
James Birren, Ph.D.	1960	Psychopathology of Aging
Benjamin Pasamanick, M.D.	1961	Future of Psychiatry
Heinz E. Lehmann, M.D.	1962	Evaluation of Therapy
Charles W. Eriksen, Ph.D.	1963	Psychopathology of Perception
Ronald Melzack, Ph.D.	1963	Psychopathology of Perception
Robert W. Payne, Ph.D.	1964	Psychopathology of Schizophrenia
Kurt Salzinger, Ph.D.	1964	Psychopathology of Schizophrenia
David A. Rogers, Ph.D.	1965	Comparative Psychopathology

Library of Congress Catalog Card Number 69-16219

Copyright © 1969
Grune & Stratton, Inc.
381 Park Avenue South
New York, N.Y. 10016
Printed in U.S.A. (K-A)

CONTENTS

PREFACE

THE MAIN PURPOSE of this symposium was to review current knowledge of central nervous system biology as it may pertain to the behavior of the mentally ill. The majority of the papers thus deal with biological observations that more or less directly reflect the state of organization of the central nervous system itself, such as its electrical activity and chemistry. The intention of the program committee was to focus more on the brain itself than on ecological, developmental, or other partly exogenous influences.

The papers of this symposium contain many hopeful indications that knowledge is accumulating about the nature of deviant central nervous system activity in psychiatric disorders. Clearly, the available knowledge is not yet sufficient for practical application in diagnosis or for guiding therapeutic interventions, except within a limited range. However, the symposium contributes some direction and perhaps methodological advances toward the general goal of obtaining more objective assessment of psychopathological behavior using neurobiological methods. It is possible, then, to expect some advance toward freeing the detection, diagnosis, and prognosis of mental disorders from the network of social-cultural factors that we know prevent basic comparisons with regard to incidence, prevalence, and course of illness between countries and between regions of the same country. Discovery of the more basic aspects of mental disorders may help to reveal some of the etiological factors underlying them; this may hasten scientific understanding and make possible more adequate intervention.

The editors acknowledge with gratitude the contribution of David Jenness to the planning of the symposium and the editing of this volume.

JOSEPH ZUBIN, PH.D.
CHARLES SHAGASS, M.D.

vii

JOSEPH ZUBIN

JOSEPH ZUBIN

Paul H. Hoch Award Lecturer, 1968

HE NAME OF Joseph Zubin has been linked with the American
Psychopathological Association for so long—and with its recent
history, its style and published achievements—that it carries its own
introduction to the Hoch Award Lecture for this year, or for any other
year. The names and the work of these two important but quite
different men have been so often joined, in fact, as to lend to them a
sort of "corporate identity," not only in the mind of the beginning
student of psychopathology but in the memory of colleagues and con-
temporaries as well. Paul Hoch is twice honored by the lecture given
this year in his name by his old friend and longtime working partner.

Joseph Zubin was born with our century in October of 1900, in
Rasseinai, Lithuania. The family, in which Joseph was the second of
six children and the oldest son, reached America during his early
boyhood and settled in Baltimore, Maryland. The events of his early
life that brought the young Zubin first to the study of psychology and
later to biometrics and psychopathology need not be traced out in
detail here, for we are concerned more with his lasting contribution
to our field of study and with his mature character as a teacher and
investigator. It may be useful to recall, however, that his discovery of
our particular knot of problems came about only gradually and through
his early work in community youth organizations with their typically
human-centered value systems and goals. I have always thought this
beginning was of lasting importance to him and a key to understanding a central theme found in much of his later scientific work. A
naturally analytic young mind—easily drawn to the study of chemistry,
German or mathematics—became early joined to the need to study
certain very human problems in a quantitative way. It has been said
that in the field of psychopathology both clinician and scientist must
deal with subjective phenomena. Those few men who can turn a
judgment about inner, personal experience into outer, objective notation—even if they succeed only in part—thus stand to make a fundamental contribution to psychopathology as a science. Far from a dis-
regard for the importance of the data of individual experience in a
rush to quantification, it is clear that any lasting value to come from
this approach will depend entirely on a skillful interpretation of the

nature of subjective evidence. Professor Zubin's legacy to us may be exactly so described.

He came to the task well prepared. Following undergraduate training at Johns Hopkins he entered graduate study at Columbia University, and was awarded the doctorate in psychology by a distinguished faculty—though at a rather unfortunate moment, the low point of the national economic depression, 1932. He found a teaching position as Instructor in Psychometry at the Columbia College of Physicians and Surgeons and, with borrowed money and characteristic optimism, married Winifred M. P. Anderson in 1934. Two sons, Jonathan and David, and a daughter, Winifred Anne, were born to the Zubins— children who have today reached astonishing heights (the boys, at least) that reflect the dashing Scots Guard who was their maternal grandfather. Dr. Zubin has since held teaching positions at the City College of New York, briefly, and at Columbia University, where he has been both Professor of Psychology (currently) and of Psychiatry. Concurrent with these academic appointments he has also served the State of New York in a research capacity for many years and is, at present, Chief of Psychiatric Research (Biometrics) within the New York State Department of Mental Hygiene, directing the work of an interdisciplinary staff of some 80 people from headquarters at the Psychiatric Institute in New York City.

In his earliest published work, one can discern three main themes or "factors," which might be the more appropriate term to use in analyzing the life of a biometrician. These emergents recur in a more evolved form throughout the remainder of his scholarly and scientific writing. *Factor I* falls in a cluster defined by experimental work on motivation, rivalry, "like-mindedness," and personality adjustment. *Factor II* is best described by published mathematical–statistical notes on transformation functions, probability, error terms, measures of the internal consistency of test-items, and pioneering use of factor analysis and covariance analysis in psychology.

Factor III, which is more widely dispersed (as is typical of factors numbered III), ranges from writings on choosing a life work through a psychometric evaluation of the Rorschach test to analyses of regional patterns in the hospitalization and care of patients with mental disease.

Robert S. Woodworth said, in his well-known autobiography, that there were actually only a few recurrent ideas in his own (seemingly remarkably varied) scientific activity over a lifetime, and suggested that this may be true of us all. What is remarkable in Dr. Zubin's work is not only the early appearance and persistence of certain consistent themes or ideas, but the fact that one does not usually find these particular clusters of interest in the same person. Of equal importance is an unmistakable trend toward growth in each area through time to a maturity in which these very different kinds of experience could be combined effectively and uniquely for his generation. This last must be given a particular emphasis, for as we see him going about his work today—setting an example for young scientists of abnormal behavior—it may seem that his biometric approach to the psychological factors associated with psychopathology is straightforward and direct and was ever thus. It does seem simple, in retrospect, as do most basic scientific and artistic organizing insights. This valuable legacy, which combines an abiding concern for those human misfortunes called psychopathology with knowledge of analytic concepts drawn from systematic psychology and mathematical statistics, has pointed a way in which we all can learn. In his person, as in all of his later writings, he embodies this useful and simple lesson: to quantify abnormal experience is essential if we are to bring it under scientific scrutiny. Any system of notation that distorts or fails to represent with sensitivity the qualitative nature of human experience, however, is no system at all.

The ability to instruct at a distance, by means of one's printed thought, is an essential attainment for all intellectual pioneers. This ability is enriched and given a more human dimension by adding some of the complementary details of individual teaching style and personal character. The prime element of an authentic teacher, we know, is not any particular platform manner but a way of encouraging young people to come to grips with the tasks or problems they have chosen for themselves. Dr. Zubin is known to many of you, as he is to me, to be specially gifted in this way. His personal warmth and openness and willingness to give of his time and thought is basic, of course, but the key quality may rest in what might be called his intellectual democracy. By this term I mean to pay homage to the natural acceptance that he has always given to the greenest and most unsophisticated of student ideas; by listening to them, helping to shape them and improve them, applying thoughtful critique and urging reformulation, so that at the end the original idea—although vastly improved and readied for action by this skilled exchange—remains recognizably the property of the student. A different aspect of the same value or attitude is shown by the immediate, simple and warm introductions he has always made between young "beginners" and their professional "seniors," as though they really ought to know each other. We have learned little that is systematic about how to encourage creativeness, but reassuring the young and challenging the old is surely a part of it—an attitude that is intuitively practiced by this grand teacher. Among his peers, these same qualities, combined with the intensity of his concentration on a task, in an abstract sense, have made it simple and natural for him to cross traditional disciplinary boundaries and even long cherished trade-union picket lines—only to be welcomed on the other side.

Cheerfully absent-minded at times, in the best professorial tradition, good friend and proud husband and father—along the way be has somehow found time to serve actively on the editorial board of half a dozen scientific journals (including our own, *Comprehensive Psychiatry*), to wear the uniform of a Lieutenant Commander in the United States Public Health Service while serving as Chief Medical Statistician in the Psychobiology Program of the War Shipping Administration during World War II, to co-edit the two dozen volumes that record the annual meetings of this society, and to write well over a hundred published articles, as well as several volumes in his own name and in collaboration with others. He has taught as visiting professor in California, Hawaii and Wisconsin, and has instructed perennially in the postdoctoral institutes held for clinical psychologists by the American Psychological Association. I think that we need not be greatly concerned about whether he gave too much of himself to his work, or to ours, or to the affairs of this society. His visible joy at being among us and joining the fray against our common problems is answer enough.

Wearing lightly the sixty-eight years of our century that he has brought along with him, Dr. Zubin speaks to us this year in honor of his lifelong friend Paul Hoch, late Commissioner of the Department of Mental Hygiene of the State of New York and, like Zubin himself, one of Columbia's great teachers and a mainstay of our American Psychopathological Association. Like Moses of old, I think that Joseph Zubin has always known that he might glimpse the Promised Land, but not himself set foot on that yearned-for soil. He has been fulfilled by his effort to try to find a way to a more scientific understanding of the psychopathological experience. Uncertain himself about the hidden turnings in that tortured road, as are we all, he has maintained a durable conviction that a way can and must be found. We celebrate his untiring and resourceful effort toward discovery.

H. E. KING, PH.D.
Western Psychiatric Institute, Pittsburgh

1

EEG CORRELATES OF PSYCHOPATHOLOGY

by LEONIDE GOLDSTEIN, D.Sc., and
A. ARTHUR SUGERMAN, M.B., D.P.M., Med.D.Sc.*

Vingt fois sur le métier remettez votre ouvrage.—Boileau

IF THIS PAPER had been written ten years ago, it would have been negative or, at best, defensive, because at that time there were no clearcut, unequivocal EEG correlates of psychopathology. Since then, however, and especially during the last five years, a number of new facts have emerged that tend to indicate not only that the brain wave characteristics of certain mental patients are indeed different from those of non-psychotics, but that they also provide information on the nature of brain malfunction in such patients.

This new appreciation of the informational content of brain waves stems from three different sources. First, the introduction of mathematical and statistical processing of EEG signals has revealed features not previously detected by conventional visual inspection of brain wave records. Secondly, the rapid advances of neuropharmacology and psychopharmacology have brought to light interesting differences in EEG reactions to drugs between normal subjects and psychotic patients. Finally, the study of sleep patterns, in terms of definite EEG characteristics, has demonstrated differences not apparent from behavioral observations alone.

Since Dr. Feinberg deals with sleep changes in mental disorders in another paper in this volume, the present review will be devoted mainly to quantitative techniques applied to the resting EEG and to the effects of drugs. Earlier clinical findings are discussed briefly to illustrate how quantitative techniques differ from conventional procedures and to allow judgment of their relative merits.

This paper will be restricted to major psychoses, especially chronic schizophrenia, both because of time and space limitations and because

---

*N.J. Bureau of Research in Neurology and Psychiatry, Princeton.

1

of the scarcity of data on neurotics and acute patients in the drug-free condition. The present-day emphasis on urgent treatment and rapid discharge has made it impossible to obtain adequate samples of such patients who are not receiving a variety of medications. This has so far confounded our attempts to separate the EEG changes due to drugs from those associated with the underlying condition. In contrast, adequate samples of chronic patients may be tested at various stages of their illnesses, both without medication and with different types of pharmacotherapy.

Clinical EEG

Hess[1] reviewed studies relating EEG and psychopathology up to 1961; his conclusions, although pessimistic, are still valid. Despite the early hopes of Berger, the EEG has not been helpful in the diagnosis of endogenous psychosis; it has been practically useful only in the borderlands between neurology and psychiatry, and decisive only in epilepsy. Where the differential diagnostic problem may be solved by demonstrating an organic brain lesion, the EEG is invaluable; also, behavioral disorders in children, more rarely in adults, are sometimes clarified by an abnormal EEG pattern. The nature of the EEG changes depends on the severity and localization of the organic lesion, and especially on the degree of impairment of consciousness, rather than on the pathological nature of the lesion.

Cathryn Walters[2] reviewed a wide range of studies relating EEG to conditioning, reaction time, intelligence, general mental activity, personality factors and psychopathology. Her conclusions, covering the period up to 1962, were that few hypotheses had been substantiated; apart from a relationship of alpha-blocking time to anxiety, there seemed to be no definite relationships between EEG and psychological measures.

In the specific area of the psychotic disorders, few EEG findings are generally accepted as specifically characteristic and none appear to be diagnostic. Pauline Davis[3] stated 25 years ago that 61 per cent of schizophrenics showed "choppy" activity, which she regarded as indicating overstimulation or irritation of the cortex. She and Sulzbach were able to evoke this pattern in mescaline psychosis, but later workers have not substantiated these findings; Hill[4] believes they may be largely due to artifact, especially muscle potentials, and to the short time constants used in Davis's recording technique. Gibbs and Gibbs[5] have described a variety of mitten pattern, the B or fast mitten, as occurring very often in the sleep of psychotic patients; but this is said to be etiologically non-specific. Lester and Edwards[6] found precentral fast activity increased in amount, amplitude and spindling in some schizophrenic and neurological patients as compared to normal controls; this finding also appears to be etiologically non-specific. Bruck[7] found less occipital average voltage and less synchrony in chronic schizophrenics than in non-schizophrenic psychiatric patients. Persistent regular alpha rhythm was found to be a predictor of unfavorable outcome by Igert and Lairy[8] and by Small and Stern.[9] Salamon and Post,[10] in a carefully designed study, found that a mixed group of acute and chronic schizophrenics showed significantly more baseline alpha and significantly less alpha blocking in response to photic stimulation than controls. These and several other early studies are summarized in Table 1.

Studies comparing psychotic and normal groups suffer greatly from the many difficulties involved in controlling differences due to such variables as age, institutionalization, medication status and cooperativeness. Although these also handicap studies in psychological areas, the investigation of electroencephalographic differences is subject to a specific difficulty: psychiatric patients consistently show more artifacts, due to eyelid tremor and blinks, eye movements, muscle tension and perspiration.[23]

Because of problems of design in between-subject studies, within-subject studies, that is, comparing recordings when patients are in and between psychotic episodes, are especially attractive. Obvious subjects for such investigations are manic-depressive and periodic catatonic patients. Harding et al.,[24] using a 4-channel low frequency wave analyzer covering 8, 9, 10, 11, 12 and 13 Hz, studied 3 cases of periodic psychosis, 2 of whom appear to have been undoubtedly manic-depressive, while the third had been diagnosed manic-depressive and schizophrenic by equally eminent psychiatrists. All 3 showed EEG changes with mood, but there was no common pattern. The two definitely manic-depressive patients appeared more alike in their EEG patterns as compared to the third patient; the most marked change was a decrease in amount and abundance of alpha activity with elation. Gjessing et al. studied[12] 140 records from 3 cases of periodic catatonia. The most prominent change was a decrease in alpha amplitude and an increase in alpha frequency during the recurrent psychotic episodes. These

TABLE 1.—EEG Findings in Schizophrenia

Characteristic	Description	Reference
Alpha activity	Incidence and amplitude decreased in periodic catatonia; frequency increased in 2 of 3 patients.	Bonkalo, Lovett-Doust and Stokes[11]
	Amplitude decreased, frequency increased in periodic catatonia.	Gjessing et al.[12]
	Incidence decreased in catatonic stupor.	Walter[13]
	Persistent and regular in poor outcome schizophrenics.	Igert and Lairy[8]; Small and Stern[9]
	More baseline alpha and less blocking than in controls.	Salamon[10]
Fast activity	More in schizophrenics and some neurological patients than in normals.	Lester and Edwards[6]
	More in schizophrenics and psychopaths than in depressives and neurotics. "Choppy activity."	Newman[14,15] Davis[3,16]
Slow activity	2-6 Hz, usually bilaterally symmetrical in catatonic stupor.	Walter[13]
Paroxysmal activity	Episodic high voltage frontal and temporal, related to hallucinatory disturbance (implanted electrodes).	Sem-Jacobsen et al.[17]
	Septal spikes (implanted electrodes).	Heath[18]
	Low voltage grouped bilateral spikes, fast spikes, paroxysmal 4-7 Hz waves.	Hill[4]
	Resemblances to psychomotor-type discharges.	Gibbs, Gibbs and Lennox[19]
Other	More non-specific abnormalities, especially in catatonics-hebephrenics.	Finley and Campbell[20]
	Abnormal, immature in childhood schizophrenics.	Kennard[21]
	B-mitten pattern, especially in reactive schizophrenics.	Gibbs and Gibbs[5]; Struve and Becka[22]

changes were correlated with changes in excretion of VMA and normetanephrine.

Some of these studies have produced intriguing findings; most could bear replication, with careful definition of patient groups and techniques. What is most disappointing in these approaches is the few reliable variables that can be obtained, and the consequent lack of sound theoretical connections with the functioning of the enormously complex organ underlying the electrodes.

Most studies have dealt with alpha activity, its presence, persistence and reactivity; this is undoubtedly because of the prominence of alpha activity in scalp recordings, but its relevance to psychopathology is still obscure. Heath's studies[18] of potentials recorded from depth electrodes suggest that schizophrenics show abnormal electrical activity predominantly in the septal area, which might not be expected to appear at the scalp. As yet, the most useful function of clinical electroencephalography in the differential diagnosis of psychosis appears to be in the discovery of the occasional patient whose abnormal behavior is associated with temporal lobe foci.

Analysis of the waking rest EEG

a) Frequency analysis. Shortly after its introduction in clinical medicine, the EEG was found to contain distinct "rhythms" characterized and defined chiefly if not uniquely by the temporal spacing of the waves. One such rhythm, the so-called alpha, present in most subjects when recorded with eyes closed, is defined by the 8-13 Hz bands. Other rhythms commonly studied are the "beta" with a band extending from 14 to 25 Hz, the "theta" occupying the 4-7 Hz and the "delta," 0.5-3.5 Hz. For a number of years attempts at quantification and classification were performed "by hand," simply by counting the number of waves per time unit. Later, semi-automatic frequency analyzers were developed (Grey Walter[25]) and used until fully automatic and highly reliable devices became available recently. There are now a number of laboratories in the U.S., Europe and Japan where extensive research is done by filtering EEG signals into their frequential components and analyzing changes produced by behavioral alterations, mental disease, drugs, etc. Most often up to 30 bands are studied. Since any strip of EEG, even of a few seconds duration, contains numerous components in the different bands, frequency analysis results in an enormous amount of data which cannot be processed "by hand" but re-

TABLE 2.—Data Obtained from Frequency Analysis

Characteristic frequential domain (Hz)	Schizophrenics and Normals	Differences between	
		Schizophrenics and Depressives	Depressives and Normals
"delta" (0.5-3.0)		More activity (Fink et al.)[27]	
"theta" (4-7)	More activity (Volavka et al.)[28]	More activity (Fink et al.)[27]	
"alpha" (7.5-12.5)	More activity (Uruyu)[26]		More activity (Volavka)[29]
"low" (7.5-9.0)	More activity (Volavka et al.)[28] with larger variance		
"high" (9.5-12.5)	with smaller variance		
"beta" (14-25)	More activity (Uruyu)[26]	Less activity (Fink et al.)[27]	More activity (Volavka)[29]

quires the use of electronic computers. Furthermore, since it is not clear at present what type of change should be sought, none of the data can be eliminated or even reduced. Thus analysis remains tedious and time-consuming, so that to date only preliminary conclusions have been reached. It should also be pointed out that no procedure has yet been developed which allows the study of data on groups of subjects. Only individual records can be processed. The between-subject likeness or unlikeness is judged qualitatively.

Several studies have appeared recently and are summarized in Table 2. Uryu and Moryia[26] found 1.7 times more alpha activity and 1.6 times more beta activity in a group of schizophrenics than in normal controls. Fink et al.[27] described more theta and less beta activity in schizophrenics than in depressives (normals were not included in this paper). However, as the authors are aware, their study has not excluded the possible effects of age differences between their patient groups. Volavka et al.[28] reported a significantly higher amount of theta and alpha activity in schizophrenics than in controls. These authors found no difference in the beta band. They also noticed a greater variance between individuals in delta and low alpha bands (7.5 to 9.0 Hz) in patients than in normals, although the reverse was true for the high alpha bands (9.5 to 12.5 Hz). The last-mentioned authors point to the fact that there were differences in normal subjects in the amount of slow activity, this being higher in younger subjects (18-25) than in older subjects (25-48). Such a difference did not exist in patients. In a recent publication Volavka et al.[29] report on EEG studies in cases of periodic endogenous depression. Using an experimental design allowing separation of the influence of medication and the clinical state on the EEG, the authors were able to show a significant increase of alpha and beta activity during the depressive phases.

Thus, frequency analysis does show differences. However, these are not highly consistent in the different laboratories where such research is performed. A possible reason for divergent findings lies in the time duration of the samples which were analyzed. The EEG being a highly variable system, it is to be expected that quite different features will be found according to the sample selected.

b) *Amplitude analysis.* In straightforward frequency analysis, the distribution of EEG signals into their frequential components is performed without regard to amplitude. In straightforward amplitude analysis (as first developed by Drohocki[30]), measurements are performed on cumulative amplitudes of brain waves regardless of their specific appurtenance to a particular frequency band. In other words, for given fixed periods of time, it is the global unfiltered cumulative amplitude of waves that constitutes the raw material for analysis.*

The way in which this is achieved is as follows: an electronic integrator is preset to deliver a pulse each time a certain cumulative voltage level has been reached. A direct proportionality between the voltage level (in reference to the microvoltage of selected calibration signals) and the number of pulses is readily demonstrable (Figure 1). In the course of a recording, the number of pulses thus expresses continuously the mean energy content (MEC), or better, mean integrated amplitude, of the EEG. The word "continuously" is justified since there is no significant delay in firing when the critical voltage level is reached and no significant latency in the integrator in resetting to zero. Pulses may be considered as units of electrical activity and counted as such. Any length of the record can be subdivided into time-units such as 1 second, 20 seconds or 1 minute or more. The total number of pulses within any such time-unit can be counted and averages calculated. In addition, one can easily compute the statistical parameters of such averages. Comparison between them becomes a matter of routine statistical procedure. Furthermore, variability levels can also be established. These levels, most often expressed as the coefficient of variation (CV), appear, as will be shown, to be most informative in relation to psychopathology and drug effects.

An important feature of amplitude measurement analysis is that, since one single value per channel is obtained for each time-unit, quantitative data as established on long periods of recordings can be processed rapidly with simple desk calculators. Instead of the usual 10-second "epoch," most often used as a sampling period in frequency analysis, recordings of 10 minutes, 1 hour or even an entire night may be processed without being submerged in a sea of numbers. This avoids the difficulty of selecting "representative" samples.

Data obtained with this method on 101 chronic male schizophrenics and a group of 104 non-patient controls (Goldstein et al.[32]) revealed the features reported in Table 3. All the recordings were obtained from subjects in the supine position, eyes closed. The only lead analyzed was the

---

*A recent development due to Murphree et al.[31] represents a combination of both methods, since what is done is to establish for successive periods of 20 seconds the amplitude and variability for each one of 33 frequency bands.

left occipital with reference to both ears. The energy and variability values are averages obtained from the MEC and CV values of all subjects in each group. As can be seen, there was no difference in the overall amplitude levels between patients and normals. However, in patients, the CV was almost 50 per cent lower than in controls. Furthermore,

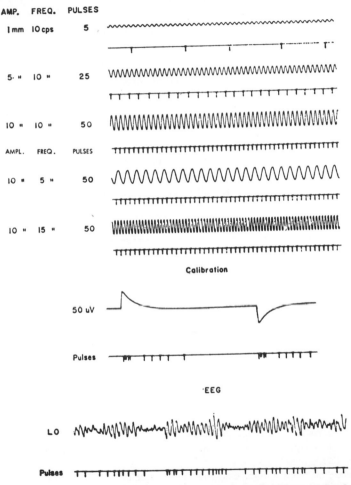

FIG. 1.—Calibration characteristics and operations of the EEG amplitude integrator. The upper part presents pulse delivery in relation to identical frequency signals delivered at different amplitudes. On the middle part one can see the performance when standard calibration signals are used. On the lower part a short strip of actual recording with corresponding integration pulses is presented.

within the patient group, the catatonics had such a low CV that it was significantly different from that of the other three groups.

These determinations were based on time-intervals of 20 seconds, with 30 to 45 values being processed for each record. To determine whether the differences in CV might have been due only to the choice of the 20-second time-basis, similar determinations of mean and CV were performed using 1, 5, 10, 20 and 60 seconds as basic periods of measurement. Records obtained on 20 controls and 20 chronic schizophrenic patients were selected on the basis of similar mean amplitude and persistence of wakefulness throughout the recording period. The variability levels in this case were calculated from data from all the subjects in each group: i.e., by pooling all 1, 5, 10, 20 or 60 second counts, rather than by averaging subject values. The data appear in Table 4 and show that the greatly reduced variability in the EEG of schizophrenics exists, whatever the basic time-unit during which integration pulses are counted. It may also be noted that however the 10-minute samples are subdivided, the statistical distributions of the values of the pulse counts during the basic time-units remain reasonably Gaussian or normal.

TABLE 3.—Overall Data on M.E.C.[1] and on C.V.[2]: 20-sec. Time Basis*

Type of subject	Number of subjects	Number of measurements	M.E.C.[1]	C.V.[2]
Non-schizophrenics				
Reformatory inmates	51	2330	36.24	18.62
Staff volunteers males	33	1550	35.85	17.52
Staff volunteers females	20	620	25.97*	17.42
Total	104	4500	32.68	18.52‡
Schizophrenics				
Chronic undifferentiated	54	2148	35.05	9.18
Hebephrenic	15	548	37.30	10.02
Paranoid	20	769	32.77	9.98
Catatonic	12	455	36.00	7.39†
Total	101	3920	35.28	9.14‡

*Difference statistically significant with values obtained on reformatory and staff volunteers (t-test) $p < 0.05$.
†Difference statistically significant with any one or all other groups taken together (F-ratio) $p = 0.05$.
‡Difference statistically significant (F-ratio) $p < 0.001$.
[1]Mean energy content.
[2]Coefficient of variation.
  * (From Goldstein et al.[22], 1965)

TABLE 4.—Differences in Levels of the C.V. in Patients and Normal Volunteers According to Time-basis of Measurement

Time basis for measurement	Normals			Schizophrenics		
	N of measurements	Mean	C.V.	N of measurements	Mean	C.V.
1 second	12,000	2.64	47.35	12,000	2.61	30.65
5 seconds	2,400	13.20	33.11	2,400	13.06	16.54
10 seconds	1,200	26.40	28.37	1,200	26.12	11.94
20 seconds	600	52.80	25.19	600	52.24	9.86
1 minute	200	158.40	20.90	200	156.72	7.02

Besides the time-unit of measurement, other possible sources of error were tested and rejected. For example, there were no significant differences in either the MEC or the CV with regard to age of the patients (at least in the range of 17 to 49 years) and no difference in either of these parameters in relation to the duration of hospitalization (at least between 1 and 20 years). Finally, the same low variability was found to exist regardless of amplitude levels.

Validation of this finding has come, thus far, from four sources. First, Burdick et al.[33] found that the difference in variability between

TABLE 5.—Mean Modulus Integrated Values from Marjerrison et al.,[34] 1968, by Subject Groups

Group (no. of subjects)	Mean integrated amplitude		Coefficient of variation	
Staff volunteers (24)	12.29		14.73	
male (12)		12.80		14.04
female (12)		11.77		15.43
Chronic schizophrenics	12.08		11.02	
male (14)		9.89		11.84*
female (14)		14.27		10.19*
Acute schizophrenics	13.23		13.44	
male (30)		13.33		14.45
female (30)		13.13		12.43
hallucinating during EEG (10)		10.93		10.23*
non-hallucination (50)		13.69		14.09

*Significant differences with controls and/or non-hallucinating patients.

EEG records obtained on normals and patients could be demonstrated under different recording conditions and with different instrumentation. Next, Marjerrison et al.,[34] in Canada, using a modulus voltage integrator and an entirely different population of both patients and normals, also found reduced levels of EEG variability in the patients, although of not so large a magnitude as reported by Goldstein et al. (Table 5). An interesting observation of Marjerrison et al. is that in acute schizophrenic patients the CV is significantly lowered during hallucinatory episodes. Thirdly, Sugerman et al.[35] detected, in a study performed on 16 chronic male schizophrenics over a year, a highly significant correlation between levels of EEG variability and behavioral states. As can be seen in Figure 2, whenever behavioral ratings revealed improvement, the CV of the EEG increased. When placebo was substituted for the active medication, following the well-known carry-over effect of phenothiazines, behavior deteriorated and the CV decreased. Needless to say, this study was performed in a blind design as regards patients, the psychiatrists performing the ratings, and the statisticians measuring EEG characteristics. Finally, Volavka et al.,[28] in

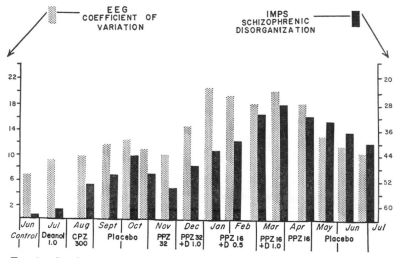

FIG. 2.—Graphical representation of behavioral scores and EEG measurements of the coefficient of variation, as established on a group of 16 male chronic schizophrenics, during a 1 year drug study. Note that the scale for IMPS scores has been reversed in order to allow a direct confrontation between behavioral ratings and CV values. D: Deanol (2-dimethylaminoethanol); CPZ: Chlorpromazine; PPZ: Perphenazine. (Drawn from the data in Sugerman et al, 1964.)[35]

Czechoslovakia, studying the variability of data derived by frequency analysis, found schizophrenics less variable than normals in the dominant alpha 2 band (9.5 - 12.5 Hz), and they related this finding to the results of Sugerman[35] and Goldstein.[42]

Statistical Considerations

Our interest in the variability in time of the EEG (chronogram) led us to consider various ways of characterizing this expression. Although the mean and the coefficient of variation are simple and appropriate when the chronogram approximates a straight line, as is the case with many schizophrenic patients, they are less appropriate statistically when the chronogram shows the points of inflexion characteristic of higher order curves. Hyams and Sugerman[36] have found that the majority of ten-minute recordings from normal subjects may be very adequately described by fitting polynomials of up to the fifth degree. It can be shown that the residuals about such higher order curves have convenient properties of randomness and normality. It follows from this model that estimates of parameters, such as the order of the accepted polynomial, its coefficients and variance, may be used in parametric design. This technique is now being applied to clarifying EEG differences between anxious and non-anxious normal subjects and to demonstrating changes produced by drugs in schizophrenic patients.

Thus amplitude measurements of the EEG do reveal a difference between normal and schizophrenic patients. This difference diminishes as the behavioral status of the patient improves. It is also likely that the difference is not an accidental finding on a particular group of patients in one particular institution.

EEG Reactivity to Drugs

a) *Barbiturates.* Goldman reported for the first time in 1959[37] and in greater detail in 1962[38] that the EEG "patterns of activation" which occur after intravenous administration of thiopental are different in schizophrenic patients from those observed in normal subjects. The patterns referred to are the so-called "fast" or "beta" activity in the range of 20 to 25 Hz with low voltage. Similar results were reported by Itil.[39] Recently Murphree et al.[40] presented data, assembled from normal subjects and schizophrenic patients treated with thiopental, measuring EEG changes by the method of amplitude measurement just described. As can be seen in Table 5, Goldman's findings were confirmed by the statistical demonstration of a decrease of the mean integrated amplitude of the EEG (5 to 8.5 minutes after injection, 1.5 mg./Kg.) significantly greater in chronic schizophrenic patients than in non-patients.

Murphree et al.[40] reported in the same paper a difference in reaction to pentobarbital (Table 6). Following an oral dose of 0.2 Gm., there occurred in normal subjects, within 30 minutes, a 30 per cent increase in the MEC and a 3.5-fold increase in variance. In patients, however, the same dose elevated the mean energy by only 15 per cent and did not affect the variance.

Shagass's data with amobarbital[41] suggests a similar differentiation in reaction to barbiturates. The technique involved determination of the drug level producing the greatest increase in fast activity amplitude. In normals, the level was approximately 3 mg./Kg.; in patients with overt anxiety the mean threshold approached 5 mg./Kg.; in psychotic depressives, the threshold was somewhat less than 3 mg./Kg.

b) *Lysergic acid diethylamide.* In 1963 Goldstein et al.[42] compared the EEG effects of LSD in non-patient volunteers and in schizophrenic patients. Here again, the method of amplitude analysis was employed. The results are summarized in Table 6. As can be seen, with 1 mg./Kg. orally, there occurred within 90 minutes a highly significant decrease of the MEC and CV in normal subjects. The reverse situation was obtained in schizophrenic patients, where both MEC and CV were elevated, although only the CV increase reached significant levels.

TABLE 6.—Quantitative Differences in Drug Effects in Normal Subjects and Schizophrenic Patients

Drug and dose	Normal subjects	Schizophrenic patients
Thiopental 1.5 mg./Kg. I.V.	"Activation" 70% decrease in MEC	"Activation" 85% decrease in MEC
Pentobarbital 0.2 Gm. orally	3.5 fold increase in variance 30% increase in MEC	No change in variance 15% increase in MEC
Amobarbital (threshold)	3 mg/kg	Less than 3 mg/kg (Psychotic depressives)
LSD-25 1 mg./Kg. orally	33% decrease in MEC 40% decrease in CV	15.5% increase in MEC 49% increase in CV
Haloperidol 2 Mg. I.M.	15% increase in MEC 15% decrease in CV	21% decrease in MEC 32% increase in CV

This effect was not due, in patients, to the stress of the recording situation. This was shown by the fact that in these same patients the experimental procedure *per se* or the experimental procedure plus placebo administration (in a double blind design) did not change in any measurable way either the MEC or the CV.

c) *Butyrophenones.* In a recent study, Pfeiffer et al.,[43,44] using amplitude analysis, compared the effects of 2 mg. IM of haloperidol in normal subjects and in chronic male schizophrenics. The results appear in Table 6. In normal subjects the so-called "neuroleptic syndrome" previously described by Meurice[45] was clearly observed, characterized by an increase in the MEC and a decrease in the CV. In patients, however, different effects were observed, with a decrease in MEC and an increase in CV. It should be pointed out that this is a small scale study on 5 patients only. Further experimentation is warranted for a more precise demonstration of such a difference.

It thus appears that for a variety of drugs, with different biochemical and physiological mechanisms of action, a difference exists in the reactions of normal subjects and schizophrenic patients. It is interesting to note that a common feature exists in the patient's reactivity: it is characterized by an increase in EEG variability whenever a drug effect is obtained. This could be due to the fact that starting from a baseline of low variability, further reductions are not possible, and rebound phenomena are likely to occur. Whatever the mechanism involved, the fact exists that a drug such as LSD, which acts as a powerful stimulant in normal subjects, appears to be devoid of any such action in schizophrenic patients.

DISCUSSION

Throughout the forty years that electroencephalography has been in existence, hope has prevailed that it could be used for diagnosis and understanding of the pathology underlying mental disease. However, at no point in this short but rich history was there any theoretical foundation for such a search. This is perhaps the main reason for the generally assumed failure of the EEG approach to psychopathology. In a "fact-rich but theory-poor" field, one can only hope to find something when one knows what to look for. In the absence of a clue of any kind, researchers have turned to the only alternative, namely the comparative method, more specifically the confrontation of tracings from non-patients with those of patients. Although this approach has yielded some interesting data (as just shown), the strict limitations it carries should be clearly spelled out.

A scientifically sound comparison between two entities such as "normals" and "patients" has validity only if these entities are strictly juxtaposable other than for their main variable. It is obvious that, when one compares qualitatively or quantitatively records obtained from normally functioning subjects to those of institutionalized patients, one violates that rule. Matching for age, sex and whatever else one can control does not remove biases. For example, according to Volavka et al.[28] maturation of EEG frequential characteristics could well be different in normals and schizophrenics. Social and sexual functioning are dramatically altered under schizophrenia. In fact, on any known criterion, there is no possible way to constitute groups which differ only by the presence or absence of the disease.

It might be that a feature of the EEG quantitative research presented above could give the one clue which bypasses the use of the comparative method; this has to do with the time-course variability in the amplitude of EEG signals. True, the low level of variability in records obtained in schizophrenics was first detected by the comparative method. Yet it did not need to be so, since this result should have appeared from purely statistical considerations. As is well known, in most parametrically distributed measurements obtained on physiological systems, the standard deviation represents 15 to 30 per cent or more of the mean. The existence of one such system with CV of 8 to 10 per cent constitutes a factual entity.

Let us examine briefly what this finding could suggest concerning the difference in brain function between schizophrenics and normals.

Consider the brain as the central homeostatic control station. According to Ross Ashby's cybernetic concepts,[46] in order to function effectively a homeostat must be endowed with a range of variability in regulating potencies equal to the diversity of the situations it has to deal with. This is the "law of requisite variety." For a given level of variability in input, when regulating capacities increase, the time required to adapt to a novel situation is extremely short, and the readjustment is highly successful. When regulating capacities decrease, the operations of the homeostat become sluggish, hectic, unpredictable and most often hyperactive.

Hypo-variability of the EEG suggests that brain function in schizophrenia may be defective in homeostasis. Any input, however trivial or apparently non-significant, brings about an inappropriate behavioral response. Most conspicuously absent is the capacity to "relax," since such a state can be achieved only when the homeostat's reactivity becomes so wide that most input is absorbed, so to speak, too quickly to be of relevance to the system. Thus the patients appear to be in a sustained state of hyper-alertness.

The question of the possible biochemical and/or physiological reasons for the existence of such a state, and its therapeutic implications, are clearly beyond the scope of this discussion. It is clear, nonetheless, that if more evidence confirms the generality of hypo-variability in brain function in certain types of schizophrenics, a new concept of the disease might emerge.

REFERENCES

1. Hess, R.: Elektrische Hirnaktivat und Psychopathologie. Schweiz. Med. Wschr. 93:449-462, 1963.

2. Walters, C.: Clinical and experimental relationships of EEG to psychomotor and personality measures. J. Clin. Psychol. 20:81-91, 1964.

3. Davis, P. A.: Comparative study of the EEG of schizophrenic and manic-depressive patients. Amer. J. Psychiat. 99:210-217, 1942.

4. Hill, D.: The EEG in psychiatry. In: Hill, D. and Parr, G. (Eds.): Electroencephalography, A Symposium on its Various Aspects. New York, Macmillan, 1963.

5. Gibbs, F. A., and Gibbs, E. L.: The mitten pattern: an electroencephalographic abnormality correlating with psychosis. J. Neuropsychiat. 5: 6-13, 1963.

6. Lester, B. K., and Edwards, R. J.: EEG fast activity in schizophrenic and control subjects. Int. J. Neuropsychiat. 2:143-156, 1966.

7. Bruck, M. A.: Synchrony and voltage in the EEG of schizophrenics. Arch. Gen. Psychiat. 10:454-468, 1964.

8. Igert, C., and Lairy, G. C.: Interet pronostique de l'EEG au cours de l'evolution des schizophrenes. Electroenceph. Clin. Neurophysiol. 14:183-190, 1962.

9. Small, J. G., and Stern, J. A.: EEG indicators of prognosis in acute schizophrenia. Electroenceph. Clin. Neurophysiol. 18:526-527, 1965.

10. Salamon, I., and Post, J.: Alpha blocking and schizophrenia. I. Methodology and initial studies. Arch. Gen. Psychiat. 13:367-374, 1965.

11. Bonkalo, A., Lovett-Doust, J. W., and Stokes, A. B.: Physiological concomitants of the phasic disturbances seen in periodic catatonia. Amer. J. Psychiat. 112:114-122, 1955.

12. Gjessing, L. R., Harding, G. F. A., Jenner, F. A., and Johannessen, N. B.: The EEG in three cases of periodic catatonia. Brit. J. Psychiat. 113:1271-1282, 1967.

13. Walter, W. Grey: Electroencephalography in cases of mental disorder. J. Ment. Sci. 88:110-121, 1942.

14. Newman, H. W.: Electroencephalography. Amer. J. Med. Sci. 196:882-887, 1938.

15. Newman, H. W., and Lawrence, R.: The electroencephalogram in functional psychiatric disorders. Stanford Med. Bull. 10:76-77, 1952.

16. Davis, P. A.: Evaluation of the electroencephalograms of schizophrenic patients. Amer. J. Psychiat. 96:851-860, 1940.

17. Sem-Jacobson, C. W., Petersen, M. C., Lazarte, J. A., Dodge, H. W., and Holman, C. B.: Electroencephalographic rhythms from the depths of the frontal lobe in 60 psychotic patients. Electroenceph. Clin. Neurophysiol. 7:193-210, 1955.

18. Heath, R. G.: Common characteristics of epilepsy and schizophrenia: clinical observation and depth electrode studies. Amer. J. Psychiat. 118:1013-1026, 1962.

19. Gibbs, F. A., Gibbs, E. L., and Lennox, W. G.: Likeness of cortical dysrhythmias of schizophrenia and psychomotor epilepsy. Amer. J. Psychiat. 95:255-269, 1938.

20. Finley, K. H., and Campbell, C. M.: Electroencephalography in schizophrenia. Amer. J. Psychiat. 98:374-381, 1941.

21. Kennard, M. A.: The characteristics of thought disturbance as related to electroencephalographic findings in children and adolescents. Amer. J. Psychiat. 115:911-921, 1959.

22. Struve, F. A., and Becka, D. R.: The relative incidence of the B-mitten EEG pattern in process and reactive schizophrenia. Electroenceph. Clin. Neurophysiol. 24:80-82, 1968.

23. Bruck, M. A., and McNeal, B. F.: Artifacts in the EEG of schizophrenic patients. Amer. J. Psychiat. 121:265-266, 1964.

24. Harding, G., Jeavons, P. M., Jenner, F. A., Drummond, P., Sheridan, M., and Howells, G. W.: The electroencephalogram in three cases of periodic psychosis. Electroenceph. Clin. Neurophysiol. 21:59-66, 1966.

25. Walter, W. Grey: An automatic flow frequency analyzer. Electr. Eng. 16:9 and 236, 1943.

26. Uryu, K., and Moryia, A.: A frequency analyzing study of electroencephalogram in schizophrenic psychoses. Dynamic observation with the overlapping method. Proc. VI Ann. Meet. Jap. EEG Soc. 12, 1957.

27. Fink, M., Itil, T., and Clyde, D.: A contribution to the classification of psychoses by quantitative EEG measures. Proc. Soc. Biol. Psychiat. 2:5-17, 1965.

28. Volavka, J., Matousek, M., and Roubicek, J.: EEG frequency analysis in schizophrenia. Acta Psychiat. Scand. 42:237-245, 1966.

29. Volavka, J., Grof, P., and Mrklas, L.: EEG frequency analysis in periodic endogenous depressions. Psychiat. Neurol. Basel 153:387-390, 1967.

30. Drohocki, Z.: L'integrateur de l'electroproduction cerebrale pour l'electroencephalographie quantitative. Rev. Neurol. 80:619-624, 1948.

31. Murphree, H. B., Goldstein, L., Pfeiffer, C. C., Schramm, L. P., and Jenney, E. H.: Computer analysis of drug effects on the electroencephalograms of normal and psychotic subjects. Int. J. Neuropharmacol. 3:97-104, 1964.

32. Goldstein, L. Sugerman, A. A., Stolberg, H., Murphree, H. B., and Pfeiffer, C. C.: Electrocerebral activity in schizophrenics and non-psychotic subjects: Quantitative EEG amplitude analysis. Electroenceph. Clin. Neurophysiol. 19:350-361, 1965.

33. Burdick, J. A., Sugerman, A. A., and Goldstein, L.: The application of regression analysis to quantitative electroencephalography in man. Psychophysiology 3:249-254, 1967.

34. Marjerrison, G., Krause, A. E., and Keogh, R. P.: Variability of the EEG in schizophrenia: Quantitative analysis with a modulus voltage integrator. Electroenceph. Clin. Neurophysiol. 24:35-41, 1967.

35. Sugerman, A. A., Goldstein, L., Murphree, H. B., Pfeiffer, C. C., and Jenney, E. H.: EEG and behavioral changes in schizophrenia. Arch. Gen. Psychiat. 10:340-344, 1964.

36. Hyams, L., and Sugerman, A. A.: A model for the quantitative area encephalogram. (Submitted for publication).

37. Goldman, D.: Specific electroencephalographic changes with pentothal activation in psychotic states. Electroencephal. Clin. Neurophysiol. 11:657-667, 1959.

38. Goldman, D.: Electroencephalographic changes brought to light under pentothal activation in psychotic (schizophrenic) patients with particular reference to changes produced by pharmacologic agents. Ann. N.Y. Acad. Sci. 96:356-374, 1962.

39. Itil, T.: Elektroencephalographische Studien bei endogenen Psychosen und deren Behandlung mit psychotropen Medikamenten unter besonderer Berücksichtigung des Pentothal-Elektroencephalogramms. Istanbul, Turkey, Ahmet Said Matabaase, Ed., 1964.

40. Murphree, H. B., Pfeiffer, C. C., Goldstein, L., Sugerman, A. A., and Jenney, E. H.: Time series analysis of the effects of barbiturates on the electroencephalograms of psychotic and non-psychotic men. Clin. Pharmacol. Ther. 8:830-840, 1967.

41. Shagass, C.: The sedation threshold. A method for estimating tension in psychiatric patients. Electroenceph. Clin. Neurophysiol. 6:445-453, 1954.

42. Goldstein, L., Murphree, H. B., Sugerman, A. A., Pfeiffer, C. C., and Jenney, E. H.: Quantitative electroencephalographic analysis of naturally occurring (schizophrenic) and drug-induced psychotic states in human males. Clin. Pharmacol. Ther. 4:10-21, 1963.

43. Pfeiffer, C. C., Goldstein, L., and Murphree, H. B.: A study of the effects of parenteral administration of antipsychotics in man. I. Normal subjects: quantitative EEG and subjective response. J. New Drugs 8:79-88, 1968.

44. Pfeiffer, C. C., Goldstein, L., and Sugerman, A. A.: A study of the effects of parenteral administration of antipsychotics in man. II. Male chronic schizophrenics: quantitative EEG findings. J. New Drugs 8:89-94, 1968.

45. Meurice, E.: Etude electro-encephalographique du R. 1625. Acta Neurol. Psychiat. Belg. 60:91, 1960.

46. Ashby, N. R.: Requisite variety and its implications for the control complex systems. Cybernetica 1:83-99, 1958.

Discussion of
Dr. Goldstein's and Dr. Sugerman's Paper

by ENOCH CALLAWAY, M.D.

Langley Porter Neuropsychiatric Institute, San Francisco

HUDSON HOAGLAND once compared a psychiatrist, using an EEG to study a patient, with a labor-management consultant using an airplane to study a factory. They both make observations at quite a distance from some complicated interactions. They can observe some byproducts of gross energy exchanges and they can detect riots and shutdowns. However, one is likely to suspect that their delightful machines entered more forcefully into their choice of techniques than did their announced problems.

Things have changed since Hoagland made that comparison only in that we now have even more delightful machines. If our knowledge of the mind had kept pace with our techniques, we should all be enormously wise.

The work of Goldstein and Sugerman and their group flies in the face of fashion. The EEG is boiled down to two numbers—one measuring energy and one measuring variability. The apparatus is simple, and, furthermore, the results are reproducible. For example, we find that schizophrenics have lower coefficients of variability than nonschizophrenics even when the EEGs are recorded from sitting subjects who watch an oscilloscope and hear haphazard tones. Simple numbers, simple equipment, and reproducible results are very unstylish these days.

The coefficient of variability seem to be a useful index of that psychophysical syndrome that we may loosely call arousal anxiety. A normal subject, lying quietly, shows a variety of EEG patterns as his mind wanders, hangs upon some thought, then wanders again. The anxious subject is much more consistent. We often think of the anxious aroused subject as having low alpha, but research doesn't bear this out. Such subjects do, however, show less alpha blocking. Wells and Wolf found this in anxious patients, Salmon and Pratt in schizophrenics, and Sayer and Torres in college students. In this latter case, high alpha–high

20

anxiety subjects showed less alpha blocking than high alpha–low anxiety subjects.

The techniques of Goldstein and Sugerman seem to tap this interesting dimension. Their findings support those of Venables and others, who find it is the chronic withdrawn nonparanoid schizophrenic who shows the greatest apparent arousal. Like a good technique should, theirs has revealed some unexpected things. For example, that LSD produces an increase in this arousal-anxiety dimension in normals, but it causes a decrease, if anything, in schizophrenics.

This work fits into a growing body of observations that show the withdrawn unresponsive nonparanoid process schizophrenic as extremely aroused, and unresponsive only in that he is pushed to the limit before the experimenter adds his challenge.

Longitudinal studies on a single patient show that the coefficient of variability tracks clinical state, so we may rule out the possibility that the novelty of the laboratory produces this arousal. One interesting alternative, however, is yet to be tested, and should be testable by the coefficient of variability. Suppose the withdrawn schizophrenic is protecting himself because he cannot select from among the conflicting demands inherent in any relatively rich environment. Any involvement with people—even in the laboratory would produce overwhelming stimulation. Familiarity would be no help. However, on return to his quiet room and to his self-imposed isolation, calm might return. Would the EEG telemetered from a patient who felt himself alone, unencumbered, and safely withdrawn show a high and more normal coefficient of variability? If so, the arousal would seem more effect than cause. If not, we would be left with more ambiguity, and we would have to consider biochemical and physiological changes due to chronic hyperarousal.

REFERENCES

1. Sayer, K. E., and Torres, A. A.: Effect of anxiety on alpha responsiveness to light stimulation. Psychol. Rep. 19:1141-1146, 1966.

2. Wells, C. E., and Wolf, H. C.: Electroencephalographic evidence of impaired brain function in chronically anxious patients. Science 31:1671-1672, 1960.

3. Salmon, I., and Post, J.: Alpha blocking in schizophrenia. I. Methodology and initial studies. Arch Gen. Psychiat. 13:367-374, 1965.

2

EVOKED POTENTIALS AND PSYCHOPATHOLOGY*

by CHARLES SHAGASS, M.D., and
JOHN J. STRAUMANIS, JR., M.D.†

DAWSON'S pioneering demonstration that cerebral responses evoked by sensory stimulation can be extracted from the obscuring "spontaneous" rhythms of the EEG was reported in 1947.[10] Very few evoked response studies were conducted in man until effective, commercially produced equipment for automating the averaging process was made available in 1960. The widespread use of the method since that time clearly indicates that lack of equipment, rather than lack of interest, was responsible for the slow progress of the previous decade.

For the student seeking neural correlates of psychopathology, the ability to record cerebral responses from the intact scalp opened new and exciting avenues for investigation. The idea that deviant reactivity or excitability of the central nervous system underlies psychopathology is at the core of every theory that ventures to consider brain function in relation to mental disorder. The problem was how to measure reactivity, and here, at last, was a relatively direct method. Considering the length of time during which the techniques have been available, there has not yet, however, been a flood of literature on evoked responses in psychopathologic states. This fact, which makes the present task of reviewing evoked response studies in psychopathology much less difficult than it might otherwise have been, reflects the embryonic state of the field.

In applying evoked response methods, one must be aware that these electrophysiological events represent the resultant of many possible influences. Consequently, abnormal mechanisms may come into play at

*Research supported (in part) by Grants MH02635, MH12507, MH12681 and 1-K3-MH-32, 932 from the National Institute of Mental Health, U.S. Public Health Service.
†Temple University and Eastern Pennsylvania Psychiatric Institute.

numerous levels of CNS functioning, and demonstration of an evoked potential correlate of psychopathology is a contribution more to problem definition than to problem solution. Furthermore, there may be disagreement about the nature of the problem being defined. Our viewpoint, or bias if you will, is that abnormal behavior reflects cerebral pathophysiology, which should also be manifested in deviant evoked response characteristics. A contrasting view, equally legitimate as of now, would be that altered evoked activity reflects no more than a normal physiological correlate of deviant behavior. For example, one may investigate deviant attention in schizophrenia and employ evoked responses to gauge the degree of deviation, as Callaway has done.[5] This approach does not negate the presence of some kind of pathophysiology, but also it does not assume that the responses measured are, in themselves, expressions of the pathophysiological process. At this time it is not possible to establish the correctness of either viewpoint, but awareness of the distinction between them may be of some value in considering the material to follow.

METHODS AND PROCEDURES

Recording Techniques

Many types of instruments have been used for automatic averaging or summation to record evoked responses from the human scalp. Special-purpose computers are in most common use. Data are frequently stored on tape for later processing in the computer. The output of the computer may be displayed in analogue or digital form; an appropriate digital read-out onto magnetic tape permits application of automatic quantification procedures by a general-purpose computer without additional data processing steps. For adequate amplitude quantification, it is desirable to have a calibration signal which is treated by the entire recording system in the same way as the evoked response.[14] Resolution which is appropriate to the characteristics of the physiological signal must be maintained in amplifiers and tape recorders and with respect to the number of memory locations per unit of time in the computer. It is desirable to record from electrodes placed near known sources of extracerebral potentials which can contaminate the evoked response, such as the orbit, at the same time as the evoked responses are taken; potential changes which are synchronous with those from known myogenic sources can then be recognized as of probable extracerebral origin.

Since the averaging procedure depends upon absence of "jitter" in activity with respect to a sharply defined point in time—i.e., the stimulus—favorite stimuli have been brief punctate ones, such as light flash, electrical shock to nerve, or auditory click. There is, however, abundant evidence that evoked response characteristics differ considerably with different stimulus patterns,[54] or when stimuli have different meaning.[58] Stimulus standardization for studies of individual differences presents serious problems. We have employed the sensory threshold to electrical stimulation of the ulnar or median nerve as a physiological zero point for somatosensory stimulus intensity; a constant-current stimulator, set for specified current values above threshold, then provides a reasonably well-defined stimulus. Standardization of visual stimuli requires control over pupil size, fixation, etc. Auditory stimuli are fairly readily controlled with earphones but, at high intensities, are more prone than other kinds of stimuli to give myogenic responses.[3] Also, since the auditory cortex is not at the surface of the brain, the initial components of the cerebral response are not generally visible.

A number of studies, including our own, have involved presentation of paired stimuli to measure recovery functions. The initial "conditioning" stimulus is followed at varying interstimulus intervals by a "test" stimulus. For most interstimulus intervals the test response overlaps the conditioning response and needs to be distinguished from it. This may be accomplished by an automatic subtraction procedure; both paired and unpaired stimuli are presented in the same sequence, and the unpaired response is subtracted from the responses to stimulus pairs, thus giving R1 + R2 minus R1, or R2.[31]

Test Procedures

In most of our own work we have simply applied repetitive stimuli to the passive subject, who was required only to stay awake with eyes shut and produce minimal electromyographic activity. This is similar to clinical EEG recording, the subject's cooperation being monitored by the investigator from electrical signals produced by him. Callaway et al.[5] introduced a more active attitude in their subjects by asking them to do their own monitoring for artifact by watching their recordings on an oscilloscope display. The procedures designed to elicit the contingent negative variation (CNV) phenomenon of Walter et al.[61] involve more subject activity; they deliberately induce attention or expectancy and often require a specific response, such as button press to an imperative stimulus when it is preceded by a particular alerting signal. Various forms of subject activity have been introduced by other investigators, such as reaction time responding[12] and guessing stimulus modality;[57] application of these procedures to psychopathological populations has not yet been reported.

Age and Sex

Evoked response characteristics vary considerably with age.[13,45,47,56] In general, amplitudes are larger and response peaks occur later in older

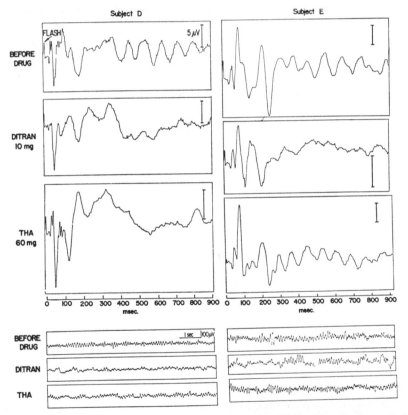

FIG. 1—Effects of Ditran and tetrahydroaminacrin (THA) on visually evoked responses and EEG in two subjects. Evoked responses recorded from leads placed 3 and 12 cm. above inion in midline; relative positivity at posterior lead gives upward deflection. Note obliteration of after-rhythm by Ditran in both subjects, with return after THA only in subject E. Modification of EEG by Ditran was reversed by THA in both subjects.

adult subjects. Responses are larger in young children than they are in young adults and the age curve appears to be U-shaped.[45] Not only does the response to an unpaired stimulus vary with age, but marked variations in recovery functions are also found. After correction for variations in the response to the conditioning stimulus, the somatosensory test response tends to be greater in older subjects.[38]

Significant evoked response variations with sex have also been found. Latencies of somatosensory and visual evoked responses are shorter in females.[45,46] Females also show greater recovery of visual evoked responses.[46]

These facts render control over age and sex imperative in studies of individual differences related to psychopathology. In our data, we have also found a number of interactions between presence or absence of psychopathology and age or sex. This possibility must be considered in the experimental design.

Alertness

As is true also for the EEG, the most dramatic shifts in evoked responses occur when the subject falls asleep.[50,62] Although not so well documented, it is likely that minor shifts in alertness affect the responses. There are also many changes associated with attention and expectation.[19,58] Since it is very difficult to achieve adequate experimental control over alertness, particularly in mentally ill subjects, some independent criterion would be desirable. It is possible that by monitoring the quantified EEG during evoked response recording, some degree of statistical correction for fluctuations in alertness can be achieved.

Drugs

It is obviously desirable to take recordings from patients in the drug-free state. Unfortunately, we do not know what length of time should have elapsed since the patients last received CNS-active drugs before they may confidently be assumed not to be affecting the records. One of us has recently reviewed the literature concerning drug effects on averaged evoked responses.[34] In general, drugs produce changes which are more correlated with their effects on the state of alertness than with the nature of the drug. The minor tranquilizers, such as chlordiazepoxide, diazepam, and oxazepam, tend to decrease evoked response amplitude. In our own work we have not been able to demonstrate statistical differences between the evoked response characteristics of patients who had drugs from 24 hours to 7 days before testing, and those with no history of drug intake for at least one month prior to testing.[35]

BRAIN SYNDROMES

Experimental Delirium

We have utilized the delirium-inducing properties of Ditran and the fact that its effects are antagonized by tetrahydroaminocrin (THA) to study the evoked response concomitants of an experimental acute brain syndrome and its relief.[4] In general, for both visual and somatosensory responses, the earlier components of the response were decreased in latency and increased in amplitude by Ditran. The latencies of later components were prolonged and amplitude reduced. The effects on the later components resembled those observed in sleep. One of the most

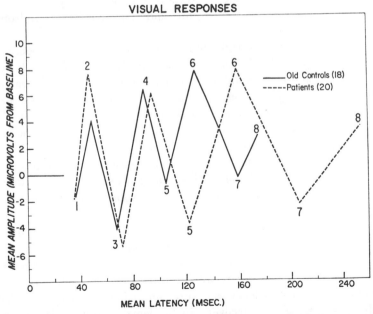

FIG. 2—Mean amplitude and latency values for visually evoked responses in 20 patients with brain syndromes due to cerebral arteriosclerosis and 18 healthy controls of same age and sex. Lead placements as in Fig. 1. Note prolonged latencies of peaks 6, 7 and 8 in the patients.

striking effects is illustrated in Fig. 1. The after-rhythm, or "ringing," component of the visual response was uniformly abolished, an effect which resembles that found in sleep.[50] Although THA produced remarkable reversals of the clinical effects of Ditran, the effects of this antidote on evoked response changes were only partial.

Chronic Brain Syndromes

In a parallel study of somatosensory and visual evoked response characteristics associated with naturally occurring delirium, a group of 20 patients with cerebral arteriosclerosis, characterized clinically by disorientation, was compared with 18 healthy subjects of like age and sex.[56] With respect to visual responses, patients differed from non-patients mainly in events occurring after 100 msec. Their latencies were prolonged and rhythmic after-activity was markedly reduced. The latter finding resembled that in acute delirium as illustrated for Ditran in Fig. 1, and agreed with that reported in a few cases by Cohn.[9] The mean results for the portions of the response preceding the after-rhythms are shown in Fig. 2; latencies were significantly longer in brain syndromes for peaks 6, 7 and 8.

More complex findings were obtained for somatosensory responses;[55] these involved a sex by diagnosis interaction. As shown in Fig. 3, non-patient males and females did not differ from one another, whereas the chronic brain syndrome females had larger evoked responses than normal and the male patients with brain syndromes had smaller responses. Somatosensory latencies for peaks 6 and 9 were significantly longer in patients than in nonpatients. Fig. 3 also shows the numbering scheme, employed by us to designate somatosensory response peaks, to which reference will be made in this paper; peaks 2 and 3, occurring between 1 and 4, are generally visible only in younger subjects and were not included in statistical analyses.

Somatosensory recovery functions were also determined in 15 of the brain syndrome subjects and their matched nonpatient controls. As had been found for the unpaired responses, sex by diagnosis interactions were demonstrated also for recovery; three of eight evoked response amplitudes and one latency measure showed this interaction. The tendency was for greater recovery in the female brain syndromes and less recovery in the males. No explanation for these evoked response differences related to sex in association with cerebral arteriosclerosis seems readily available. In another analysis of recovery functions, in which the arteriosclerosis group was enlarged by adding 10 patients with brain syndromes of diverse etiology, recovery of peak 4 was found to be less during the first 20 msec. (see Fig. 6).

Goff et al.[18] have suggested that the somatosensory evoked response peaks corresponding to peaks 6 and 8 in our scheme might reflect extra-lemniscal activity, perhaps mediated by reticular formation, and that the later peaks may represent nonspecific mechanisms. The fact that the later peaks appear to occur bilaterally suggests nonspecific mediation. The general slowing of these components in patients with brain syndromes might then implicate impaired reticular functioning. However, Domino et al.[11] have shown in man that lesions in nucleus ventero-postero-lateralis (VPL) reduced all somatosensory components during

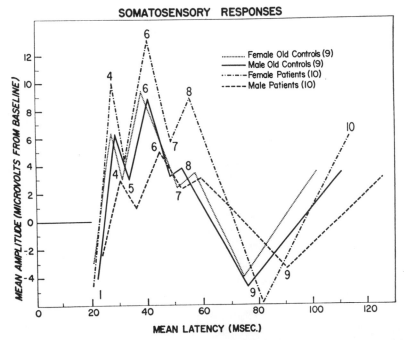

Fig. 3—Mean amplitudes and latencies of responses evoked by right median nerve stimulation at intensity 10 ma above sensory threshold. Responses recorded from electrodes placed 6 cm. apart over left hemisphere in parasagittal plane 7 cm. from midline; relative positivity in posterior lead, 2 cm. behind interauricular line gives upward deflection. Note that male and female controls did not differ from one another, while female brain syndrome patients had larger and male patients had lower amplitude responses than controls.

the first 125 msec. Furthermore, Liberson[26] has found that, in patients with aphasia from cerebrovascular accidents, there is no trace of ipsilateral response to median nerve stimulation if the contralateral response is absent. The data of Domino and Liberson indicate that the later, as well as earlier, somatosensory response effects are mediated via specific sensory pathways and that reticular mediation is not directly reflected in the response. If impaired reticular functioning is involved in brain syndromes, as seems possible in relation to altered awareness, this would affect evoked responses in some indirect manner.

The findings in acute and chronic brain syndromes may be cited to support a position concerning the behavioral dimension most relevant for neurophysiological studies of consciousness. The evoked response and EEG changes in these conditions bear many resemblances to those found in sleep, but the subjects were not asleep in any usual sense. They did all, however, have impaired ability to perceive and integrate cues from the environment—i.e., their sensorium was impaired. This is, of course, also the case with sleep. It thus seems more reasonable and useful to relate neurophysiological events to the *perceptual dimension* involved in sensorium than to the motor dimension, which is commonly used to evaluate sleep.

INTELLIGENCE AND MENTAL RETARDATION

Chalke and Ertl[7] have reported that the latency of flash evoked potentials is correlated with psychometric intelligence. Higher IQ was associated with shorter latencies for responses recorded over the left motor area; the results appeared more striking with the later components. These findings, which are of great interest, require confirmation in other laboratories. Our own data for visual and somatosensory evoked response measurements in subjects for whom intelligence test scores were available gave equivocal results.[33] Although we substantiated Chalke and Ertl's findings for some peaks, significant correlations in the opposite direction were found for other peaks. However, the results of Chalke and Ertl are certainly in accord with the differences between elderly brain syndrome patients and nonpatients illustrated in Fig. 2.

The findings of Barnet and Lodge[1] in developmentally retarded infants also suggest that evoked responses may be deviant in association with impaired intellectual functioning. These workers studied click evoked responses in 55 normal infants and 15 infants with the diagnosis of mongolism. Chromosome studies revealed trisomy-21 in all but one of the mongol patients; the exception had 21/15 translocation mongolism. The evoked responses were measured particularly during sleep. A statistical analysis was performed on the largest averaged evoked response for patient–nonpatient pairs matched for age and sex. Response amplitudes were about twice as large in the mongoloid subjects as in the normals, but significant latency differences were not found. Since these results were obtained in infants 14 months of age or younger, and particularly during the sleep state, one may ask whether the differences would be present also in older age groups and in the waking state. In any case, the results indicate clearly that further investigation of the evoked response characteristics in mental retardation may prove to be rewarding. The interpretation of results put forward by Barnet and Lodge, which seems most attractive to us, is that the abnormally large responses indicate defective inhibitory mechanisms, which would normally result in response habituation to repetitive identical stimuli.

Effects of LSD

Particular interest attaches to the evoked response changes associated with the effects of lysergic acid diethylamide (LSD), as an agent capable of eliciting "model psychosis." Several studies have been reported. The major effect observed in visually evoked responses has been reduction or elimination of after-activity.[8,29] However, our own studies, which involved recordings from multiple electrode placements, indicated that there was actually an augmentation of after-activity.[32] As seen in Figure 4, this was not observable in records from electrodes placed near the main zone of origin of the visual response, but was seen in records from electrodes adjacent to the central pair. This suggests that a high dose of LSD (2.5 μg./Kg. given intravenously) produced increased synchronization of the after-activity over a larger area than was involved in the response before LSD was given. The absence of effect from the central pair of electrodes would be due to the fact that both were located within the enlarged zone of response.

We found no significant effects on the initial somatosensory response components with 60 μg. of intravenously given LSD in an earlier study[48]; 2.5 μg./Kg. did produce reduction of amplitude in the early components of both somatosensory and visual responses.[32] However, no consistent association between the immediate symptoms produced by the

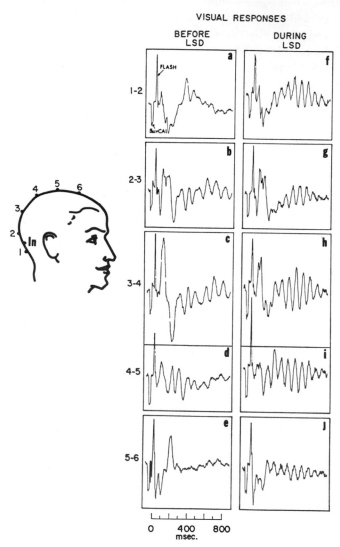

Fig. 4—Effects of LSD, 2.5 μg./Kg. intravenously, on visually evoked responses in one subject. Upward deflection indicates positivity in posterior electrode. Note minimal effects observed in recordings from electrode pair 2-3, whereas after-rhythms were augmented in records from other leads. Note also reduction in amplitude of early components and increase in after-rhythm frequency.

drug and the nature of the electrophysiological events was observed. Any electrophysiological changes with LSD were gone after 24 hours. We did note one possible association with remote behavioral effects of LSD. LSD experiments were carried out in the context of a therapeutic trial of this drug for conduct disorders,[36] and we found that those subjects who had the largest evoked responses to begin with, and who also showed the greatest reduction of amplitude of early components with LSD, tended to display greater subsequent behavioral improvement.

FUNCTIONAL PSYCHOTIC DISORDERS

Evoked Response Characteristics in Psychotic Depression

Under the heading of psychotic depressions we have included the following diagnostic categories: manic depressive psychosis, depressed; involutional psychotic depression; and psychotic depressive reaction. With somatosensory evoked responses we found two measures which discriminated psychotic depressions from nonpatient subjects. These were based on the initial components of the response (peaks 1 to 4, Figure 3). One was the intensity-response function, which showed larger responses in the depressed patients over a range of stimulus intensities.[42,43] The other was the recovery function obtained with paired, relatively intense stimuli of equal strength; recovery was less in patients, particularly during the initial recovery phase taking place during the first 20 msec.[39,42] We were able to carry out serial studies of recovery functions in a group of depressed patients, most of whom were treated with electroconvulsive therapy. The results showed a return to normal recovery function values as the depression responded to effective treatment.[40] Similar results were obtained in the few patients treated with antidepressant drugs.[48]

In a more recent study, employing additional controls and more sophisticated procedures both for recording and data analysis, we were unable to verify the previously found amplitude differences.[47] These may have emerged as a consequence of inadequate control over age. However, the absence of amplitude difference is still not fully understood, since we have observed amplitude reduction with effective antidepressant therapy.[48] Our recent data once again confirmed the reduced recovery in patients with psychotic depression. Fig. 5 shows the mean amplitude recovery curves for three peaks giving significantly less recovery in the patients than in nonpatients. The recovery values represent R2 measurements adjusted for covariance with R1 in each interstimulus interval; this procedure avoids some of the problems encountered with ratios. Some latency recovery differences were also found; these are rather puzzling, since they suggest earlier latency recovery in patients. Amplitude and latency recovery seem to be governed by different mechanisms.

In a study of visual recovery functions,[46] there were only 6 patients with psychotic depressions in our sample; these gave results similar to other patients—i.e., a tendency for increased amplitude. Speck et al.[54] reported visual response data for 7 depressive patients in their sample; they found nonsignificant trends for increased amplitude and latency and reduced recovery in the depressives. Data on more cases are obviously required.

The possible relation of reduced recovery in depression to deviant mineral metabolism was investigated by Gartside et al.,[17] who ad-

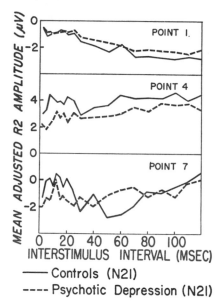

Fig. 5—Amplitude recovery curves for 3 somatosensory response peaks in 21 patients with psychotic depressions and 21 age and sex matched nonpatients. Amplitudes of response to second stimulus, R2, were adjusted for covariance with amplitude of response to first stimulus, R1. Mean recovery was greater for nonpatients. This is also true for point 1 where a larger response is indicated by greater negativity.

ministered lithium ion to nondepressed subjects. They were able to demonstrate that lithium carbonate altered the somatosensory recovery function curves from the normal configuration to one resembling that found by us in psychotic depression. However, they did not observe a concomitant clinical depression in their subjects. As will be noted below, the recovery function deviation in depression is by no means specific to that class of disorders. It seems reasonable to assume that additional factors are required for clinical mood changes, even though shifts in mineral metabolism have altered the electrophysiological activity.

Evoked Response Characteristics in Schizophrenic Disorders

Our initial results in schizophrenic disorders were quite similar to those in psychotic depression. We found increased amplitudes and attenuated recovery functions for the early component of somatosensory responses.[39,43,44] In a study of visually evoked responses and their recovery functions, there were no significant amplitude differences for the early components, but there was, in the schizophrenic patients, some tendency for reduced latency.[40] No significant differences were found with respect to visual recovery functions between schizophrenic patients and nonpatients. We did, however, find that the amount of rhythmic after-activity in the visual response was significantly less in patients than in nonpatients, and our schizophrenic subjects showed the lowest after-activity values of any patient group. The reduced after-rhythms in schizophrenics are difficult to reconcile with similar findings in conditions of impaired sensorium; they could be due to *hyper*alertness, which may also reduce rhythmic after-activity.

In our most recent study of somatosensory evoked responses, we were not able to confirm the finding of larger amplitudes in schizophrenic patients.[35] The only amplitude difference we found showed patients to have a smaller peak 10 deflection; this peak occurs about 90 msec. after the stimulus. On the other hand, the previously found reduction of amplitude recovery was verified and extended to several additional response peaks; mean recovery curves for two amplitude variables, comparing 18 schizophrenic patients with 18 nonpatients matched for sex and age, are shown in Fig. 6. Furthermore, several differences were found with respect to latency recovery, this being faster in patients. The somatosensory recovery function measures have thus been consistently deviant.

In contrast to our own failure to show significant visual response recovery differences between schizophrenic patients and nonpatients, Speck et al.[53] and Floris et al.[16] have succeeded in demonstrating such differences. Speck's data showed reduced early recovery in 39 schizophrenic patients when compared with 41 nonpatients. It may be important that her sample was larger than ours and was drawn from a state hospital instead of from a small university hospital, as was ours. Heninger and Speck[20] also found a significant relationship between symptom change and visual evoked response measures.

Rodin et al.[30] obtained somewhat different findings with visual evoked responses than other workers. Comparing 20 nonpatients with 20 schizophrenic patients, they found smaller amplitudes in the patients. Sampling factors may have been important in Rodin's different results, since the patients were a selected group involved in biochemical studies.

Callaway's Two-Tone Procedure in Schizophrenia

Callaway and his group have employed auditory evoked responses as an indicator of differences in response sets. According to Shakow[15] the integrating and organizing functions that provide for the establishment of generalized or major sets are impaired in schizophrenia. Consequently, patients are thought to employ multiple, enduring, minor, or "segmental" sets for categorizing sensory inputs and directing action. On the basis of Shakow's formulation, Callaway predicted that the responses evoked by two tones of different frequency—e.g., 1000 or 600 cps—would be more dissimilar in schizophrenic patients than in nonpatients and most dissimilar in nonparanoid schizophrenics. The results[5] supported these predictions, but did not support predictions of difference between process and reactive or between acute and chronic schizophrenics. In subsequent studies, Jones et al.[23,24] demonstrated that the evoked response similarity index changed in relation to clinical improvement in schizophrenic patients. Improved patients were more like normals when tested again than were unimproved patients. Nonschizophrenic patients did not show similar shifts. These workers also presented data showing that scores derived from factor analysis of nurses' clinical rating correlated with evoked response changes. The related factor scores were most loaded with items such as disorganized thinking, inappropriate affect, suspiciousness, craziness, withdrawal, and confusion. Their data also suggested that a normal two-tone response similarity index, coupled with a highly disturbed clinical picture, would predict a poor prognosis for response to drug therapy. This last result is reminiscent of Igert's and Lairy's[21] data, showing that a "hypernormal" EEG in a disturbed psychotic is associated with poor prognosis.

Although Callaway's data supported the original formulation of segmental set, he has more recently obtained evidence to suggest that this model does not fit the findings. Patients with Korsakoff's psychosis

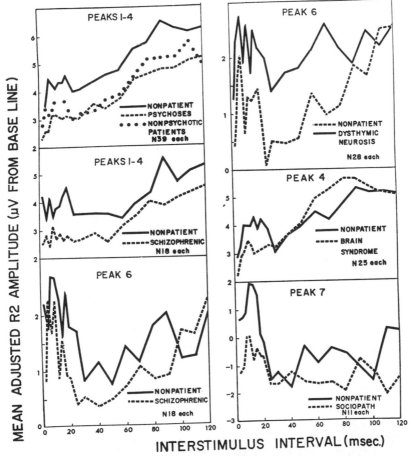

FIG. 6.—Amplitude recovery curves for certain somatosensory response peaks obtained in various psychiatric diagnostic groups and nonpatient groups matched for age and sex. In all cases recovery was significantly greater in the nonpatient samples, particularly during the first 20 msec.

gave two-tone evoked response results quite similar to those of schizophrenics, even though their set characteristics are of opposite kind.[6]

Grey Walter's Contingent Negative Variation

Walter et al.[61] have described another kind of evoked response event that appears to have psychological relevance. This has been named the contingent negative variation (CNV) or expectancy wave (E-wave). Although discussion of CNV may be more appropriate under the heading of nonpsychotic disorders, it will be introduced at this point in order to describe relevant findings and to discuss methodological issues which seem particularly important for the study of psychotic disorders.

When an initial signal has the significance of indicating to the subject that he is to prepare for a response to a forthcoming stimulus, there is a shift in the base line toward negativity of the vertex following the warn-

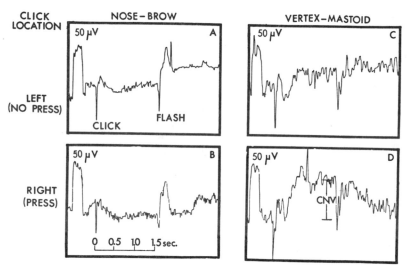

FIG. 7—Recordings obtained from one subject in an experiment designed to elicit contingent negative variation (CNV). Click precedes flash by 1.5 sec.; subject was instructed to press button after flash following right click but not to press after left click. Negativity at vertex and nose gives upward deflection. Note greater negativity at vertex following right click (press condition) than after left click. Note also absence of change in nose-brow recording taken simultaneously.

ing signal. The shift, the CNV, is a slow event; and DC, or long time-constant, amplifiers must be used to record it. Walter states that, in normal subjects, the CNV follows an extremely regular time course, commencing about 200 msec. after the warning signal and rising slowly to a peak at the moment of the imperative response. Fig. 7 gives an example of CNV recorded in our laboratory. The experimental paradigm was one in which auditory clicks were presented by means of earphones at random to either the right or left ear. A flash of light followed the click by 1.5 sec. The subject was instructed to press a button to the flash when the click sounded in the right ear, but not to press when the click sounded in the left ear. Recordings were made from a series of electrodes in bipolar linkage from the tip of the nose to the inion, as well as from vertex to mastoid, in an attempt to determine whether any reversal of phase could be discerned. Our amplifiers had a time constant of 10 sec., and we used an automatic device, designed by Dr. Donald Overton, to return the base line to zero during intertrial intervals, when the computer was inactive. Figure 7C shows that the base line remained fairly steady between the response to the left click, to which button press was not required, and the response to the flash. In contrast, Fig. 7D shows that there was a rather large negative shift between right click, requiring a button press to the subsequent flash, and flash. In this subject, the CNV was maximum over the vertex, and there was no accompanying shift in recordings from leads between nose and brow (Figs. 7A, 7B), providing evidence that the response was not originating in the orbit.

Although no systematic study of CNV in schizophrenic patients appears to have been reported, Walter[60] believes that many patients with schizoid features studied by him at the Burden Neurological Institute would probably be rated as more nearly psychotic in America than in Britain. He states that the feature of CNV which seems to characterize these patients is variability from trial to trial, and suggests that a measure of variance would indicate greater CNV fluctuations in such subjects.

In view of the obvious potential value of the CNV phenomenon in psychiatric research, we planned to compare CNV in various psychiatric groups. However, since Bickford et al.[2] had drawn attention to possible contamination of the CNV by the large potentials originating in the orbit, we decided first to conduct a study in nonpatients, using multiple electrode placements in an attempt to assess the contamination problem and to learn more about the distribution of CNV. The results are still being analyzed statistically, but at the present time it seems quite clear that, in nonpatient subjects, records of the type shown in Fig. 7 are the exception rather than the rule. The more common finding in the two experimental situations involved in the study, which are similar to those used by Irwin et al.,[22] is that the negative shift at the vertex is accompanied by an even greater negative shift at a lead placed between the eyes. This is illustrated in Fig. 8; the relative positivity at the nose can be shown to reflect a negative event reversing in phase at the brow. Furthermore, if one measures the amplitude of the CNV (difference between press and no-press conditions) at a set point in time corresponding to that indicated by the horizontal lines in Fig. 8D, there is a significant correlation between the amount of shift near the eyes and that at the vertex. We are therefore forced to conclude that, in the great majority of subjects under these conditions, it is extremely difficult to distinguish slow activity of the CNV variety from activity originating in the orbit.

We do not claim that there is no CNV phenomenon and, in fact, Fig. 7 seems to illustrate quite clearly that there is. However, from a practical point of view, the phenomenon appears to be an extremely difficult one to measure, particularly in psychiatric patients. Recordings resembling CNV may be voluntarily produced by initiating downward gaze following the alerting signal. Such events may be inhibited by careful control over eye fixation, but we cannot feel confident that our psychotic subjects will regularly be capable of this kind of prolonged cooperation.

Other Psychoses

The numbers of patients with "functional" psychoses other than depressions or schizophrenias in which evoked response studies have been carried out have been too small for any significant findings.

NONPSYCHOTIC DISORDERS

Psychoneuroses

In our original studies of the somatosensory intensity-response and recovery functions, we found that dysthymic psychoneurotic patients—i.e., those with primary symptoms of anxiety and depressions or with diagnoses of psychophysiologic reactions—gave results which were indistinguishable from those of nonpatient subjects.[39,42,43,44] There was some indication that the intensity-response gradients in patients with conversion or dissociative reactions differed from those of dysthymics[43] and were more like those of "functional" psychoses or personality disorders. Also, the conversion-dissociation group showed a tendency for less amplitude recovery than dysthymic psychoneurotics.[44] On the other hand, with respect to visual responses, patients, with psychoneurotic disorders showed significantly larger amplitudes than nonpatients and displayed a tendency for prolonged latency recovery, which was not, however, statistically significant.[46]

There were 42 psychoneurotic patients in our recent study of somatosensory recovery functions.[35] Of these, 28 were classified as dysthymic and 14 were diagnosed as conversion or dissociative reactions. The dysthymic group differed significantly from age and sex matched nonpatients in only one R1 characteristic; they had a significantly longer latency for peak 7. This difference, significant at the 5 per cent level, could have arisen by chance. However, the recovery functions of the dysthymics did differ considerably from those of nonpatients. Dysthymics showed less recovery for peaks 4, 5, 6 and 7 over the entire 2.5 to 120 msec. recovery curve and also significantly less recovery of peak 8 during the first 20 msec. Figure 6 shows mean recovery curves for peak 6 in dysthymics and matched nonpatients. Dysthymics displayed little difference in latency recovery. In contrast to dysthymics, the number of differences found between the conversion group and matched nonpatients was so small as to have possibly occurred by chance. Examination of the mean values obtained in these analyses reinforced the conclusion that, in this series, which was carefully matched for age and sex, the dysthymics differed from nonpatients to a considerably greater extent than did the patients with conversion or dissociative reactions. These results, which constitute a reversal of previously found trends, are still consistent with the idea that the psychoneurotic group may not be treated as a uniform one with respect to evoked potential characteristics. However, the best available data now suggest that the dysthymic group may be more deviant electrophysiologically than the conversion-dissociative group.

Walter[60] has described the CNV in chronic anxiety states as developing slowly and irregularly and rarely reaching the amplitude of that of normal subjects. He reports that, in anxious patients, the CNV may easily be extinguished by unreinforced trials and may be eliminated when distraction by interfering signals is introduced. Walter has also indicated that patients with obsessive-compulsive neuroses show differences in their CNV, particularly in failure of decline to the base line as the operant action is completed.

Personality Disorders

In our initial studies, patients with personality disorders—i.e., personality trait disturbances, personality pattern disturbances, and sociopathic disturbances—gave essentially the same results as patients with "functional" psychoses. They showed greater amplitudes of initial somatosensory response components than nonpatients and their amplitude recovery functions were reduced.[41,43] The visual responses of patients with personality disorders were larger than those of non-patients, but their recovery functions were not significantly different.[45]

Our most recent sample[35] of personality disorders was classified as follows: personality trait disturbance, emotionally unstable type, 13 cases; passive-aggressive type, 13 cases; sociopathic personality disturbance, antisocial reaction, 11 cases. Comparing somatosensory responses in these groups with nonpatient groups matched for age and sex, the passive-aggressives were found to have significantly larger initial components, this being a repeat of previous findings; the Rl's of the other groups did not differ. Recovery function differences were

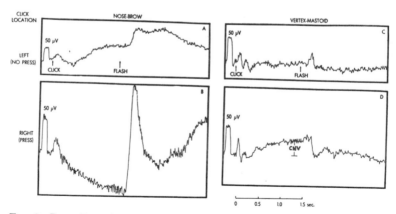

FIG. 8—Recordings from another subject obtained under same conditions as Fig. 7. Negativity at vertex follows right click (press condition) and not left click (no press condition). Note also, however, that in this case, the nose became markedly positive at the same time as vertex became negative with left click (no press condition). Other data indicate that nose positivity reflects increased negativity at brow.

found only in the later components and involved both amplitude and latency. The only outstanding difference was obtained in comparing 11 sociopathic, antisocial reaction patients with 11 matched nonpatients with respect to amplitude recovery of peak 7. The recovery curves for these groups are shown in Fig. 6. Patients displayed much more negativity, particularly during the first 20 msec. of the recovery function. Only one subject in each group overlapped the other with respect to mean R2 values during the first 20 msec.

Sociopathic patients also seem to be markedly deviant in CNV. Walter[60] reports that "psychopathic deviants," who seem comparable to the American "sociopathic personality, antisocial reaction," do not seem capable of producing more than a trace of CNV. He suggests a significant inverse relation between "neuroticism" and CNV amplitude.

BROADER DIAGNOSTIC CATEGORIES

It will have become evident that the major conclusion to be reached from our most recent study of somatosensory evoked response characteristics in a fairly large, heterogeneous sample of psychiatric patients and matched nonpatients is that patients differ from nonpatients in their recovery functions and that very little diagnostic specificity has been demonstrated. We carried out two sets of analyses to determine whether evoked response differences were specifically related to major classes of psychiatric disorder—i.e., psychosis, psychoneurosis, and personality disorder.[35] One analysis compared all patients with a diagnosis of "functional" psychosis with nonpsychotic patients and nonpatients matched for age and sex; there were 39 subjects in each group. There were many significant differences, but nearly all were found between patients and nonpatients. Only one measure discriminated between psychotics and nonpsychotics, that for the R2 of the measurement from peak 1 to peak 4 in the first 20 msec. of the recovery curve ($p<.05$). The mean value for nonpsychotics was intermediate between those of nonpatients and psychotics; this is illustrated in the upper left-hand curve of Fig. 6. In another set of analyses, comparisons were made between matched nonpatients, patients with psychoneuroses, and patients with personality disorders; there were 36 subjects in each group. The personality disorders and psychoneuroses showed virtually no significant differences.

The curves of Fig. 6 illustrate some of the amplitude recovery function differences found between various diagnostic groups and nonpatient controls matched with them. Figure 9 compares mean amplitude recovery curves for six peaks which yielded significant differences between the entire heterogeneous group of 162 patients and 54 nonpatients matched for age and sex. It will be seen that the differences in Fig. 9 are quite similar in character to those shown in Fig. 6, recovery being generally less in patients. Fig. 10 compares all patients with matched nonpatients with respect to peaks giving significant differences in latency recovery. The patients actually showed more rapid latency recovery than nonpatients for three of the four peaks, suggesting that mechanisms involved in latency and amplitude recovery may be quite different.

RESULTS OBTAINED WITH PERSONALITY TESTS

We have employed various personality tests as criterion variables in an attempt to determine psychological characteristics correlated with evoked response measures. In a study of visual evoked response characteristics, we administered the Bender Gestalt test (scored), the Maudsley Personality Inventory, and the Rod-and-Frame test, and measured the duration of Archimedes spiral after-image and the amobarbital sedation threshold in most of our patients.[49] There were few significant relationships, and most were provided by the Bender Gestalt and the Maudsley neuroticism (N) and extraversion (E) scores. Patients with poor Bender performances, high N and low E had larger responses. Since patients differed nonspecifically from nonpatients in the same direction with respect to these test scores, the results supported the conclusion that psychopathology was associated with larger evoked potentials, but they did not permit further specification of the relevant psychological variables.

In our recent somatosensory evoked response study, most of the patients received the Rod-and-Frame test and the Minnesota Multiphasic Personality Inventory (MMPI); a smaller number also had the Bender Gestalt test.[37] Although the number of significant relationships between evoked response and personality test variables far exceeded that expected by chance, the pattern of these relationships was relatively inconsistent and did not suggest clear formulations of the kind of psychopathology associated with evoked response deviation. Some individual findings were, however, of interest. One showed that patients who were more field-dependent, as indicated by Rod-and-Frame test performance, had larger initial components in their unpaired somatosensory response; this result had been predicted from the idea that greater field-dependence may involve less inhibitory activity of the kind required for perceptual discrimination and that large evoked responses may also reflect decreased inhibition. The other findings of interest also involved the initial component of the unpaired somatosensory response and showed larger responses in patients classified as psychotic than in those classed as nonpsychotic by the Meehl-Dahlstrom rules applied to the MMPI[27]; this agreed with the diagnostic finding shown in Fig. 6. Thus, on the whole, our results employing objective psychological tests were rather disappointing as regards specification of psychological factors contributing to patient-nonpatient evoked response differences.

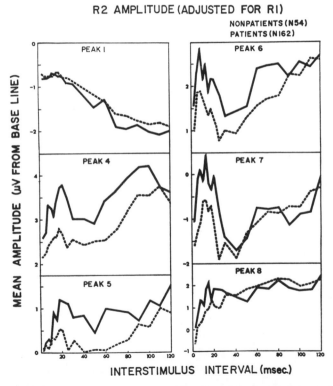

FIG. 9—Mean amplitude recovery curves for six peaks of somatosensory response, comparing a heterogeneous group of 162 patients (broken line) with 54 nonpatients (solid line) matched for age and sex. Note greater recovery in nonpatients.

In nonpatient subjects alone, we did find that the Maudsley E-score was related to age and evoked response amplitude.[45] Subjects under 20 with above median E had larger somatosensory responses than subjects with below median E values. In contrast, high E subjects 40 years of age or older had smaller responses than low E subjects.

Knott and Irwin[25] have recently employed a questionnaire–type anxiety scale to select high- and low-anxious college students for an experiment attempting to relate anxiety to CNV. Half of the subjects received 100 light-light pairings, which were regarded as nonstressful, and the other half received 100 light-shock pairings, regarded as stressful. The only difference between high- and low-anxiety subjects occurred for the response condition under stress, with high-anxiety subjects showing significantly smaller CNV's than low-anxiety subjects. Knott and Irwin attempted to explain their paradoxical findings, of lower CNV during the stressful response conditions for high-anxiety, by suggesting that combinations of stress and anxiety may operate to limit the range in which the cortical slow potentials may occur. Their results

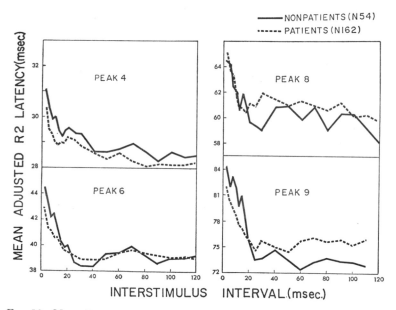

FIG. 10—Mean latency recovery curves for four somatosensory response peaks in heterogeneous patient group and nonpatients. Latency during first 20 msec. recovery was greater in patients for peaks 4, 6 and 9.

seem to be in line with those of Walter,[60] who reports reduced CNV in anxiety states; one could assume that Walter's patients were under stress by virtue of their clinical condition alone.

DISCUSSION

Many significant associations between evoked response characteristics and presence or absence of psychopathology have already been found. The psychopathological states range from mental retardation and organic brain syndromes to "functional" psychoses, psychoneuroses, personality disorders, and drug-induced conditions. On the other hand, very little specificity has so far been shown. To demonstrate specificity in future research will require greater sophistication at both the electrophysiological and psychological levels than has so far been applied. It seems fair to state that, at the electrophysiological level, we now have available most of the tools required to answer our questions. We need to learn how to ask the proper questions. Learning how to do this will, however, not be dependent upon electrophysiology alone; psychological insight and sophisticated psychological technology are required.

Looking toward the future, it seems probable that we shall learn much by combining computer methods for quantifying EEG and averaging evoked potentials to study their interrelationships. In our laboratory, we have recently found that, within a healthy college student population, superior and inferior performers on perceptual tests could be discriminated by the group correlation between EEG and evoked response amplitude. We are also studying intra-individual relationships between EEG and evoked response characteristics. We know from the results of Fedio et al.[15] that, in the reaction time experiment, the relationships between EEG blocking to the alerting signal and reaction time differ between schizophrenic patients and normal subjects. It seems possible that, whereas the discriminative power of individual indicators may be limited, much greater significance may be obtained by looking at interrelationships.

The most consistently discriminating evoked response indicator of those so far applied to patient and nonpatient groups has been the amplitude recovery function. It may be noted, however that the procedures employed have usually involved quite intense stimuli and that the finding of reduced recovery in patients probably represents increased inhibitory activity induced by the intense conditioning stimuli. We have recently been exploring a method for studying recovery functions which involves varying the intensity of conditioning stimuli so that inhibitory responsiveness will be favored in some averaging sequences and facilitatory in others. Very preliminary data suggest that patterns of "excitation-inhibition" measured by this method may be quite different from normal in the presence of psychopathology. It also seems possible that evoked response characteristics studied in this way may provide objective CNS measures corresponding to behavioral concepts of stimulus "reducers" and "augmenters."[28,52]

It seems a fair possibility that relevant pathophysiological processes affect brain areas with important regulatory functions. This idea is supported by the effects of major somatic therapies in psychosis; these tend to normalize behavior, rather than to shift it in one direction alone. For example, electroconvulsive therapy relieves both stupor and excitement and phenothiazines improve both agitation and withdrawal.[59] Such therapeutic effects may be most readily understood as reversal of abnormal function of regulators. If we are measuring two or more electrical events controlled by such regulators, dysfunction could be manifested more in changed relationships between them than in marked shifts in any event by itself. In pursuing the study of EEG-evoked response relationships and interactions to more complex varieties of stimuli, we hope that information will be gained concerning cerebral regulatory functions and their deviations in association with psychopathology.

ACKNOWLEDGEMENTS

Dr. Donald A. Overton contributed to various aspects of the more recent research described here.

REFERENCES

1. Barnet, A. B., and Lodge, A.: Click evoked EEG responses in normal and developmentally retarded infants. Nature 214:252-255, 1967.

2. Bickford, R. G., Cant, B. R., Cracco, R. Q., and Bickford, J. A.: Problems in the application of evoked potential techniques in psychiatry. Proc. IV World Congress of Psychiatry, Madrid, 1966, Abstract No. 313.

3. ——, Jacobson, J. L., and Cody, D. T.: Nature of average evoked potentials to sound and other stimuli in man. Ann. N.Y. Acad. Sci. 112:204-223, 1964.

4. Brown, J. C. N., Shagass, C., and Schwartz, M.: Cerebral evoked potential changes associated with the Ditran delirium and its reversal in man. In: Wortis, J. (Ed.): Recent Advances in Biological Psychiatry, Vol. VII. New York, Plenum Press, 1965, pp. 223-234.

5. Callaway, E., Jones, R. T., and Layne, R. S.: Evoked responses and segmental set of schizophrenia. Arch. Gen. Psychiat. 12:83-89, 1965.
6. —— and Jones, R. T.: Evoked responses for the study of complex cognitive functions. Presented at Conference on Objective Indicators of Psychopathology, Sterling Forest, N.Y., Feb., 1968 (in press).
7. Chalke, F. C. R., and Ertl, J.: Evoked potentials and intelligence. Life Sci. 4:1319-1322, 1965.
8. Chapman, L. F. and Walter, R. D.: Action of lysergic acid diethylamide on averaged human cortical evoked responses to light flash. In: Wortis, J. (Ed.): Recent Advances in Biological Psychiatry, Vol. VII. New York, Plenum Press, 1965, pp. 23-36.
9. Cohn, R.: Rhythmic after activity in visual evoked responses. Ann. N.Y. Acad. Sci. 112:281-291, 1964.
10. Dawson, G. D.: Cerebral responses to electrical stimulation of peripheral nerve in man. J. Neurol. Neurosurg. Psychiat. 10:134-140, 1947.
11. Domino, E. F., Matsuoka, S., Waltz, J. and Cooper, I. S.: Effects of cryogenic thalamic lesions in the somesthetic evoked response in man. Electroenceph. Clin. Neurophysiol. 19:127-138, 1965.
12. Donchin, E. and Lindsley, D. B.: Averaged evoked potentials and reaction times to visual stimuli. Electroenceph. Clin. Neurophysiol. 20:217-223, 1966.
13. Dustman, R. E. and Beck, E.: Visually evoked potentials: amplitude changes with age. Science 151:1013-1015, 1966.
14. Emde, J.: A time locked low level calibrator. Electroenceph. Clin. Neurophysiol. 16:616-618, 1964.
15. Fedio, P., Mirsky, A. F., Smith, W. J., and Parry, D.: Reaction time and EEG activation in normal and schizophrenic subjects. Electroenceph. Clin. Neurophysiol. 13:923-926, 1961.
16. Floris, V., Morocutti, C., Bernardi, G., Amabile, G., Rizzo, P. A., Sommer-Smith, J. A., and Vasconetto, C.: Cortical recovery cycle modifications in schizophrenics and dysthymic patients. Symposium on Use of Electronic Devices in Psychiatry, IV. World Congress of Psychiatry, Madrid, 1966 (in press).
17. Gartside, I. B., Lippold, O. C. J., and Meldrum, B. S.: The evoked cortical somatosensory response in normal man and its modification by oral lithium carbonate. Electroenceph. Clin. Neurophysiol. 20:382-390, 1966.
18. Goff, W. R., Rosner, B. S., and Allison, T.: Distribution of cerebral somatosensory evoked responses in normal man. Electroenceph. Clin. Neurophysiol. 14:697-713, 1962.
19. Guerrero-Figueroa, R. and Heath, R. G.: Evoked responses and changes during attentive factors in man. Arch. Neurol. (Chicago) 10:74-84, 1964.
20. Heninger, G. and Speck, L.: Visual evoked responses and mental status of schizophrenics. Arch. Gen. Psychiat. 15:419-426, 1966.
21. Igert, C. and Lairy, G. C.: Prognostic value of EEG in the development of schizophrenics. Electroenceph. Clin. Neurophysiol. 14:183-190, 1962.
22. Irwin, D. A., Knott, J. R., McAdam, D. W., and Rebert, C. S.: Motivational determinants of the "contingent negative variation." Electroenceph. Clin. Neurophysiol. 21:538-543, 1966.
23. Jones, R. T., Blacker, K. H., Callaway, E., and Layne, R. S.: The auditory

evoked response as a diagnostic and prognostic measure in schizophrenia. Amer. J. Psychiat. 122:33-41, 1965.

24. Jones, R. T., Blacker, K. H., and Callaway, E.: Perceptual dysfunction in schizophrenia: Clinical and auditory evoked response findings. Amer. J. Psychiat. 123:639-645, 1966.

25. Knott, J. R. and Irwin, D. A.: The contingent negative variation during stress and non-stress situations with high- and low-anxiety subjects. Presented at American EEG Society Meeting, Atlantic City, June, 1967.

26. Liberson, W. T.: Study of evoked potentials in aphasics. Amer. J. Physical Med. 45:135-142, 1966.

27. Meehl, P. E. and Dahlstrom, W. G.: Objective configural rules for discriminating psychotic from neurotic MMPI profiles. J. Consult. Psychol., 24:375-387, 1960.

28. Petrie, A., Holland, T. and Wolk, I.: Sensory stimulation causing subdued experience: audio-analgesia and perceptual augmentation and reduction. J. Nerve. Ment. Dis. 137:312-321, 1963.

29. Rodin, E. and Luby, E.: Effects of LSD-25 on the EEG and photic evoked responses. Arch. Gen. Psychiat. 14:435-441, 1966.

30. ——, Zacharopoulos, G., Beckett, P. and Frohman, C.: Characteristics of visually evoked responses in normal subjects and schizophrenic patients. Electroenceph. Clin. Neurophysiol. 17:458, 1964.

31. Schwartz, M. and Shagass, C.: Recovery functions of human somatosensory and visual evoked potentials. Ann. N. Y. Acad. Sci. 112:510-525, 1964.

32. Shagass, C.: Effects of LSD on somatosensory and visual evoked responses and on the EEG in man. In: Wortis, J. (Ed.): Recent Advances in Biological Psychiatry, Vol. IX. New York, Plenum Press, 1967, pp. 209-227.

33. ——: Discussion of W. T. Liberson's paper on EEG and Intelligence. In: Zubin, J., and Jervis, G. A. (Eds.): Psychopathology of Mental Development. New York, Grune & Stratton, 1967, pp. 626-628.

34. ——: Pharmacology of evoked potentials in man. Presented at 1967 meeting of Amer. College of Neuropsychopharmacology, San Juan (in press).

35. ——: Averaged somatosensory evoked responses in various psychiatric disorders. In: Wortis, J. (Ed.): Recent Advances in Biological Psychiatry, Vol. X. New York, Plenum Press, 1968, pp. 205-219.

36. ——, and Bittle, R. M.: Therapeutic effects of LSD: A follow-up study. J. Nerv. Ment. Dis. 144:471-478, 1967.

37. ——, and Canter, A.: Some personality correlates of cerebral evoked response characteristics. Proc. XVIII Internat. Congress of Psychology, Moscow, 1966, Symposium No. 6, pp. 47-52.

38. —— and Overton, D. A.: Measurement of cerebral "excitability" characteristics in relation to psychopathology. Presented at Conference on Objective Indicators of Psychopathology, Sterling Forest, N.Y., February, 1968 (in press).

39. —— and Schwartz, M.: Excitability of the cerebral cortex in psychiatric disorders. In: Roessler, R. and Greenfield, N. S. (Eds.): Physiological Correlates of Psychological Disorder. Madison, U. of Wisconsin Press, 1962, pp. 45-60.

40. —— and ——: Cerebral cortical reactivity in psychotic depressions. Arch. Gen. Psychiat. 6:235-242, 1962.

41. —— and ——: Observations on somatosensory cortical reactivity in personality disorders. J. Nerv. Ment. Dis. 135:44-51, 1962.

42. —— and ——: Cerebral responsiveness in psychiatric patients. Arch. Gen. Psychiat. 8:177-189, 1963.

43. —— and ——: Psychiatric disorder and deviant cerebral responsiveness to sensory stimulation. In: Wortis, J. (Ed.): Recent Advances in Biological Psychiatry, Vol. V., New York, Plenum Press, 1963, pp. 321-330.

44. —— and ——: Psychiatric correlates of evoked cerebral cortical potentials. Amer. J. Psychiat. 119:1055-1061, 1963.

45. —— and ——: Age, personality and somatosensory cerebral evoked responses. Science 148:1359-1361, 1965.

46. —— and ——: Visual cerebral evoked response characteristics in a psychiatric population. Amer. J. Psychiat. 121:979-987, 1965.

47. —— and ——: Somatosensory cerebral evoked responses in psychotic depression. Brit. J. Psychiat. 112:799-807, 1966.

48. ——, —— and Amadeo, M.: Some drug effects on evoked cerebral potentials in man. J. Neuropsychiat. 3:S49-S58, 1962.

49. ——, —— and Krishnamoorti, S. R.: Some psychologic correlates of cerebral responses evoked by light flash. J. Psychosom. Res., 9:223-231, 1965.

50. —— and Trusty, D.: Somatosensory and visual cerebral evoked response changes during sleep. In: Wortis, J. (Ed.): Recent Advances in Biological Psychiatry, Vol. VIII. New York, Plenum Press, 1966, pp. 321-334.

51. Shakow, D.: Segmental set: A theory of the formal psychological deficit in schizophrenia. Arch. Gen. Psychiat. 6:1-17, 1962.

52. Silverman, J.: Variations in cognitive control and psychophysiological defense in the schizophrenias. Psychosom. Med. 29:225-251, 1967.

53. Speck, L. B., Dim, B. and Mercer, M.: Visual evoked responses of psychiatric patients. Arch. Gen. Psychiat. 15:59-63, 1966.

54. Spehlmann, R.: The averaged electrical responses to diffuse and to patterned light in the human. Electroenceph. Clin. Neurophysiol., 19:560-569, 1965.

55. Straumanis, J. J.: Somatosensory and visual cerebral evoked response changes associated with chronic brain syndromes and aging. Unpublished M. S. Thesis in Psychiatry, U. of Iowa, 1964.

56. ——, Shagass, C. and Schwartz, M.: Visually evoked cerebral response changes associated with chronic brain syndromes and aging. J. Gerontology 20:498-506, 1965.

57. Sutton, S., Braren, M. and Zubin, J.: Evoked-potential correlates of stimulus uncertainty. Science 150:1187-1188, 1965.

58. Sutton, S., Tueting, P., Zubin, J. and John, E. R.: Information delivery and the sensory evoked potential. Science 155:1436-1439, 1967.

59. The National Institute of Mental Health Psychopharmacology Service Center Collaborative Study Group. Phenothiazine treatment in acute schizophrenia: Effectiveness. Arch. Gen. Psychiat. 10:246-261, 1964.

60. Walter, W. G.: Electrophysiologic contributions to psychiatric therapy. In: Masserman, J. (Ed.): Current Psychiatric Therapies, Vol. VI. New York, Grune and Stratton, 1966, pp. 13-25.

61. ——, Cooper, R., Aldridge, V. J., McCallum, W. C. and Winter, A. L.: Contingent negative variation: An electric sign of sensorimotor association and expectancy in the human brain. Nature 203:380-384, 1964.

62. Weitzman, E. D. and Kremen, H.: Auditory evoked responses during different stages of sleep in man. Electroenceph. Clin. Neurophysiol., 18:65-70, 1965.

Discussion of Dr. Shagass' Paper

by W. T. LIBERSON, M.D., PH.D.

Loyola University

IT IS A PRIVILEGE to discuss the paper of Dr. Shagass. All those who have followed his efforts to derive new ways of understanding psychopathology with the new techniques of recording evoked cerebral potentials have admired his work.

From the very beginning of this work, he was inspired by "the idea that deviant reactivity or excitability of the central nervous system underlies psychopathology" and, therefore, "should . . . be manifested in deviant evoked response characteristics."

I would accept this proposition with some reservation. Psychopathology is not necessarily related to the initial processes underlying perception, but might affect the cerebral activity which follows immediate perception of the stimulus. It apparently affects the degree of attention that the patient extends toward differential stimuli and, as Dr. Shagass mentions, Dr. Callaway has given us some information covering this aspect of the problem. From this point of view, the late components of the evoked potentials may be of greater interest to psychopathologists than the earlier ones. As Dr. Shagass mentioned in his paper, I have presented evidence that late potentials, at least in the area of somatosensory perception, are not transmitted to the cortex via reticular formation pathways, but are carried out through the lemniscal sensory afferents. The changes in these late components, so readily produced by sleep or anesthetics, may, therefore, have for a locus the cortex and not necessarily the deeply seated reticular core.

The animal experiments which we conducted recently in collaboration with Dr. Karczmar, show that different components of the evoked potentials are not affected in the same way by "decision-making processes." Thus, for example, at the beginning of a behavioral latency period preceding the rat's jump to one of two windows of the Lashley jumping stand, selected by the rat, the early negative component (40 msec. peak latency) to meaningful visual stimuli is of lower amplitude than the following (N_2) negative component (140 msec. peak latency), while the ratio of N_1/N_2 is inverted just prior to the jump. This finding suggests that behavioral correlations of evoked potentials should be considered *differentially* in relation to each of these components, particularly the late ones. Although Dr. Shagass' present review of the correlations of evoked potentials in sleep, delirious states and organic mental disturbances is most encouraging, his findings concerning functional mental disorders are less promising. He recently found that the difference between various functional mental disorders found in the past may be explained by the effect of age and sex, with the exception of the recovery rate of the evoked potentials, respectively, for the normal individuals and for patients with functional mental disorders. However, all the involved groups of mental patients, whether schizophrenic, depressive, psychopathic or neurotics, manifest the same deficiency in recovery of evoked potentials. This seems to limit the significance of his findings, as such general factors as attention, cooperativeness, etc. may explain these results. It is hoped that when the late components of the potentials are considered differentially, more specific correlations will be found.

Dr. Shagass' findings concerning the possibility of contaminating the "expectancy wave" by eye movement artifacts is somewhat distressing. If his results are confirmed, they would suggest the possibility of correlating directly recorded eye movements with expectancy. Mrs. Liberson and I have recently reported significant correlation of eye movements, slow or rapid, with different types of mental content during alert states and drowsiness.

3

BEHAVIORAL AND AFFECTIVE RESPONSES TO BRAIN STIMULATION IN MAN

by FRANK R. ERVIN, M.D.,* VERNON H. MARK, M.D.,† and
JANICE STEVENS, M.D.‡

E LECTRICAL stimulation of discrete regions of the subcortex in waking man provides a wealth of titillating anecdotal material. To relate this material to the problem of cerebral organization in psychopathological states is conceptually difficult. A few of the more obvious difficulties in interpretation should be noted:

1. A synchronous electrical discharge is quite different from the exquisitely patterned afferent volley of physiologic signals.

2. In a complex neural aggregate the electrical input may activate excitatory and inhibitory; afferent, efferent, and integrative; or cholinergic and adrenergic systems indiscriminately.

3. The instantaneous state of cerebral organization—i.e., all the other influences acting on the object structure at the time of stimulation—is unknown.

4. At best, the site stimulated is part of an integrated system, so that the stimulus is like a rock thrown in a pond—perhaps influencing by waves a distant lily pad. The stimulation of a structure says what it *can* do under certain circumstances, not what it *does* do normally.

5. It should be further emphasized that ablation is not the reciprocal of stimulation in other than very simple input or output systems.

It might best be said that both stimulation and ablation experiments should be described with the emphasis on how the organism functions in

*Department of Psychiatry, Massachusetts General Hospital, Boston, Mass.
†Neurosurgical Service, Boston City Hospital, Boston, Mass.
‡Department of Neurology, University of Oregon Medical School, Portland, Ore.
This project was supported in part by: USPHS research grant #CA 07368-05; DHEW Social and Rehabilitation research grant #UD 2685 M-68; Neuroresearch Foundation grant; and FRE career awardee USPHS #5 KO3 MH 19434-05.

the new state of cerebral organization necessitated by the experimental intervention.

With these caveats I should like to try to summarize the results of ten years' experience in cooperation with the Neurosurgical Service at the Massachusetts General Hospital in human brain stimulation; in particular, with Drs. William H. Sweet, Vernon H. Mark and Raymond J. Kjellberg. In addition, Dr. Janice Stevens has provided welcome critique and creative ideas. The latter part of this paper is quite directly derived from a study performed with Dr. Stevens.[1]

The most secure data comes from those patients with intractable pain due to terminal carcinoma, because a) they have no intrinsic structural disease of the brain, and b) after the patient's death, histological examination permits accurate anatomical localization of electrode sites.[2-6]

Using the experience gained from such cases, however, one can make certain cautious extrapolations of the data from patients with intrinsic brain disease. For example, phenomena observed following limbic system stimulation in the epileptic may be related to normal mechanisms if also seen in the pain patient. I shall assume this privilege in discussing the data.

It is difficult to know whether one should organize the data by anatomic or behavioral categories. I have chosen to use anatomic ones to provide some solid base of reference. I should, however, like to draw particular attention to the distinction between long-lasting and transient effects.

I. Posterior Thalamus

a. Lateral (VPM, VPL)

The primary relay nuclei of the somatosensory system provide the simplest and most understandable model. Stimulation here at threshold produces a subjective report of contralateral paraesthesias, "tingling," or "electric shock-like" sensations. These sensations are well localized, somatotopic (e.g., ulnar fingers of one hand), and clearly referred to the body surface. At increasing stimulus intensity there is an increase in subjective intensity and a spread of sensation by contiguity (fingers to hand to wrist to face.) Quite medial placements, evoking peri- or intra-oral sensations, are usually described as bilateral. At a given frequency of stimulation a thalamic homunculus could be described. Even in this simple system, however, change in frequency of stimulation might change both the quality and the anatomic site of referred sensation at threshold. With constant parameters the results are highly reproducible, including the current threshold for subjective awareness (the ascending threshold always slightly higher than the descending). For stimulus trains up to five seconds in duration, the subjective sensation is contemporaneous with the stimulation. With protracted or intense stimulation there is sometimes an "after-sensation" of a few seconds.

b. Intralaminar Nuclei (PF, CM, CI)

A few millimeters medially, in the diffuse thalamic system, the results are different. At threshold the subject expresses dismay and aversion: "Stop!" "Good God, what's that?" "I'm falling apart!"—but finds it difficult to describe the quality or location of the sensation. It seems to be internal, generalized, *sometimes lateralized,* and universally unpleasant. On probing, one can elicit analogies to the reaction to fingernails scraping on blackboard, sudden fright (as in a near accident,) nauseating pain (as with a crushed finger), etc.

Stimulation at levels below this subjective reporting threshold elicits increasing irritability, diffuse complaints of fatigue, headache, general discomfort and restlessness. Both the low–level and more dramatic phenomena have quite constant thresholds for evocation and extinction. The phenomena disappear abruptly on termination of the stimulus. Repeated or protracted low–level stimulation may lead to an irritable, anxious patient for an hour or two, but this seems more parsimoniously explained on experiential than physiologic grounds.

The occasional lateralization of the dysphoria might be noted, for we have also seen lateralized euphoria—both equally puzzling to the subject (and observer).

II. Anterior Thalamus (DM, AV)

Brief unilateral stimulation of these anterior thalamic structures may elicit no subjective response. On protracted bilateral stimulation, there may well appear a cumulative confusion and disorientation (especially in AV), as is seen after ablation. Of particular interest is the occasional evocation of a structured affective response.

A case example may be helpful: a very intelligent, articulate 40-year-old lady had a history of many years of abrupt incapacitating pananxiety attacks, which had been absent for 12 months as her current depression deepened. On stimulation of a region in AV of about 3 mm. in diameter, her characteristic anxiety attacks were reproduced in detail, the intensity directly proportional to the stimulus current. The attacks disappeared on termination of stimulus, would wax and wane with variations of current, and could be aborted by stimulation of a nearby electrode pair. Sham stimulation, unexpected stimulation during distraction, and repeated determination of the threshold for onset were convincing as to the unique relationship of stimulus site and symptoms. Similar, though much less dramatic, findings characterized a few other patients with electrodes in this region, none of whom had a history of gross psychopathology.

III. LIMBIC SYSTEM

a. Medial Forebrain Bundle—Anterior Hypothalamus

Responses from this region are very sensitive to precise electrode position and stimulus parameters. By carefully dissecting away the autonomic responses by parametric manipulation, an interesting effect remains, consistent with Heath's reports of stimulation in this region.[7] In our experience, stimulation might produce early visible relaxation in the pain patient, but the response was most obvious after 10 to 15 minutes. By that time the patient reports relaxation, mild euphoria (like two martinis"), is more communicative, shows less muscle spasm, directly denies pain, etc. This effect persists for several hours following 30 to 45 minutes of stimulation. Stimulation carried beyond that point gradually produces more dyscontrol and the patient looks slightly "drunk".[8]

The striking features of this stimulation are the protracted effect of stimulation without persistent EEG changes. This point will be discussed in more detail in reference to the amygdala.

b. Hippocampus

Stimulation in the region of the hippocampus produces complex and varied subjective reports, which are highly individualized. Some examples of these will be shown later. Three generalizations can be made, however:

1. Bilateral stimulation of the hippocampus produces a total amnesia for coincident events (with a slight retrograde component) without otherwise altering the patient's ongoing behavior or appearance (e.g., reading aloud is carried out quite adequately, but neither the content

nor the act can be recalled). Unilateral stimulation may produce a feeling of "reminiscence" without specific content; this is particularly true in the anterior, perhaps peri-amygdaloid, region. Occasionally, but rarely, is a "memory" evoked; and when it is, it usually has an affective (e.g., "an orchard at home in the spring") rather than a substantive quality.

2. At other sites one often evokes clearly dysphoric behavioral responses of fear, disgust or horror, often with an apparently hallucinatory content, but with frustrating concurrent amnesia.

3. Protracted or recurrent stimulation at low frequencies ultimately produces a state of increasing disorientation and "organic confusion" typified by hippocampal slow waves. The condition resembles a mild post-EST confusional state, but often without scalp EEG changes.

c. Amygdala and Periamygdaloid Region

It is the affective states accompanying stimulation, ablation, and epileptic abnormality of the amygdaloid complex that are to us the most provocative for the study of psychopathology. Let us begin with 3 detailed case examples:

The first case is that of a 33-year-old male whose history of seizures began some fifteen years before admission, when, following hemorrhage from a gastric ulcer resulting in severe vascular shock, he began to have blank spells with staring, salivation, licking, swallowing, head turning to the left, an impulse to run, searching movements, and rapid speech followed by a feeling of intense "hurt" and depression. Treatment with anticonvulsants controlled the early motor seizure and unconsciousness, but he began to have frequent episodes of violent aggressive behavior that commenced with the same feeling of "hurt" and hypersensitivity that had followed the previous ictal episodes. Violent verbal and physical aggressive behavior was directed most often toward his wife, lasting for minutes to several hours and followed by crying spells. The patient was only partially conscious of what took place in these episodes. Occasional spells were accompanied by an aura of smelling ether. Scalp EEGs prior to electrode implantation showed some non-specific bitemporal theta activity. The depth studies from amygdala and hippocampus disclosed spike activity bilaterally. From both amygdala sites, stimulations gave the patient a "tremendous" feeling of relaxation after some 10 to 30 seconds. The patient had a variety of interesting ways of describing this sensation, such as "super relaxation," relief from the intense anxiety and depression that he frequently experienced, "detachment," "displacement," and so on.

These pleasurable sensations usually began some 30 seconds after the current was turned on and persisted for minutes to hours following cessation of the stimulation. There was no attendent EEG change, nor were blood pressure, pulse or respiration regularly affected. The rapid and lasting relief of tension or somatic distress following stimulation suggested the possibility of a conditioned effect from the situation. This could not, however, be substantiated by placebo stimulations, stimulation of other intracerebral sites, nor warningless stimulation by remote telemetry methods. The patient became "addicted" to stimulation, given several times weekly, and when it was withdrawn became extremely depressed, complaining of multiple aches and pains, tension and despair. On occasion the stimulation induced a peculiar ether-like odor, which was regularly followed by a strong relaxing effect. When RF lesions were made at the site of maximum spiking in the right amygdala, the patient experienced no immediate effect. However, on the following day there was a sharp depression in mood, which persisted for approximately a week. When a second lesion was made on the opposite side several months later, a much more severe mood depression accompanied by delusions occurred and persisted for nearly two weeks, requiring the use of mood elevators to maintain the patient's nutrition and activity.

The second patient is a 28-year-old unemployed Navy veteran discharged from the service because of typical psychomotor automatisms, which were only partially controlled with anticonvulsants. Further studies were performed because of warningless attacks of violent impulsivity which frequently got him into difficulties with others and for which he had no memory. Recordings from the scalp demonstrated some mild sharp and slow activity over the temporal regions, more prominent on the left. From deep sites, left amygdala and hippocampus spike discharges of more than 300 microvolts were recorded. Electrical stimulation of the amygdala electrodes induced occasional after-discharges with lipsmacking and head turning but no duplication of the complex seizure automatism of rage attacks. Metrazol activation caused an electrical seizure in the right amygdala with a sense of "whirling" but no clinical seizure. A summary of the effects of electrical stimulation at the 48 depth points in the amygdala and hippocampus is given in Fig. 1.

Again, as in patient I, patient II was affected by the stimulations long after the current was turned off, despite the fact that this kaleidoscope of sensations was not associated with an after-discharge. Unlike patient I, who became calm and euphoric after stimulation, this man's post-stimulus effects were subjective confusion, excitability, press of speech, rushing thoughts, over-activity, restlessness, difficulty with concentration, and vivid imagery and recollection of old situations that induced anger and excitement. Chlorpromazine, 200 mg. daily, controlled these symptoms quite well. In an effort to localize the origin of the rage attacks, we recalled the important studies of Eidelberg, Lesse and Gault[9] with cocaine induction of amygdala seizures in rat and cat, and introduced a relatively small amount of this drug intranasally in our patient while recording from the depth and scalp electrodes.

Seizure activity elicited in the amygdala of the cat by intraperitoneal cocaine was particularly remarkable not only in that the electrical discharge was restricted to the amygdala; it was also resistant to phenobarbital and Dilantin, but could be blocked by adrenolytic agents such as reserpine, chlorpromazine, or dibenamine, and could be potentiated by the monoamine oxidase inhibitors. Fig. 2D illustrates the results of the instillation of 80 mg. of cocaine intranasally while the patient was still premedicated with Thorazine. One week later, with the pa-

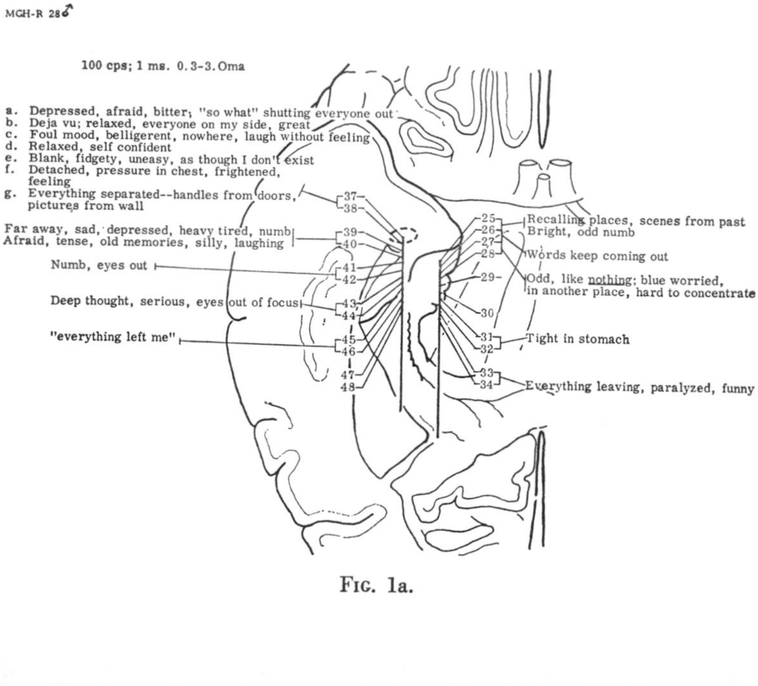

MGH-R 28♂

100 cps; 1 ms. 0.3-3.0ma

a. Depressed, afraid, bitter; "so what" shutting everyone out
b. Deja vu; relaxed, everyone on my side, great
c. Foul mood, belligerent, nowhere, laugh without feeling
d. Relaxed, self confident
e. Blank, fidgety, uneasy, as though I don't exist
f. Detached, pressure in chest, frightened, feeling
g. Everything separated--handles from doors, pictures from wall

Far away, sad, depressed, heavy tired, numb
Afraid, tense, old memories, silly, laughing

Numb, eyes out

Deep thought, serious, eyes out of focus

"everything left me"

Recalling places, scenes from past
Bright, odd numb

Words keep coming out

Odd, like nothing; blue worried, in another place, hard to concentrate

Tight in stomach

Everything leaving, paralyzed, funny

FIG. 1a.

tient off Thorazine, the intranasal cocaine was repeated, as seen in Figs. 2A, B, and C.

The seizure discharge demonstrated was associated with improved performance on psychological speed and accuracy tests and the characteristic autonomic effects of cocaine. The patient was elated and there was considerable speech pressure which lasted for some three hours during this prolonged one-per-second discharge. Phenobarbital failed to block the activity. The test was repeated one week later with similar results. At this time nasopharyngeal leads were used simultaneously to determine whether it would be possible to make this test in patients without intracerebral electrodes. Although a high-amplitude discharge was again induced in amygdala, it was not evident at nasopharyngeal or scalp leads.

In summary, like patient I, patient II displayed two types of response to depth stimulation: a short-latency effect of relatively simple stereotyped nature, inducing fear, visual disturbance, *déjà vu*; and long-duration changes commencing 5 to 30 seconds after onset of current and consisting of much more complicated mood and thought changes.

The third patient, a 63-year-old mild-mannered machinist with terminal squamous cell carcinoma of piriform sinus, suffered from intractable localized pain in head and neck. He received treatment with x-

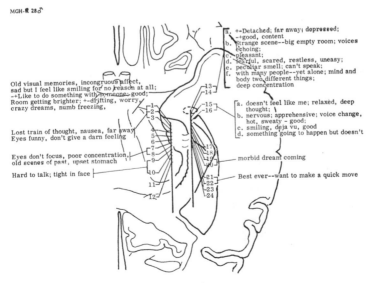

FIG. 1b.

ray, local denervation, electric shock therapy and narcotics, without relief. In March of 1966, electrodes were implanted in nucleus parafasicularis and in posterolateral thalamus. Lesions of the latter two sites were unsuccessful in relieving pain. In February, 1967, bilateral amygdala implants were placed for chronic stimulation. When the patient was brought to the laboratory for stimulation of the depth points in the search for a region that might give relief of pain or elevation of mood, a total of one and one-half hours was spent in the first stimulation trial. No change in subjective state or relief of pain was obvious from any site. However, the second most distal pair of electrodes in the left amygdala induced a sharp blood pressure rise which persisted for nearly an hour despite cessation of stimulation. The patient was returned to the ward at the end of the hour-and-a-half session. Approximately 20 minutes later he became wide-eyed, would not permit his nurse to come near, breathed hard, appeared extremely angry, had a vacant stare, started climbing on the bed, attacked anyone nearby, and was incontinent, proceeding to hurl feces at all who came near. This behavior continued for about 10 minutes until a group of nurses and orderlies were able to restrain him long enough to administer Thorazine, after which his behavior rapidly calmed and deep sleep ensued. He awoke with total amnesia for the episodes. The following day, stimulation was again carried out in the right amygdala, but for a much briefer period—some 20 minutes. Again no EEG or clinical change occurred, and this time the blood pressure was unchanged. Shortly after return to the ward he again had an attack similar to that of two days before and was belligerent and assaultive, but for a much briefer period. The patient had never had any sort of epilepsy or behavioral disturbance in the past, and these aggressive episodes were totally at variance with his usual courtly and dignified manner. Subsequent stimulations were limited in duration of sessions, and no further episodes of this nature occurred. The patient died twelve weeks following the amygdala implants. Electrodes were seen to be squarely on target in right and left amygdala.

These long-latency, long-lasting effects of deep temporal stimulations suggest that neurohumoral changes may contribute fundamentally to the clinical effects. That the prolonged stimulations are not acting as temporary lesions seems likely from the very different effects of stimulation and ablation at these sites. While previous reports of the effects of electrical stimulation of these structures and other cerebral sites in man have emphasized the well-known responses of short latency, limited in duration to passage of the current or subsequent after-discharge, this report emphasizes a different response, very similar to the delayed rage and other effects following prolonged amygdala stimulation in cats as reported by Gunne.[10] The reports of mood elevation with electrical changes are of course not available from experimental animals.

To summarize our interpretation of the phenomena in these patients, it is necessary to consider a feature of temporal lobe epilepsy to which

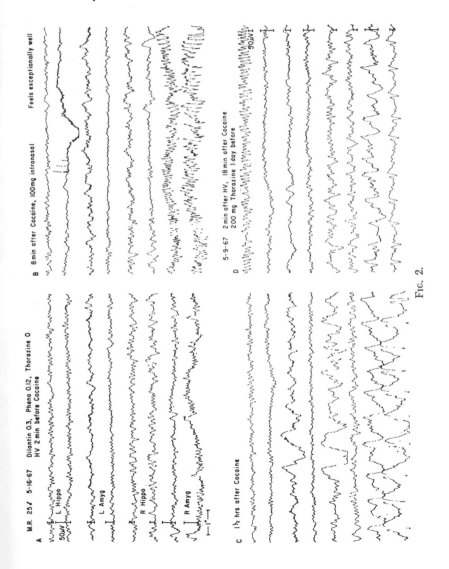

Fig. 2.

we have previously drawn attention. The patient with temporal lobe seizures often has a severe personality disorder characterized by episodes of affective dyscontrol, often by mood swings, and by an aggressive, irritable, pre-ictal state. The psychopathological syndrome often seems worse on effective anticonvulsant medication and is improved by phenothiazine medication (which may worsen the seizure). Our surgical therapeutic experience is that a discrete subcortical lesion may on occasion improve either the behavior or the fits, without affecting the other. The implied reciprocity of these conditions is epitomized by those cases who develop a frank (self-limited) psychosis and disappearance of seizures, with or without the so-called "forced normalization" of the EEG.[11]

The dramatic and prolonged effects on mood and thought process seen in the patients described (and in others) after stimulation suggest that neurohumoral rather than neuroelectric processes are involved. We should like to propose for discussion the hypothesis that in the amygdaloid complex there are at least two neural systems involved. One is a noradrenergic system, which on brief stimulation produces a prolonged elevation of transmitter catecholamine with mood elevation and a later rebound phenomenon. It is this system which is also activated by median forebrain bundle stimulation. Interruption of the system by amygdalectomy consistently leads to a depression of both catechols and mood. (Noradrenalin is suggested, in line with the work of Kety[12] and of Schildkraut[13] on neurohumoral relations to mood. Serotonin would fit the argument as well.) The other is a cholinergic system, which on activation accounts for the transient, mostly motor and autonomic, phenomena characteristic of the "fit." In a massive electrical discharge, of course, both systems might well be involved, which would account for the often profound affective changes following a clinical seizure. In a total functioning organism we would imagine these systems to be in some dynamic balance, upset by disease, by anticonvulsants, or by phenothiazines.

There are numerous conceptual problems with so simple a dichotomization both of neurohumors and of complex behavior. For example, most speculations on the relationship of catecholamines to mood have emphasized depression and elation as affective opposites. In our discussion, we are emphasizing anger as opposed to "tranquility" or mild euphoria. Yet the psychodynamic and phenomenologic kinship of anger and depression is well known. Further, the variable of specific neural subsystems in which humoral changes have particular significance has barely been explored. We should like to return for further speculation on the Neurobiological Aspects of Psychopathology, the topic of this symposium, after acquiring more data. In this paper we have not attempted to describe techniques, therapeutic indications or results, or the host of clinical, social and practical problems accompanying stereotactic surgery. In particular, we do not here elaborate on, but do wish to call attention to, the long-range social implications of the rapidly increasing technological ability to predictably modify behavior (including pharmacological and conditioning techniques, as well as direct neural intervention).

REFERENCES

1. Steven, J. R., Mark, V. H., Ervin, F., Pacheco, P., and Seumatsu, K.: Long-latency long-lasting psychological changes induced by deep temporal stimulation in man. Arch. Neurol., 1968 (in press).

2. Mark, V. H., Ervin, F. R., and Hackett, T.: Clinical aspects of sterotactic thalamotomy in the human: treatment of chronic severe pain. A.M.A. Arch. Neurol. 3:35, 1960.

3. Ervin, F. R. and Mark, V. H.: Stereotactic thalamotomy in the human: II. Physiologic observations on the human thalamus. A.M.A. Arch. Neurol. 3:368, 1960.

4. Mark, V. H., Ervin, F. R., and Yakovlev, P. I.: Stereotactic thalamotomy. III. Verification of anatomical lesion sites in the human thalamus. A.M.A. Arch. Neurol. 8:528, 1963.

5. Mark, V. H. and Ervin, F. R.: Studies on the human thalamus. IV. Evoked responses. Ann. N.Y. Acad. Sci. 112:81, 1964.

6. Sweet, W. H., Mark, V. H., and Ervin, F. R.: Stereotactic thalamic surgery for relief of pain. In: White, J. C. (Ed.): Pain and the Neurosurgeon. Springfield, Ill., Charles C Thomas, 1968 (in press).

7. Heath, R. G.: Brain centers and control of behavior—man. In: Nodien, J. H. and Moyer, J. H. (Eds.): Psychosomatic Medicine, 1st Hahnemann Symposium. Philadelphia, Lea and Febiger, 1962, pp. 228-240.

8. Ervin, F., Brown, C. C. and Mark, V. H.: Striatal influence on facial pain. Confin. Neurol. 27:75-86, 1966.

9. Eidelberg, E., Leese, H. and Gault, F. P.: An experimental model of temporal lobe epilepsy: Studies of the convulsant properties of cocaine. In: Glaser, G. II., (Ed.): EEG and Behavior. New York, Basic Books 1963, pp. 272-283.

10. Gunne, L. M. and Reis, D. J.: Changes in brain catecholamines associated with electrical stimulation of amygdaloid nucleus. Life Sci. 2:804-809, 1963.

11. Landholt, H.: Serial electroencephalographic investigations during psychotic episodes in epileptic patients and during schizophrenic attacks. In: de Hass, Lorentz (Ed.): Epilepsy. New York, American Elseiver, 1958, pp. 91-133.

12. Kety, S. S.: Biogenic amines and the affective state. Neurosciences Research Program Bulletin 5:81-86, 1967.

13. Schildkraut, J. J. and Kety, S. S.: Biogenic amines and emotion. Science 156:21-30, 1967.

4

THIS chapter is an invited paper, standing both as a discussion of the work of Ervin and Mark (Chapter 3) and as a thoughtful assessment of some of the issues, scientific and ethical, that are raised by research of this kind on patients. The contribution to knowledge represented by research such as Ervin's and Mark's is unassailable, but it behooves a professional association such as this one to consider its complex social implications, lest the furtherance of such research be jeopardized by doubt and misunderstanding in the larger community.

—*The Editors*

SOME REFLECTIONS ON STIMULATION OF THE HUMAN BRAIN

by HERBERT G. VAUGHAN, JR.*

IN 1870 Fritsch and Hitzig published their pioneering work on the electrical excitability of the cerebral cortex. Four years later the surgeon Roberts Bartholow thrust a stimulating electrode into the brain of a maidservant through a cancerous lesion of her skull, both confirming their findings and causing the death of his patient. Although advances in surgical skill and judgment have largely precluded repetition of the disastrous outcome of this experiment, the striking experiential and behavioral effects which may be induced by human brain stimulation demand a continuing review of the objectives and implications of this procedure.

The extensive clinical experiences with stimulation of the human cerebral cortex reported by Foerster and later by Penfield firmly established the technique as a method for accurately locating those cortical areas giving rise to sensory and motor responses. The sometimes

---

*Saul R. Korey Department of Neurology, Albert Einstein College of Medicine, Bronx, N.Y.

dramatic effects of cortical stimulation in man have led many to impute to it a precision and specificity justified neither by the necessarily limited human observations nor by the more detailed parametric studies in experimental animals. Since the manifestations of cortical stimulation may be drastically modified by alterations in stimulus parameters or by prior stimulation, conclusions concerning the functional specificity of any brain region, based primarily upon the results of stimulation, must be viewed with caution. Nonetheless, electrical stimulation survives as a technique of brain research, encouraged and facilitated by technical and therapeutic developments of the past few decades. Since the advent of stereotaxic surgery, few regions within the human brain remain untouched by recording, stimulating, or lesion-making probes.

The therapeutic rationale for exploration of structures deep within the human brain derives from success in the amelioration of some forms of epilepsy, movement disorders, intractable pain, and psychopathology through localized lesioning or excision. Since the early days of brain surgery, stimulation has been justified largely as a means for defining the desired location of the therapeutic lesion. Accordingly, it is ordinarily utilized only in those patients suffering from conditions considered suitable for such drastic treatment. This limitation, although serving to curb grossly excessive adventures in human brain stimulation, also impedes the rational development of this procedure as a potential therapeutic technique. In several respects the appropriately applied stimulation appears to possess significant therapeutic advantages in comparison with brain lesions. Advantages are particularly apparent in those situations in which the lesion is designed, not to destroy a pathological region of brain tissue, but to produce a strictly functional effect. In the latter instance the crudity, uncertainty, and irreversibility of lesion effects represent a serious limitation of this approach. This is particularly so when the treatment may produce deleterious effects which may be subtle, complex, or not immediately apparent, as in frontal lobotomy and temporal lobectomy. In psychosurgery, the rationale for treatment by lesions possesses little credibility in the light of present knowledge of brain mechanisms. Although sporadic attempts to achieve some therapeutic result through stimulation appear to have failed due to its seemingly crude and transient effects, it is surprising that the clinical implications of certain important experimental effects of brain stimulation have not been more actively explored. Indeed, a creative and judicious combination of modern technology and behavioral techniques with selective brain stimulation appears to offer some promise in several clinical areas.

The modern era of experimental work on brain stimulation was heralded by the discovery of its motivational effects (Delgado, Miller and Roberts; Olds and Milner) and of its effectiveness as a conditioned stimulus (e.g., Giurgea and Doty). While the full clinical impact of these findings cannot yet be estimated, even the most cautious interpretation of the facts makes it clear that the effects of brain stimulation in human patients need be neither transient nor behaviorally trivial.

Although neither the details of physiological response to electrical stimulation nor the nature of neural change associated with the process of conditioning are understood, some elementary features of brain responses to stimulation are worthy of note. At the cellular level, externally applied currents are believed to exert their effects through two mechanisms: 1) suprathreshold depolarization producing a propagated action potential, and 2) subthreshold depolarization or hyperpolarization of the neuronal membrane resulting in a modulation of the effects of synaptic transmission. Inasmuch as even the directly elicited propagated effects of stimulation are subsequently mediated by complex central and efferent processes before becoming manifest as behavior, all effects of stimulation are influenced by the state of the brain at the time of stimulation.

Furthermore, an experiment by Olds has shown that stimulation of brain sites possessing the capability for behavioral reinforcement can also "shape" the firing pattern of individual neurones in sensory cortex by selectively "rewarding" responses which approach features selected by the experimenter. This demonstration suggests some aspects of transynaptic neural interaction which may be important in the production of prolonged experiential or behavioral effects of brain stimulation, that is, in learning. The existence of subthreshold neuronal effects of stimulation greatly enhances the possibilities for subtle and behaviorally significant effects of brain stimulation, for example the facilitation of conditioning induced by mild anodal polarization of the cortical region of the CR (Rusinov, Morrell). In any analysis of the detailed physiological effects of brain stimulation it is necessary, therefore, to take into account not only the local and distant effects of propagated neuronal excitation, but the local modulation of synaptic "efficiency" which may modify ongoing experience and behavior without disrupting it.

In considering the experiential and behavioral significance of these modifications of neuronal activity, the physiological effects of brain stimulation may be divided into three categories reflecting gross distinctions in the observed effects of stimulation. At one extreme, the output from a brain region may produce its functional effect primarily through the algebraic summation of its excitatory and inhibitory projections. The specific spatiotemporal patterning of its output may be largely irrelevant, except in increasing or prolonging its characteristic effects. In such a system, stimulation might be expected to mimic normal physiological processes. The behavioral impact of stimulation in regions eliciting arousal, affective changes, and motivational effects may conform to this simple functional notion.

The second situation, familiar through the classic studies of sensorimotor cortex, presents a qualitative specificity of effects due to the presence of direct afferent or efferent connections with receptor or effector systems. Despite this qualitative specificity, complex sensory experience or behavior elicitation is not achieved merely by quantitative changes in stimulus parameters; a finer organization of the pattern of neuronal activation is required. For this reason it is generally assumed that the induction of organized perceptual experience or of motor performance by external stimulation is virtually impossible, technically if not conceptually. We shall suggest later that this may not be so.

The third level of neural organization comprises the vast "silent" regions of the brain which yield neither behavioral or experiential responses when stimulated by the usual techniques. Herein, connections with sensory, motor, arousing, and motivating regions are both complex and indirect, their patterns of organization being defined largely by learning. Address and retrieval of experientially or behaviorally significant patterns from these regions require an input specifically coded to the phenomenon under consideration. This requirement is extraordinarily stringent, as it demands not only an appropriate addressing stimulus but also specification of the pattern of experience or behavior to be elicited thereby. The latter requirement poses a problem of greater subtlety than may immediately be apparent. Inasmuch as stimulation effects in the "silent" areas possess no obligatory sensory or motor signature, but intrude upon highly organized neural networks subserving complex patterns of experience or behavior, effects may ordinarily be manifested only when an individual is actively engaged in appropriate experiences or actions at the time of stimulation. Such "arrest" responses are commonly obtained with stimulation of the cortical language areas during spontaneous speech, whereas coherent verbalizations are never induced by stimulation of these areas. Although stimulation will not ordinarily elicit organized behavioral patterns, due to inadequate differentiation, highly complex experiential and behavioral sequences may sometimes be obtained by stimulation of the brain in patients suffering from temporal lobe seizures and occasionally in other types of focal epilepsy. These phenomena are the distant responses, psychical hallucinations, and automatisms described by Penfield which, due to their habitual elaboration by the seizure discharge, may be elicited in turn by the crude electrical stimulation which mimics or elicits the seizure discharge. Penfield himself first suggested that these responses might arise by a fortuitous concurrence of the neural events corresponding to an external situation or the memory thereof with the pathological discharge, so that the experiential hallucination or automatism might be considered a conditioned response with the seizure discharge serving as conditioned stimulus. The mechanisms whereby such effects might occur are not entirely obscure. It is well known that synaptic activity arising from a cortical focus of epileptic discharge and impinging upon the homologous contralateral region will, after a time, induce a "mirror focus" which becomes independent of the original pathogenic discharge. This effect has been proposed as a model for learning by Morrell, who has also demonstrated that responses by an individual neurone to a specific stimulus may be modified (conditioned) by repeated pairing with another stimulus. This effect, taken together with the demonstration by Olds of the effects of stimulation of rewarding sites, tends to support the generalization that repeated temporal association of inputs to a single neurone results in the unknown cellular modifications responsible for learning. Taken as a whole, the results of experiments which have explored brain stimulation and conditioning, including an important series of studies by Doty and colleagues, make it likely that by repeated temporal pairing of cortical or subcortical stimulation with a selected experiential or behavioral sequence, the stimulus may come to cue and/or reinforce the total associated pattern of neural events.

Extrapolating from these considerations, clinical applications of brain stimulation may be foreseen in the areas of sensory prosthesis, inhibition of epileptic seizures, and in treatment of certain types of psychopathology.

A visual prosthesis for the blind, employing a complex spatiotemporal pattern of electrical stimulation to the visual cortex, comprises the most technically challenging application of brain stimulation. Such an approach, although utilizing the specificity of the occipital cortex for visual experience, requires that the pattern of electrical information imposed upon it be interpreted as an organized, veridical representation of the external visual world. This requirement has until recently been considered unattainable due both to technological limitations, and perhaps even more important, the lack of evidence that a mosaic of cortical stimulation would be interpreted as a comparable subjective visual mosaic. The feasibility of this approach has recently been dramatically verified by Brindley, who has demonstrated in a blind volunteer subject implanted with a cortical mosaic of 80 contacts, that each stimulus point is interpreted subjectively as a small point of white light with a substantial topologic preservation of visual space. Developments in microelectronics, materials, and optical systems now permit an incredibly complex pattern of photically controlled brain stimulation to be produced. The visual information thus available to a blind individual would consist of a coarse mosaic of spots of varying intensity, corresponding in some areas to the mosaic image of external space received by a photosensitive matrix, but discontinuous here and there, due to infolding of the cortical surface. Can such a broken image of space serve a useful and psychologically acceptable visual function? Studies in adaptation to degradation and distortion of visual input indicate that association of visual input with kinesthetic experiences and previously learned representations of external space will serve to reintegrate the visual image, suppressing the incongruous aspects of the perceived space. Thus the brain may learn to treat the artificial and grossly inaccurate stimulation of afferent input produced by patterned electrical stimulation of the visual cortex as a crude but veridical representation of spatial data.

The conditional inhibition of epileptic seizures may be proposed as another important potential therapeutic application. Inhibitory effects within brain structures may be induced by several methods, including external sensory stimulation and electrical excitation of certain central structures. The physiological defect in epilepsy may be viewed as a disorder in inhibitory stabilization of neural activity, the purpose of treatment being to impose such inhibition in as selective a manner as possible, so as to avoid disturbances of function more troublesome than the seizures themselves. This objective is not now achieved in many patients whose seizures are resistant to doses of anticonvulsant medication sufficient to significantly impair their behavior. In these patients, it has become customary to attempt surgical excision of the epileptogenic region when the seizure discharge is thought to arise from a single pathological focus. This approach has a number of drawbacks: it is applicable to but the small minority of epileptics with surgically accessible foci; excision, particularly the standard temporal lobectomy for psychomotor epilepsy, carries with it subtle but definite psychological impairment; and finally, even significant amelioration or cure of seizures may leave unaffected serious personality disturbances which seem to have at least in part some origin in the pathophysiology of the seizure disorder. Brain stimulation, applied immediately upon initiation of each epileptic discharge by means of an electronic sensing and stimulating system, may be empirically manipulated so as to provide optimal inhibition of each discharge, each repeated cycle of paired discharge and inhibiting stimulus serving to reinforce the conditioned inhibition of the seizure. A prototype for this mechanism, employing an external stimulus as the conditional inhibitory stimulus, has been reported by Efron.

The preceding illustrations of therapeutic applications of brain stimulation have been outlined to set the stage for exploration of the most powerful potential of this technique: the modification of human behavior applied to amelioration of psychopathology. Already, striking affective changes and lessening of concern for painful or distressing conditions have repeatedly been demonstrated in human patients with stimulation of sites within the limbic system, attesting that behavioral observations in experimental animals have their counterpart in human experience.

Although the etiology of the various patterns of behavior which we designate as psychopathology is both diverse and compounded of constitutional and experiential factors, deviant behavior of all sorts appears to be susceptible to modification by application of suitable reinforcement. While social reinforcers may be seemingly ineffective or even perverse in their effects, even the most regressed and intractable patients are capable of responding to appropriate rewards or punishments. Unfortunately, it may be quite difficult if not impossible to discover in an individual patient effective reinforcers for socially desirable patterns of behavior. In such instances, could not motivation be directly induced by stimulation of sites within the limbic system which possess potent capacity for positive or negative reinforcement? The efficacy of intracranial stimulation in behavioral modification is unquestionable, and techniques for implementation are readily available. Indeed, several attempts to ameliorate psychopathological conditions by intracranial stimulation have been reported, usually with transient beneficial results. Curiously, none of these efforts seem to have utilized the specific reinforcing action of stimulation, but have relied upon a general beneficial effect upon the patient's affective state such as that reported by Lilly in monkeys subjected to prolonged stimulation of the septal region. However, dependence upon such tonic effects of brain stimulation ignores its most potent and specific effect: the capacity to selectively reward or punish patterns of experience or behavior. It is hardly surprising that long-term benefits have not been realized from brain stimulation, since few efforts have been made to apply the procedure in a manner conducive to formation of conditioned association between specific patterns of behavior and their positive or negative reinforcement.

Despite potential beneficial effects, concern must be expressed that these potent applications of brain stimulation to modification of human behavior will appear upon the clinical scene with insufficient consideration of their individual and social implications. As with prefrontal leukotomy, a relatively simple and potent technique may be widely exploited before its effects are adequately apprehended and explored. It is quite clear that such considerations will not hinder the development and application of procedures for selective modification of human behavior. The demands of pathology are compelling, and there are always those prepared to employ new procedures and technologies without full consideration of individual risks and social implications.

The responsibility for reviewing these issues falls squarely upon the psychiatric community, despite the conceptual and technical contributions to behavior modification derived from other disciplines. Unfortunately, certain common clinical prejudices may impede a rational and comprehensive consideration of the issues involved in the selective modification of human behavior. These impediments derive, on the one hand, from the residuum of dualistic philosophy implicit in the dichotomy of "organic" and "functional" origins of psychopathology; and, on the other, from certain widely held beliefs concerning the nature of psychiatric disease and its treatment.

A persistent confusion exists concerning the validity of dualism as a basic philosophical principle rather than as a conceptual and methodological convenience. There can be little argument with the necessity for analysis of natural phenomena at differing levels of observation and description. That physiology and psychology may coexist as distinct scientific disciplines need not be seriously questioned. However, when one considers perception, thought, and feeling to be independent of the physiological processes giving rise to these phenomena, the fact of the biological basis of experience and behavior is ignored. Within the scientific community such a position derives not from philosophical principle but from undue emphasis upon disciplinary integrity. These views emphasize psychological or physiological factors in contexts which may ordinarily be quite appropriate, while tending to deprecate the utility of alternative descriptive systems. However, when faced with potent and selective effects of physiological manipulations upon experience or behavior, the concordance of psychophysiological processes must be recognized. The implications of physiologic manipulation of human experience and behavior cannot be derogated in the service of any strictly psychological system of belief. Some danger of such parochial response exists within the behaviorist and psychoanalytic schools of psychology. These systems, valuable in their emphasis upon important psychological techniques and concepts, must accept the ultimate physiological determinants of experience and behavior. It would be most unfortunate if the precision of behavioristic methodology and the sensitivity of the psychoanalytic insight were jointly unresponsive to the challenge of current conceptual and operational advances in brain physiology.

Beyond these considerations the relation of brain function to human experience and behavior lie the questions of the nature of psychopathology and the methods appropriate to its amelioration. Psychiatric theory and practice have long followed the accepted medical principles of nosology, etiology, and therapy despite the awkward fact that such principles are ill suited to the phenomena of psychopathology. The notion of etiology or single cause permeates even the thought of "dynamic" psychology. In this view a specific psychopathological entity may be generated through the action of a specifiable agency, whether a toxic product of disordered metabolism or a distortion of personality organization initiated by environmental trauma. The therapeutic corollary of this etiologic position asserts the efficacy of removal of the basic cause, or if this cannot be accomplished, of suppression of its effects. Thus, the application of an antidote for the postulated biochemical determinant of certain psychoses or the release of the normal mechanisms of personality from the bonds of neurotic fixation may be expected to free the psyche from pathology, much as antibiotics cure a bacterial infection. However, the known facts concerning the physiology of learning indicate that patterns of behavior, once consolidated, may be lastingly modified only through additional learning. Thus, the removal of a hypothetical psychic or metabolic noxus would not leave a new and healthy brain which might then function unencumbered, but rather a brain functionally constrained by its stored record of pathological behavior and its associated reinforcement patterns. While it can hardly be argued that nothing would be changed through elimination of the etiologically significant process, neither is it reasonable to anticipate that this would achieve a functional "cure," or even a state of affairs which would permit self-corrective learning on the part of the patient. These considerations suggest that active modes of behavior modification are required for a satisfactory therapeutic result, at least in the more severe and chronic types of psychopathology.

It is in this area that the potent effects of brain stimulation might be seen to play a role. The shaping of this role requires the most detailed consideration of the points briefly touched upon above, constrained by the acceptable bounds for external control of human behavior. Consideration of these issues should not be left solely to those who are directly concerned with human brain stimulation. The problem is far too difficult and complex for resolution by a single specialized group of medical scientists, even if it were characteristic of human nature to face such issues squarely. Such is not the case, as may be affirmed by a careful reading of the history of "psychosurgery." As in that area, the critical problems tend to be swept aside by the apparently fruitful activity of the proponents of a therapeutic approach. The muted and often ambivalent warnings of others may long go unheeded unless highlighted by the occurrence of some unexpected disaster such as the profound amnesia following bilateral mesial temporal lobectomy. Some of the present and potential hazards in brain stimulation need little imagination to identify. The report given in this volume by Dr. Ervin and Dr. Mark, as well as similar observations from other laboratories, attests to the striking influence of limbic system stimulation on the primary affective and motivational processes. The surprisingly prolonged duration of some of these effects, whatever their mechanism, represents a factor of some significance in the physiology of learning. The occurrence of tonic effects in motivational systems following a brief activating input creates a situation in which motivational or affective properties may be associated with an extended period of experience. Inasmuch as one notion concerning the neural mechanism of learning postulates a facilitatory effect of the limbic system upon the site or sites of storage during the consolidation period of memory formation, it can be seen that these observations might well be relevant to such a process. The dangers of unselective activation of such a mechanism are rather clear, inasmuch as the haphazard and possibly quite inappropriate association of environmentally defined experiences with an arbitrarily evoked affective state constitutes one model for the development of certain forms of psychopathology. Further exploration and application of such effects demands, therefore, the closest attention to all of their implications and should hardly be pursued without the most careful definition of the clinical situation and continuing critical review.

A further and somewhat unexpected outgrowth of brain stimulation research, possessing highly disturbing implications, derives from the interest shown by the military and space industry. As an offshoot of the biological programs of NASA and the military agencies, there has been an increasing awareness of brain research within the engineering community. Liaisons have been established with a number of medical and physiological research laboratories, and the possibilities for profitable exploitation of the biomedical area are being actively explored. Some of the developments envisioned by this group relate to brain—machine interfaces intended to extend or modify the activity of the brain to meet conditions demanded by space exploration and to certain military applications. These developments have no direct medical relevance, although their indirect impact may be enormous. Most significantly, however, such developments do not fall within the purview of the Public Health Service and its system of research review. Imperfect as that system may be, it has the effect of subjecting a large proportion of biological research to the scrutiny of competent scientists, as well as bringing the results of such research into the public domain. Such is not the case with the work alluded to above. There is an essential need for review and disclosure in this area, since those familiar with the intent and implications of this research view it with foreboding and dismay. Lest the impression be given that the "military-industrial complex" bears the major onus for secret and diabolical schemes for brain manipulation and control, let me hasten to note that perhaps a more hazardous situation exists in the accepted customs of medical practice. Procedures deemed of diagnostic or therapeutic significance may well not be defined by their practitioners as "research," despite their innovative or exploratory nature. The history of brain lesioning and stimulation has established a precedent for this arbitrary practice, which in effect permits the surgeon to enter into a contract with his patient providing great latitude of action through the device of "informed consent." In the hands of knowledgeable and sensitive practitioners the rights of a patient may thus be reasonably well protected. It is a matter of argument, however, whether informed consent has much meaning when the effects of a procedure may be largely unknown in advance, and the patient is either strongly motivated to intervention by a distressing disease process or is in some instances even unable to comprehend the procedures and their implications. This problem will not be further elaborated here, although the interested reader is encouraged to critically review the literature on psychosurgery and other neurosurgical approaches to amelioration of functional disturbances of the nervous system for further insight into this problem.

The current situation in brain stimulation demands immediate, continuing, and effective analysis by scientists concerned with all aspects of the problem. The following specific proposals are offered to meet this need. First, a Commission on Human Brain Stimulation should be appointed under the joint auspices of the National Institute of Mental Health and the National Institute of Neurological Diseases. This panel should be charged with the responsibility of reviewing in depth: 1) the current development and practice of brain stimulation and related procedures; 2) the issue of protection for the individual, particularly in situations wherein his judgment may be seriously impaired by the presence of disease; 3) the future impact of increasing knowledge of brain mechanisms and technological capability upon neuropsychiatric practice; and 4) the implications for society of what might be called the "bidden brain." The Commission should make specific recommendations for continuing review in this area. Means for identification and study by appropriate review groups of patients subjected to stimulation should be established. Inasmuch as these cases are ordinarily "elective" and not emergent in nature, procedures for selection and approval might be developed. It should be emphasized that the steps proposed are not intended to obstruct or inhibit activity in this area, but rather to provide for a constant review of possible adverse individual or social effects, and to establish the means for control of such inimical situations prior to their widespread appearance. Prudence and scientific responsibility demand such a course. The lesson of the atomic bomb should remind the biologist of the hazards of science or therapeutic art pursued without unremitting attention to the intrinsic amorality of nature.

5

AUTONOMIC AND SOMATIC REACTIVITY IN RELATION TO PSYCHOPATHOLOGY

by RICHARD A. STERNBACH, Ph.D., A. A. ALEXANDER, Ph.D., and N. S. GREENFIELD, Ph.D.

IT IS CLEAR to us that there is a real need for data-based dimensions in the parametric measurement of individual differences in normal and psychopathological populations. Our work with clinically psychopathological groups in a psychophysiological laboratory has brought us ever closer to the conviction that the variables of psychophysiological research have immediate relevance to both the impressions of clinical experience and the phenomena of psychopathology.

In no sense do we mean to deprecate or reject the foundations of knowledge upon which dynamic psychiatric thought is based, when we point out that it has done little to establish psychopathology as a scientific discipline, as a body of verifiable knowledge. When we interact with our patients who have difficulty with problems of living, we believe, as Freud said, that the essential thing is to grasp psychological facts psychologically. But at each point of clinical concern, from diagnosis to prognosis and treatment, we are confronted primarily with a language of constructs which fail to pass even the most generous tests of scientific method. It would be pointless here to review the many studies which demonstrate the absence of agreement among clinicians making standard psychiatric diagnoses, not to mention making more esoteric formulations such as dream analyses. We note that the psychodynamic models of psychopathology have become top-heavy with mini-formulations which depart more and more from the data of experience and observation. As they become more and more elaborate, they contribute less and less to a research approach; and it is indeed

From the University of Wisconsin Medical Center and Wisconsin Psychiatric Institute.

lamentable that in an era when men are about to fly to the moon, we still have only the barest outline of what might be called an experimental psychopathology.

In our quest for a more rigorous science of psychopathology—for greater precision, greater verifiability, and greater dependence on the data of observation rather than on the metaphors of inference—we are seeking one kind of conceptualization of psychopathological behavior—i.e., an empirically based language of dynamic psychophysiology. More heuristically, we suggest that there is great value in the development of a psychophysiological taxonomy of individual differences, especially with regard to psychopathology. We can even envision the possibility of generating profiles of individuals, based on psychophysiological parameters.

Let us hasten to repeat that we are not advocating a simplistic reductionism, implying that there is a psychophysiological level of explanation or of meaning that is superior to that of dynamic psychiatry. We are not so naive as to believe that the richness of subjective experience may be reduced to squiggles on polygraph chart paper or blips on FM recording tape. And certainly we do not believe that physiological events are any more *real* than psychological events. We clearly recognize that feelings of fear are just as real as fluctuations in blood pressure, that free associations are just as real as changes in galvanic skin responses. Similarly we know that dreams are just as real as rapid eye movement recordings, but we know as well that knowledge of dreams and of dreaming advanced little over a fifty-year period until the advent of the new dream research methodology which, in a sense, is paradigmatic of the approach we are proposing. Even with the great unknowns which still exist regarding dreams, much of our ignorance has been swiftly replaced by the systematic induction of lawfulness resulting from contemporary dream research. We believe that a psychophysiological approach to psychopathology in general will permit the introduction of this same kind of systematic order which will facilitate the identification of regularities and the emergence of patterns. This brings us to the question of the relationships between psychophysiology and psychopathology.

Without a higher order of abstraction, there is no logical relationship between the empirical findings of the two fields: the data in psychophysiology consist of measurements of various physiological systems, whereas psychopathological conditions are typically defined as certain mental (or affective) aberrations which are inferred from behavioral observations. To relate these disparate areas of observation requires that we develop concepts which, although deriving from the data in one field, may have descriptive or explanatory value also in the other. As we have pointed out elsewhere,[46] psychophysiological research constitutes a major *experimental* approach to the ancient question of the relationship between mind and body; however, attempts to relate mental and physical phenomena require more than a merely experimental approach to the collection of data—there is also the need for concepts enabling us to relate these otherwise different realms of discourse.

In a 1967 paper, Graham[17] pointed out the difficulties in the traditional approaches to the mind-body problem; psychophysical parallelism and psychophysical interactionism. Such views are based on the premise that a dualism in fact exists; it is projected onto human phenomena, and then attempts are made to assay the proportion of mental and physical "attributes" or their mode of "interaction." However, such approaches beg the question. The human being is a totally, holistically functioning organism, not a mind and a body. Neither the mental nor the physical nor their interaction are inherent in human phenomena. Rather, dualism is inherent in our descriptions and our attempts to explain.

Graham's point of view seems to us to have the merit of acknowledging the practicality of dualistic thinking, which has been with us for centuries despite many attempts to eliminate the concept, and also of avoiding the fallacy of imputing the dualism into the human phenomena being observed. His approach, which he calls "linguistic parallelism," is simply that an event or state may be described in different but parallel "languages"—that is, now in mental, now in physical, terms. Our preference for one or the other will depend on which is most useful for our purposes, purposes which may vary from understanding and treating a particular patient to designing a research program.

Our purpose in this paper is to indicate some ways in which we may approach the construction of a "dictionary" enabling us to "translate" from one "language" to another. In the past, dynamic psychiatric concepts have been used to develop hypotheses for psychophysiological research e.g.,[5]. Our approach, as we suggested above, will be quite the opposite: we will examine some concepts which have been emerging from psychophysiological research, and show how these may be applied to psychopathological phenomena. But let us say first what we mean by "psychophysiology." For us it is that discipline which emphasizes the simultaneous recording and measurement of multiple physiological responses in human subjects of theoretical interest. The more traditional area of physiological psychology has a great emphasis on manipulating physiological processes and observing changes on some behavioral parameters, usually with animal subjects. In psychophysiology, mental or emotional conditions are varied, and their effects observed on several physiological systems in the human. Thus the physiological events are the dependent, rather than the independent, variables.[41] A typical psychophysiological experiment, therefore, might employ differing degrees of severity of a psychopathological state as the independent variable, and the conditionability of heart rate and palmar skin conductance as the dependent variables.

Let us now turn to the experimental literature in psychophysiology to examine the principles which seem to us to be emerging and promising for the development of new dimensions in psychopathology.

EMERGING PSYCHOPHYSIOLOGICAL CONCEPTS

Homeostatic Concepts

Homeostatic concepts seem to us to have wide applicability in both psychological and physiological descriptions. The homeostatic nature of much of physiological function has long been known,[8] and often demonstrated for such variables as endocrine functions, metabolism, temperature regulation, etc. Moving to broader categories of physiological functioning, Wenger's work with *autonomic balance* represents a modern, operationally defined version of homeostasis. It consists of a way of quantifying the relative tonus of the sympathetic and parasympathetic branches of the autonomic nervous system in the resting state. Wenger and his colleagues have demonstrated, by means of factor analytic studies in large samples of children,[52,53,58] young adult males,[54] and young adult females,[29] that it is possible to derive an autonomic factor score which is relatively normally distributed in an unselected sample. A given individual's score of autonomic balance, as compared with the distribution of scores in the sample, will show him to have relatively more or less apparent sympathetic or parasympathetic dominance. These scores of autonomic balance have been shown to be highly reliable and stable for a given individual, yet more interesting for our purposes is that the scores are also sensitive enough to reflect both normal and pathological reactions to stress. (Let us briefly note here that although a number of different response systems are represented in the overall autonomic balance scores, there are four variables which recur in the three different factor analyses of the populations mentioned: salivary output, palmar skin conductance, volar forearm conductance, and heart period.)

As an example of the responsiveness of this index, Smith and Wenger (1965) found that acute anxiety in graduate students, just prior to their oral examinations, resulted in their autonomic balance scores showing a shift of more than 1½ standard deviations in the direction of apparent sympathetic dominance.[40] A number of other studies have shown various psychopathological states also to be associated with excessive sympathetic tonus in the resting state. In a 1966 report, Wenger summarized these data: paranoid schizophrenics, catatonics, other schizophrenics, and anxiety neurotics all show scores of autonomic balance between ½ to 2 standard deviations from the mean in the sympathetic direction—a highly significant difference.[55]

Studies of autonomic activity in our own laboratories originated by A. A. Alexander have also brought us to concepts of homeostasis, or self-modulation, in both physiological and psychological aspects. These began with the discovery of a rhythmic component in the non-specific (i.e., non-stimulus induced) resting autonomic activity of human subjects, which we refer to as *periodicity*. A brief description of the methods used to detect physiological periodicity will help to explain the nature of the phenomenon. Various autonomic and somatic variables, such as skin resistance, heart rate, muscle potentials, finger blood volume, etc., are continuously recorded while the subject is at rest. These variables are then sampled and scored electronically every half second for periods ranging from six minutes to twenty minutes. The resultant digitalized data are then subjected to a variance (or power) spectrum analysis[7] to determine whether a statistically significant proportion of the variance for the entire time span recorded is accounted for by any one of a series of frequencies. The technique of the power spectrum involves the correlation of a given record with itself over time. These "auto-correlations," when themselves properly analyzed, will indicate whether or not there is a periodic wave form within the record under analysis. Such rhythms can thereby be detected even when masked by random or other physiological activity, and most importantly, allow quantification of such periodicities as to frequency and amplitude.

Results to date indicate that the presence of a significant periodic component can be discovered in the resting activity of one or more physiological variables of 85 per cent to 90 per cent of all subjects tested.[3] Furthermore, these periodicities can be classified as "fast" or "slow" (i.e., high frequency or low frequency) on the basis of the range of frequencies explored, and individuals differ according to whether any "fast" (high frequency) activity shows up in one or more of the variables sampled.[4]

In keeping with an interest in the heuristic application of somatic phenomena to psychopathological principles, we were motivated to study the relationship of physiological periodicity to ego strength, or general adaptive capacity of the individual. The theoretical reasons for choosing this particular psychological parameter have been stated elsewhere[21] and will not be repeated here. Suffice to say that periodicity itself is seen as part of physiological homeostasis, and that the process of adapting successfully to life would also represent a psychological homeostasis (a concept to which we will return later). Results to date relating the specific physiological periodicity phenomenon to successful or unsuccessful psychological adaptation, operationally defined, are as follows:

High frequency periodic activity can be found in at least one or more physiological variables of 90 per cent of all psychiatric inpatients tested.[2]

High frequency periodic activity can be discerned in one or more physiological variables of 75 per cent of all basic airmen studied who were "washed out" of initial USAF training for psychological reasons.[1]

Only 10 per cent of the normal control subjects matched for age and sex with psychiatric patients demonstrate high frequency activity, and roughly 20 per cent of "successful" basic airmen exhibit high frequency activity.[1]

The greater the number of variables in which high frequency periodicity appears for a given individual, the greater the probability that he will be maladaptive as defined by patient status, success of training, or psychological test measures of ego strength.[4]

The phenomena we have described, autonomic balance and periodicity, are examples of homeostasis in resting (non-specific stimulus induced) physiological activity. We have seen how these parameters can be predictive of psychopathological conditions, and later in this paper we will return to consider the implications of such homeostatic concepts for psychopathological models. Now, however, we wish to consider the responses of the reacting subject—i.e., behavior induced by specific experimental stimuli.

General Activation

This is the concept referring to the diffuse discharge of the sympathico-adrenal system, increased muscle tonus, and low amplitude, fast activity in the EEG. Malmo (1959) and Duffy (1962) have shown how this phenomenon, variously called arousal, energy mobilization, etc., is useful for ordering a variety of physiological and behavioral data.[11,30] For example, it has frequently been shown that moderate amounts of activation improve performance on perceptual and motor tasks, but a great deal of activation leads to a deterioration of such performance, a phenomenon referred to as the inverted-U curve. In addition, as we have already seen and will further demonstrate below, measures of activation can in themselves be used to differentiate normal and pathological populations. There are several reasons for this. First, as we have shown elsewhere,[42] different measures or indices of activation are not always in agreement with each other, and this in turn reflects the extent of individual differences both in resting conditions, as already mentioned, and in patterns of responsiveness, as we will indicate further on. Second, the general principle of the so-called "law of initial values" affects the form of activation observed. This principle is simply that the direction and degree of physiological responsivity will be in part a function of the prestimulus level of activity. Since different pathological groups often have different prestimulus levels, we may expect that they may also be differentiated by their reactivity.

We may note parenthetically that a number of factors other than pathology can contribute to the initial values and the reactive responses. Such "psychological" factors as explicit instructions have been shown to have this effect.[44,45] Likewise, pre-experimental, implicit sets associated with ethnic membership have been demonstrated to influence the degree of activation responses.[48,49] The point to be made here is that although the general concept of activation is a useful one, it is even more useful to examine the ways in which patterns of reactivity are differentiated, and how these differential responses can be used to sort individuals and groups along different dimensions. We believe this will contribute more to our understanding of psychopathology.

Stimulus-Response Specificity

Within the general framework of activation there exist clearcut patternings of physiological responses to stimulation. The "stimulation" may be, in the laboratory, lights, sounds, or tasks, but in the typical pa-tient "stimulation" is usually an interpersonal situation which produces relatively strong emotions and their concomitant physiological responses. In addition to making up a generalized activation pattern, these sets of responses will be characteristic both for the individual, and for the emotion which the interpersonal situation arouses.

The concept that a unique pattern of physiological responses occurs to each stimulus-situation is referred to as *stimulus-response specificity*. Actually, only a few such unique response patterns have been convincingly demonstrated. Davis, Buchwald and Frankmann (1955) ob-tained several response patterns characteristic for each of several simple laboratory stimuli, and Wenger and Cullen (1958) found 14 autonomic patterns to such stimuli.[10,57] Although artificial laboratory situations are not particularly rewarding for producing standardized emotional stimuli, there has been some success. Ax (1953) could distinguish fear vs. anger responses,[6] and Schachter (1957) confirmed and extended his findings by distinguishing fear, anger, and pain responses.[37] Similarly, we were able to demonstrate some differentiation among autonomic responses associated with feelings of sadness and fear in children, as produced by a movie.[43] From these and a few other similar studies, it seems reasonable to suppose that within the generalized activation framework, each emotion has some degree of unique patterning of responses.

One major difficulty in studies of this sort, as we have suggested, is the problem of inducing authentic emotions in the laboratory with stand-ardized stimuli. Another, somewhat related problem, is that of quan-tifying emotional stimuli. If emotional stimuli could be graded or quan-tified in some way to reflect intensity, then it would be possible for the first time to generate the equivalent of dose-response curves. A most promising beginning in this respect has been made by Holmes, Rahe and their colleagues.[24,35] They have been able to obtain reliable magnitude estimates for a variety of life stress situations, either positive or negative ones, ranging in severity from death of a spouse, down through marriage, illness, to the receiving of a parking ticket. Different subject populations apparently quantify these stressors quite similarly.

Furthermore, these authors have shown, it is possible quite accurately to predict the occurrence of an illness or accident episode in an individual if he has accumulated a sufficient number of "life change units" over the recent past. These are most intriguing findings, and we are in the process of checking them out in a longitudinal, prospective study of college student adaptation.

The quantification of life stressors is, technically, rather different from the laboratory study of stimulus-response specificity, but they have in common a focus on the input to the human organism. From what we have seen so far, an individual's response is in part a function of the nature of the emotion induced by some stimulus-situation; whether his response becomes pathological seems to be independent of the nature of the emotion induced (whether fear, anger, grief, or joy), but in large measure a function of the intensity of the emotional responses and their rate of occurrence. However, we also know that the individual's responses may also be uniquely characteristic of him, somewhat independently of the stimulus. Let us turn to this concept now, emphasizing the patterning of the output of the human organism.

Individual Response Stereotypy

Malmo and Shagass,[31] and Malmo, Shagass and Davis[32,33] showed that patients produced maximal responses to stressful stimulation in the organ-systems related to their symptoms, even though the patients were symptom-free when tested. Thus, cardiovascular responses were greatest in patients with cardiac complaints, neck muscle responses greatest in those with headache complaints. From their findings these authors formulated an hypothesis of "symptom-specificity," namely, that patients would show maximal physiological responsiveness in their symptom organs. Following this up, the Laceys[26,27] and Engel[12,13] found that this form of organ response specificity could be found distributed in the normal population as well, and the original hypothesis has now been generalized to the concept of response-stereotypy.

This principle suggests that, in the general population, there exists a continuum of reactivity such that those at one extreme demonstrate marked response-stereotypy, and those at the other show marked heterogeneity of response patterns from one situation to the next. The former, whom we may designate as "rigid reactors," are those who always respond maximally with one organ-system (gastric, respiratory, cardiovascular, etc.) no matter what the stimulus-situation. The latter group, "random reactors," will respond maximally now with one system, now with another. The bulk of the population will consist of those with varying degrees of "preferred" response patterns, but neither "rigid" nor "random" maximal responses. (We should note here that "maximal" response is defined by statistical procedures which permit comparisons among several physiological variables with different units of measurement, as well as permitting comparisons among individuals with different levels of prestimulus functioning.)

It is tempting to think that "rigid reactors" are those most likely to develop psychosomatic symptoms in their maximally responsive systems, but there is no evidence yet to support this idea. In fact, although other investigators have also obtained data supporting the concept of response-stereotypy,[56] there is some doubt about the stability of the phenomenon. Oken et al. (1962) obtained stereotypy patterns on 18 subjects, but could not recover them on retesting a week later.[34] Johnson, Hord and Lubin (1963) had similar difficulty in testing 24 subjects on two occasions 48 hours apart.[25] It is difficult to understand how so replicable a phenomenon can be so evanescent; only further studies, especially longitudinal ones, can answer this, although we should note that Lacey and Lacey (1962) reported good reproducibility of response patterns obtained on 37 children on two occasions four years apart.[28] Clearly, more information is necessary before these findings can be reconciled.

Another kind of specificity, which seems characteristic of individuals and related to psychosomatic symptoms, has been called the "specificity of attitudes" by Graham and his colleagues.[15,20] These workers found that patients with given psychosomatic diseases would verbalize attitudes toward interpersonal situations in unique and characteristic ways, so that similar statements would be made by patients in the same diagnostic group which differed from those made by patients in the other groups with different symptoms. Furthermore, in a remarkable series of experiments, Graham and his co-workers found that when the statement representing the attitude of a given patient population (hives, or Raynaud's disease, or hypertension) was suggested to hypnotized normal subjects, they responded with the appropriate change in the relevant physiological system, and only with such changes.[16,18,19] Thus, these normal subjects, when told they would like to hit or choke someone (the Raynaud's attitude), showed significant decreases in finger temperature, and no other significant response. When told they were taking a beating (the hives attitude), skin temperature rose, with no other significant change. And when told they must be on guard (the hypertension attitude), diastolic blood pressure rose, with no other significant change. Altogether 18 attitudes have been specified, although only these three have been experimentally tested so far. These findings suggest that, in the absence of "objective" evidence of interpersonal stress, such stress may nevertheless exist for the patient because he *perceives* all interpersonal situations in a chronic, uniquely stressful way. Elsewhere we have shown how this specificity of attitude concept, together with the concepts of response-stereotypy and homeostatic restraints, can be used as an explanatory schema for understanding psychosomatic phenomena.[47] Later, we will indicate how other chronic attitudinal styles may be used to investigate other psychopathological conditions. We wish first, however, to consider some other differentiated patterns of reactivity.

Other Activation Patterns

An interesting attempt at psychophysiological model building has recently been made, with impressive results which have yet to generalize to the psychopathological literature. Claridge[9] has attempted an integration of studies of autonomic functioning with a systematic theory of personality and psychopathology based largely on Eysenck's work.[14] Claridge is concerned primarily with an activation concept which, for the most part, is operationally defined by the sedation threshold technique first developed by Shagass and his co-workers.[38] Systematic efforts were made to study a variety of central nervous system, autonomic nervous system, and psychological task performance correlates of two continuous dimensions of psychopathology, running from dysthymia to hysteria and from active to retarded psychosis. Between these extremes lie different modes of personality functioning extending from the normal to the abnormal.

Claridge's findings based on this psychophysiological model have led him to advance the theory that central nervous system arousal is a function of the interaction between a tonic arousal system, and an arousal modulating system which serves to maintain central nervous system homeostasis and filters sensory input into the nervous system. In normal functioning these two mechanisms work in equilibrium at different levels of arousal. The theory holds that variations in excitability may account for the behavioral dimension of dysthymia-hysteria, and psychosis results when the mechanisms become dissociated, so that normal equilibrium cannot be maintained. Dissociation, so the theory goes, may occur in the direction of poor modulation of sensory input and poor inhibitory control over tonic arousal, or it may occur in the direction of increased modulation, excessive inhibition, and a reduction in tonic arousal. Furthermore, the dimension of psychoticism, extending from active to retarded psychosis, is related to these two kinds of dissociation.

Now let us turn to the consideration of specific instances of dissociation in activation, in order to see how useful this approach may be in helping to illuminate previously murky areas in particular psychopathological conditions.

Activation Deficits

Some years ago it was thought that the withdrawn chronic schizophrenic was defective in physiological responsiveness, since there would typically be little reactivity to stimuli as compared to that of normals and acute patients. However, keeping in mind the concept of activation and the law of initial values, it is possible to hypothesize that the chronic schizophrenic is already so highly aroused that there is little more in the way of responding that is possible; he is close to his ceiling. This hypothesis has been tested and supported in a study reported by Venables and Wing (1962).[51] These workers have shown that the extent of social withdrawal in hospitalized chronic schizophrenics is highly correlated with their skin potential; the more withdrawn the patient, the higher is his potential and thus, by inference, the higher his degree of activation.

This work, and other studies as well, has led Venables to distinguish between acute and chronic schizophrenics, as well as subtypes, on the basis of differences in activation deficit.[50] The acute patient, and the reactive and paranoid patient, apparently suffer from an inability to restrict their range of attention. Clinically, we observe an active scanning process, especially noticeable in the paranoid. This broad span of attention, as well as their physiological functioning, seems to reflect a low level of activation, or apparent parasympathetic dominance. Accordingly one would expect that any drug or procedure which increased activation would reduce the scanning and otherwise improve behavioral symptoms. On the other hand the chronic patient, and the process and withdrawn schizophrenic, are already highly activated and have consequently narrowed attention span, which is why, clinically, they seem so unresponsive to many stimuli, including noxious ones. Therefore any technique or drug that reduced activation should result in clinical improvement. Note that these hypotheses run counter to the traditional attempts to calm the acute patient and stimulate the chronic one. Improved psychophysiological measurement techniques, and the application of these concepts, can generate new and potentially useful ways of thinking about psychopathological conditions. The following section is an illustration of the approach advocated above.

Developing Psychophysiological Models for Psychopathology

In clinical parlance, when we speak of intrapsychic tensions, or interpersonal conflicts, or environmental stresses, or ego assaults, or even constitutional predispositions, what we are referring to is a human organism who is facing or undergoing a psychological disequilibrium. A disequilibrium in behavior, affect, thought process, or any combination of these may be what is threatened, and threatening, to the individual. Much of what we term "character," "defense," "coping," "neurosis," and "psychosis" can be seen as attempts to re-establish equilibrium. Whatever else these terms might mean to the psychoanalyst, psychotherapist, or academic psychologist, the psychophysiologist can find much that is fruitful in a consideration of psychological homeostasis.

A first question might be: Does psychopathology represent a failure in homeostasis? Our answer would be in the negative—rather that psychopathology is an instance of homeostatic function at a great expense. By "expense" we refer to a grossly inefficient, inappropriate, or widespread use of many processes to achieve homeostasis. Perhaps a comparison will help to illustrate this point.

An hysteric and an obsessive-compulsive, as described recently by Shapiro[39] have widely different "styles" of attending to and responding to the world. The hysteric may be characterized as one, usually a woman, who discharges relatively great amounts of affect impulsively and sometimes inappropriately, with relative indifference to her own behavior and its effect. An obsessive-compulsive, more often male, is one who delays, restrains, curbs and controls his emotion and behavior. Where the hysteric might be labile and histrionic, the obsessive-compulsive might be rigid and unemotional. Where an hysteric might react to the slightest cues or hunches—i.e., respond on the basis of ambiguous stimuli—the obsessive-compulsive would need very clear, definite signs indeed before he committed himself to any course.

What both styles are "designed" to do is control and modulate, that is, maintain homeostasis. In the case of the hysteric this is accomplished by immediate discharge at the slightest provocation, using any and all means available to her, including intense emotionality, acting out behavior, manipulation of other people, etc. The swings are wide, and relatively frequent, but between them there is peace for her. The obsessive-compulsive, on the other hand, stores, controls, monitors, and immediately modulates the slightest deviation from his "normal" state. The number of negative feedback systems needed to attenuate the slightest increase of emotion, impulsivity of behavior, or intrusion of fantasy, can become enormous. They might range from seeing to the cleanliness of his household to prissily refusing to become involved in a social or interpersonal life. While the obsessive-compulsive lives in fear of "losing control," the hysteric is never much bothered that she has had "tantrums" or "hysterics." The fact is that both maintain control psychologically by virtue of their styles, and it is our thesis that these styles should be discernible physiologically.

We would therefore expect that were each of these neurotic character types subjected to a series of stimuli of graded intensity (e.g., bursts of sound of increasing intensity), their physiological response patterns would be demonstrably different. Disregarding the phenomenon of in-dividual response-stereotypy for the moment, we would predict that the maximum magnitude of physiological response for the hysteric would be reached more frequently and at a lower intensity of the graded stimulus than would be the case for the obsessive-compulsive. Similarly, the fluc-tuations of the physiological response to the stimulus would be expected to be much narrower in range and to have much less "rebound" in the case of the obsessive-compulsive as compared to the hysteric. Data from our laboratory has already shown this to be the case when using a wider system of categorization based on ego strength.[23,36] Briefly, we demonstrated that the greater the adaptive capacity of the individual, the more appropriate or congruent the physiological response to the ex-ternal psychological or physical stimulus.

Working from such a model, the number of testable predictions which can be made unfold rapidly. Related to the established psychophysiological phenomena we have described above, we might suspect that: an hysteric would have greater parasympathetic dominance than the obsessive-compulsive; the obsessive-compulsive would show a greater degree of stimulus-response specificity; activation levels would generally be higher for the hysteric; the obsessive-compulsive would show high frequency activity on a greater number of physiological variables in periodicity analyses; and the hysteric would show response-stereotypy more frequently in the musculo-skeletal and cardiovascular variables, the obsessive-compulsive more frequently in gastrointestinal and endocrine system variables. And when one introduces other clinical types into the scheme, the physiological distinctions compound rapidly. How might a paranoid person respond physiologically to qualitatively different stimuli, as compared to a depressive? Our guess is that responsivity would be highly differentiated in the paranoid, based on the nature and meaning of the stimuli to him, but relatively un-differentiated for the depressive patient,[22] or for that matter for the person with an anxiety reaction.

Our purpose here is not, however, to issue "suggestions for future research." It is instead to argue for a systematic approach to what we have come to call "dynamic psychophysiology," whereby profiles of physiological function could be developed for individuals and clinical entities. Our speculations above cannot be either confirmed or discon-firmed by looking into the research literature of the past 30 years, and it is our belief that this reflects both the lack of a psychophysiological tax-onomy, and an undue effort to equate psychological and physiological functions too directly. The more useful level of conceptualization seems to us to lie a level higher than the operational ones usually employed. In other words, *principles* of psychological or psychopathological functions may translate into the physiological domain, and vice-versa, but we do not believe *specific* physiological or psychological phenomena ever will. The research literature to date seems to bear this out.

CONCLUSION

In this paper we have shown how psychopathological concepts have contributed to the development of psychophysiology, which in turn has supplied a number of new dimensions for ordering individual differences in, and for elucidating mechanisms of, pathological con-ditions. A growing awareness of the promise of such reciprocal cross-fertilization has been increasingly influencing our own research efforts, and our purpose in this presentation will have been well served if we have indeed kindled any interest in others.

REFERENCES

1. Alexander, A. A.: Physiological periodicity in unsuccessful basic airmen. Psychophysiology, submitted.

2. ——, Greenfield, N. S., and Roessler, R.: Psychopathological correlates of physiological periodicity. Psychophysiology, in press.

3. ——, Roessler, R., and Greenfield, N. S.: Periodic nature of spontaneous peripheral nervous system activity. Nature 197:1169-1170, 1963.

4. ——, Roessler, R., and Greenfield, N. S.: Ego strength and physiological responsivity. III. The relationship of the Barron ES Scale to spontaneous periodic activity in skin resistance, finger blood volume, heart rate and muscle potential. Arch. Gen. Psychiat. 9:142-145, 1963.

5. Alexander, F.: Psychosomatic Medicine, Its Principles and Applications. New York, W. W. Norton, 1950.

6. Ax, A. F.: The physiological differentiation between fear and anger in humans. Psychosom. Med. 15:433-442, 1953.

7. Blackman, R. B., and Tukey, J. W.: The measurement of power spectra. Reprinted by Dover Publications, N.Y., from Bell Sys. Tech. J., 37: Nos. 1 and 2, 1958.

8. Cannon, W. B.: Bodily Changes in Pain, Hunger, Fear and Rage (2nd ed.). New York, Appleton-Century, 1936.

9. Claridge, G. S.: Personality and Arousal. Oxford, Pergamon Press, 1967.

10. Davis, R. C., Buchwald, A. M., and Frankmann, R. W.: Autonomic and muscular responses, and their relation to simple stimuli. Psychol. Monogr., 69:1-71, 1955.

11. Duffy, E.: Activation and Behavior. New York, John Wiley, 1962.

12. Engel, B. T.: Stimulus-response and individual-response specificity. Arch. Gen. Psychiat. 2:305-313, 1960.

13. Engel, B. T., and Bickford, A. F.: Response-specificity: Stimulus-responses and individual-response specificity in essential hypertensives. Arch. Gen. Psychiat. 5:478-489, 1961.

14. Eysenck, H. J.: The Biological Basis of Personality. Springfield, Ill., Charles C Thomas, 1967.

15. Grace, W. J., and Graham, D. T.: Relationship of specific attitudes and emotions to certain bodily diseases. Psychosom. Med. 14:243-251, 1952.

16. Graham, D. T.: Some research on psychophysiologic specificity and its relation to psychosomatic disease. In: Roessler, R. and Greenfield, N. S. (Eds.): Physiological Correlates of Psychological Disorder. Madison, Univ. of Wisconsin Press, 1962.

17. ——: Health, disease, and the mind-body problem: Linguistic parallelism. Psychosom. Med. 29:52-71, 1967.

18. ——, Kabler, J. D., and Graham, F. K.: Physiological response to the suggestion of attitudes specific for hives and hypertension. Psychosom. Med. 24:159-169, 1962.

19. ——, Lundy, R. M., Benjamin, L. S., Kabler, J. D., Lewis, W. C., Kunish, N. O., and Graham, F. K.: Specific attitudes in initial interviews with patients having different "psychosomatic" diseases. Psychosom. Med. 24:257-266, 1962.

20. ——, Stern, J. A., and Winokur, G.: Experimental investigation of the specificity of attitude hypothesis in psychosomatic disease. Psychosom. Med. 20:446-457, 1958.

21. Greenfield, N. S., and Alexander, A. A.: The ego and bodily responses. In: Greenfield, N. S. and Lewis, W. C. (Eds.): Psychoanalysis and Current Biological Thought. Madison, University of Wisconsin Press, 1965.

22. ——, Katz, D., Roessler, R., and Alexander, A. A.: The relationship between physiological and psychological responsivity: Depression and galvanic skin response. J. Nerv. Ment. Dis. 136:535-539, 1963.

23. ——, Roessler, R., and Alexander, A. A.: Ego strength and physiological responsivity. II. The relationship of the Barron ES Scale to the temporal and recovery characteristics of skin resistance, finger blood volume, heart rate and muscle potential responses to sound. Arch. Gen. Psychiat. 9:129-141, 1963.

24. Holmes, T. H., and Rahe, R. H.: Life crisis and disease onset. Mimeographed unpublished manuscripts.

25. Johnson, L. C., Hord, D. J., and Lubin, A.: Response specificity for difference scores and autonomic lability scores. USN Med. NP Res. Unit Rep. 63-12, Aug., 1963.

26. Lacey, J. I., Bateman, D. E., and Van Lehn, R.: Autonomic response specificity: An experimental study. Psychosom. Med. 15:8-21, 1953.

27. —— and Lacey, B. C.: Verification and extension of the principle of autonomic response-stereotypy. Amer. J. Psychol. 71:50-73, 1958.

28. —— and Lacey, B. C.: The law of initial value in the longitudinal study of autonomic constitution: Reproducibility of autonomic responses and response patterns over a four-year interval. Ann. N.Y. Acad. Sci. 98:1257-1290; 1322-1326, 1962.

29. Lucio, W. H. and Wenger, M. A.: Prediction of teacher performance and emotional stability: A psychophysiological pilot study of female student teachers. Final report to U.S. Office of Education, Contract No. SAE 8311; Sept. 30, 1961.

30. Malmo, R. B.: Activation: A Neuropsychological dimension. Psychol. Rev. 66:367-386, 1959.

31. —— and Shagass, C.: Physiologic study of symptom mechanisms in psychiatric patients under stress. Psychosom. Med. 11:25-29, 1949.

32. ——, —— and Davis, F. H.: Symptom specificity and bodily reactions during psychiatric interview. Psychosom. Med. 12:362-376, 1950.

33. ——, —— and Davis, F. H.: Specificity of bodily reactions under stress: A physiological study of somatic mechanisms in psychiatric patients. Res. Publ. Ass. Res. Nerv. Ment. Dis. 29:231-261, 1950.

34. Oken, D., Grinker, R. R., Heath, H. A., Hertz, M., Korchin, S. J., Sabshin, M., and Schwartz, N. B.: Relation of physiological response to affect expression. Arch. Gen. Psychiat. 6:336-351, 1962.

35. Rahe, R. H., McKean, J. D., Jr., and Arthur, R. J.: A longitudinal study of life-change and illness patterns. J. Psychosom. Res. 10:355-366, 1967.

36. Roessler, R., Alexander, A. A., and Greenfield, N. S.: Ego strength and physiological responsivity—I. The relationship of the Barron ES Scale to skin resistance, finger blood volume, heart rate and muscle potential responses to sound. Arch. Gen. Psychiat. 8:142-154, 1963.

37. Schachter, J.: Pain, fear, and anger in hypertensives and normotensives. Psychosom. Med. 19:17-29, 1957.

38. Shagass, C., and Schwartz, M.: Excitability of the cerebral cortex in psychiatric disorders. In: Roessler, R., and Greenfield, N. S. (Eds.) : Physiological Correlates of Psychological Disorder. Madison: Univ. of Wisconsin Press, 1962.

39. Shapiro, D.: Neurotic Styles. New York: Basic Books, 1965.

40. Smith, D. B. D., and Wenger, M. A.: Changes in autonomic balance during phasic anxiety. Psychophysiol., 1:267-271, 1965.

41. Stern, J. A.: Toward a definition of psychophysiology. Psychophysiol., 1:90-91, 1964.

42. Sternbach, R. A.: Two independent indices of activation. EEG Clin. Neurophysiol., 12:609-611, 1960.

43. ———: Assessing differential autonomic patterns in emotions. J. Psychosom. Res., 6:87-91, 1962.

44. ———: The effects of instructional sets on autonomic responsivity. Psychophysiol., 1:67-72, 1964.

45. ———: Autonomic responsivity and the concept of sets. In: Greenfield, N. S., and Lewis, W. C. (Eds.) : Psychoanalysis and Current Biological Thought. Madison: Univ. of Wisconsin Press, 1965.

46. ———: Principles of Psychophysiology. New York: Academic Press, 1966.

47. ———: Psychophysiological bases of psychosomatic phenomena. Psychosomatics 7:81-84, 1966.

48. ——— and Tursky, B.: Ethnic differences among housewives in psychophysical and skin potential responses to electric shock. Psychophysiology 1:241-246, 1965.

49. Tursky, B., and Sternbach, R. A.: Further physiological correlates of ethnic differences in responses to shock. Psychophysiology 4:67-74, 1967.

50. Venables, P. H.: Input dysfunction in schizophrenia. In: Maher, B. A. (Ed.): Progress in Experimental Personality Research, Vol. I. New York, Academic Press, 1964.

51. ——— and Wing, J. K.: Level of arousal and the subclassification of schizophrenia. Arch. Gen. Psychiat. 7:114-119, 1962.

52. Wenger, M. A.: The measurement of individual differences in autonomic balance. Psychosom. Med. 3:427-434, 1941.

53. ———: The stability of measurement of autonomic balance. Psychosom. Med. 4:94-95, 1942.

54. ———: Studies of autonomic balance in Army Air Forces personnel. Comp. Psychol. Monogr., Vol. 19, No. 4. Berkeley, Univ. of Calif. Press, 1948.

55. ———: Studies of autonomic balance: A summary. Psychophysiology 2:173-186, 1966.

56. ———, Clemens, T. L., Coleman, D. R., Cullen, T. D., and Engel, B. T.: Autonomic response specificity. Psychosom. Med. 23:185-193, 1961.

57. ——— and Cullen, T. D.: ANS response patterns to fourteen stimuli. Amer. Psychol. 13:423 (abstract), 1958.

58. ——— and Ellington, M.: The measurement of autonomic balance in children: Method and normative data. Psychosom. Med. 5:241-253, 1943.

Discussion of Dr. Sternbach's Paper

by ROBERT B. MALMO, Ph.D.,

Allan Memorial Institute and McGill University, Montreal

DR. STERNBACH and his colleagues at Madison are obviously engaged in significant research on physiological aspects of psychopathology. This is reflected in their paper. To my mind they are asking the right questions, and there can be no doubt about their kindling the interest of listeners in this audience.

Physiological response specificity. How right they are about psychopathology providing the means for deepening the significance of physiological data. Take, for example, the principle of physiological response specificity. Removed from the context of bodily symptoms in psychiatric patients, the findings are interesting; but what greater depth of meaning they have in the context of psychopathology! It is interesting, for instance, that a given individual under stress will show greater increase in forehead tension than another individual. But how much greater significance this physiological finding takes on when we realize that in pathological cases the forehead muscle tension can rise to exceedingly high levels, producing such excruciating discomfort that the patient has to leave his job. While certain specific physiological reactions may turn out to be evanescent, *this* kind of specificity, once it has reached the symptom stage, persists over long periods of time.

The electromyography employed to show these specific tension reactions is essential for probing beneath the surface, so to speak, to reveal clearly what otherwise would not be visible. To extend our observations, such instruments are indispensable. But I would not like to see recording instruments regarded as all-sufficient, nor as being necessarily more objective (and "scientific") than behavioral observations.

We may hope to gain a deeper understanding of the patient and his symptoms by various means, including of course his own subjective reports, although it is clear from the failure of introspectionistic psychology that it is impossible to directly perceive one's mental content. Here a quotation from Hebb (1967, p. 6) seems apt:

Objective behavior theory may seem unpalatable to the analytical psychiatrist, but he must realize that psychoanalysis itself is the great fore-

96

runner of objectivism. The whole theory of the unconscious tells us that verbal report is unreliable as an index of mental content, and that one can learn more about the presence of hostility or anxiety as an inference from a person's nonverbal behavior (and some of his verbal behavior) than one can by simply asking for a subjective report. Freud anticipated Watson as a behaviorist.[1]

Homeostatic mechanisms. If I may turn to the question of homeostatic concepts, I believe they are truly useful only when worked out in detail, like those for temperature and water regulation. On the basis of physiological data from psychiatric patients with severe anxiety, we have suggested that there may be a deficiency of homeostatic mechanisms in pathological anxiety. It seems possible that such homeostatic mechanisms normally prevent physiological overactivation and related losses in behavioral efficiency. Inhibitory components of the reticular and limbic systems, which have been relatively neglected in theories relating the nervous system and behavior, are considered as possibly playing a major role in the homeostatic control of physiological over-reaction in response to stress.

Here physiological activation is not anything so unitary nor so simple as sympathetic dominance. In fact, some of the most compelling evidence for this homeostatic notion comes from reactions of the skeletal motor system (e.g., muscle potentials and involuntary finger movement). Neurophysiological and neuropsychological experiments are throwing more and more light on inhibitory mechanisms in the brain. In my opinion, it is not a vain hope that eventually the kind of regulating mechanism we are hypothesizing may in fact be discovered and understood in detail. The behavioral and psychophysiological experiments with psychiatric patients seem to point the way to such a discovery. It would only be another one of the many instances where clinical observations have lighted the way to basic discoveries in neurophysiology.

With regard to the evidence for high physiological activation in many schizophrenics, recent research by Orzack, Kornetsky, and Freeman (1967)[2] is of interest. These workers reasoned that if poor attention in the chronic schizophrenic is partly due to hyperarousal, a tranquilizer acting on the reticular activating system ought to improve such a person's score on their continuous performance test (a test designed to measure selective attention). They found such improvement, using carphenazine.

It is not claimed that hyperarousal accounts for all impairments in performance, because the drug did not improve performance on a Digit Symbol Substitution Test. But it is of interest that clinical ratings were correlated with the test that showed improvement, and not with the Digit Symbol Test—suggesting, they thought, that clinical improvement was related to the subject's ability to attend selectively.

Clearly, we have a long way to go, but the research of Dr. Sternbach, with his co-workers, and the work of others pursuing related lines of investigation are helping to get us there.

REFERENCES

1. Hebb, D. O.: Cerebral organization and consciousness. Res. Publ. Ass. Nerv. Ment. Dis. 45:1-7, 1967.

2. Orzack, Maressa H., Kornetsky, C., and Freeman, H.: The effects of daily administration of carphenazine on attention in the schizophrenic patient. Psychopharmacologia (Berlin) 11:31-38, 1967.

6

PSYCHOMOTILITY: A DIMENSION OF BEHAVIOR DISORDER

by H. E. KING, Ph.D.*

I. INTRODUCTION

A SYSTEMATIC relation between states of behavior disorder and faulty psychomotor functioning is, by now, an experimentally well-established phenomenon. Briefly stated, it has been found that the speed and smoothness of simple psychomotor movement is defective whenever an individual finds himself under notably less-than-optimal conditions, whether these arise from changes in physiological, psychological or neurological events.[73,76] Whenever the balance of total organismic factors is affected by persistent strong emotion, marked physiologic imbalance, or structural damage to the central nervous system—great enough to produce clinically reliable disorganization of adaptive behavior—the psychomotor adequacy of the individual may be shown to be affected proportionately. This contingency has long been suspected, especially among the schizophrenias, but did not take clear form until recently when the search was narrowed, by a more explicit definition of the responses in question, and broadened, at the same time, to include virtually all of the forms that disorganized human behavior can assume. More plainly said, by turning experimental attention to a level of action more complex than the *neuromotor* (e.g., reflexes or positioning responses), yet simpler than the *perceptuomotor* (where movement is combined with discrimination, memory, or other cognitive process), and by observing performance in just these behaviors across a wide spectrum of adaptive disorder, a more orderly kind of data has emerged that is remarkably coherent. Since few measures have been found to relate in a systematic way to the diverse disruptions of personal and social behavior called "psychopathology," this general formulation of the psychomotor correlate of behavior disorder may seem oversimple. It

*University of Pittsburgh School of Medicine.

99

is based on a large body of empirical data that cannot easily be reviewed here.[73,76] We can sketch its broad outline in a few sentences, however,
and cite its experimental sources, before turning our attention more
particularly to certain aspects of psychomotor covariation with the
psychopathic state that may shed some light on the mechanism underlying this regularly observed association.

Basic (simple, irreducible) psychomotor dimensions need a clearer
delineation than they now enjoy, with a return to their logical place in
study as a component of most of the observable behavior of any
organism, rather than serving as a topic for applied research only. One
useful distinction that has been made within the limits of the definition
here imposed is that of Seashore (1951) between *fine* psychomotor action, depending more on speed or accuracy than strength, and *gross*
movement patterning, which calls for action by large muscle groups and
strength or stamina.[116,117] Centering our attention on only *fine*
psychomotor movement for the moment—for the practical reasons of
ease in accomplishment and repeatability—it has been further shown
(by factor analytic technique) that several sub-factors can be identified,
among which are clearly: the speed of initiating movement, speed in
continued oscillating movement, and speed in controlled (dextrous)
fingertip movement.[44,64,67,116] Specific tasks and procedures that tap
these essentially independent principal factors of *fine* psychomotor
movement speed have been applied, in comparable ways, to populations
as diverse as the psychotic, mentally deficient, and socially delinquent,[13,14,15,30,67,73,76,144] to the seriously brain-damaged,[9,16,72,73,108] as
well as to those whose central nervous system is influenced less radically
by drugs, direct electric, or chemical stimulation or by a limited surgical
intervention,[42,50,68,73,125,126] and to normal subjects whose behavior is
temporarily deranged by sleep loss, oxygen lack, starvation, or other
form of manipulated physiologic or psychologic stress.[21,73,90,138,139,154]
A synthesis of the empirical findings reported by many different investigators—working with quite varied hypotheses, populations, and
procedures—makes clear the following main themes.

Psychomotor retardation is found at all three levels of function (sub-
factors) tested among the psychoses, most notably among the
schizophrenias but in depression and mania as well. The degree of slowing follows closely clinical estimates made of the severity of disorder,
where these are demonstrably reliable. The speed loss of chronic
schizophrenic patients (where speed is about one-half the rate for

matched control subjects) is significantly greater than that observed among the acutely ill; and their deficit in turn is greater than that found among the subacute schizophrenic disorders of the kind most often managed on an out-patient basis. Psychoneurotic patients, in contrast, show little or no impairment in performance on identical tasks, although they are reported to display greater skeletomuscular dyscontrol and over-reaction, compared with the normal, when measured under conditions of mild experimental stress. One psychomotor deficit or another has also been described, on a less systematic basis, for such varied population groups as: "unstable children," schizophrenic children, adult speech-defectives (e.g., stammerers), and the socially delinquent (i.e., juveniles in trouble with the law, convicted felons). The brain-injured human adults, classified by neurological criteria, form a most heterogeneous group descriptively, which is reflected in the varying degrees of simple psychomotor slowing, depending on the neural problem. Marked speed decrements have been found to accompany severe forms of cerebral damage—for example, supratentorial disease, cerebral neoplasm, or in the wake of corrective lobectomies. A lesser psychomotor speed reduction is measurable if the brain-damage is more limited or diffuse—among restricted cerebrovascular accidents, for example, or in multiple sclerosis. Still less is found—although it is significantly present—among the epilepsies (between seizures) and for otherwise normal subjects in great age (70 years and above). Intelligence, in the normal range, seems in no way to be correlated with simple psychomotor speed, but among the severely retarded (IQ less than 60) decrements in measured speed, on tests that sample these same three basic factors, become systematically greater until, for the imbecile or mongol, they are the equal of the deficits seen in the chronic schizophrenic or the seriously brain-damaged individual. Not all of these conditions have been explored equally well, and the hypothesis will profit by further study and replication using the improved technology and conceptual clarification now available. The general outline is quite clear, however, and the essential findings are robust, resistant even to what might seem to be overpowering differences between examiners in procedure or measurement technique.[73,76] What may account for this broad covariation of simple psychomotor speed with varied kinds of behavior disorganization that often seem to have but little in common? Is the psychomotor slowing only a byproduct of the subjects' diffused attention, limited cooperation, lowered motivation or arousal, or does it reflect an inability to process information quickly or to change the mental "set"? Each of these explanations has been urged to account for the phenomena, at one time or another, usually reflecting the dominant psychological theme of the day. Whatever the nature of the mechanism responsible, it is decidedly more complex than would at first appear. In seeking a common base on which to compare psychomotor speed loss among the strikingly dissimilar states and grades of behavior disorder just described, we may begin by turning attention to the kinds of *change* in psychomotor speed constants that can be observed when normal subjects are placed under conditions intended to produce marked derangements in their over-all adaptive behavior.

II. Induced Psychomotor Slowing

Most investigators have found it difficult to improve by very much the *fine* psychomotor speeds of the normal subject, measured when he is rested, moderately alert, and well-practiced on the test-task. Neither stimulant drugs, raised psychophysiologic arousal, nor manipulations of reward and punishment exert strong influence on these behaviors, and if made too emphatic may produce instead a paradoxic slowing in measured response. The "usual" performance of the normal subject, recorded under experimentally favorable conditions, appears to fall close to his "maximal" or "optimal" psychomotor responsivity.[11,73,76,88] The ease with which some of these same responses can significantly be slowed, however, by any of a variety of changed organismic conditions, stands in marked contrast to this. A sleep loss of 30-78 hours has been shown to slow reaction time notably and to increase greatly the variability of individual response, with baseline speed and variance restored following a single night's sleep.[154] Even very small amounts of alcohol (10-20 cc.) begin to slow the initiating of psychomotor response[139] and intoxication is well known to affect both the initiation and coordination of simple psychomotor movement,[42] and to reduce the rate of voluntary continued movement to a somewhat lesser degree.[59] Barbiturates and psychotomimetic agents, when used in strength sufficient to derange adaptive behavior, also temporarily limit measured simple psychomotor speeds.[42,67,76,113] A significant slowing of *fine* psychomotor performance has been observed to accompany states of marked physiologic imbalance produced by oxygen lack,[139] starvation,[21] exposure to extreme environmental cold,[134] and by the *after*-effect of sleep deprivation—which is thought to disturb the pattern of the diurnal rhythm.[152] It is interesting to note that the psychomotor performance so degraded is subject to reversal, within limits, by further manipulating "excitor" conditions. That is to say, if a performance is found to be distinctly subnormal by reason of fatigue, sedating drug, boredom or sleeplessness, it may be improved and even restored, at times, by the use of stimulant drugs, such as amphetamine; by a raised state of psychophysiologic arousal; or by the use of procedurally sharpened incentives—e.g., increased stimulus intensity, the avoidance of noxious stimuli, or a knowledge of results.[42,45,88,95,149,153] These changes in performance may merely be more visible than for subjects near normal at the start, where similar but attenuated improvement might be present but less easily detected. A number of possibly interacting factors make it difficult to summarize beyond doubt all experimental work of the kind—differences in test methods and procedure, as well as the control of variance by population factors, dosage, time-course, and the like. It seems fair, however, to extract from the data available the following very general statements. 1) When adaptive behavior is deranged by experimentally changed conditions, psychomotor speed losses are observed. 2) A lessening of these losses can often be achieved by counter-manipulations of excitors that would have little visible influence on performance not originally degraded. 3) The extent of this reversibility is determined by the power of the degrading influence, the nature of the excitor influence, and the sensitivity of the tests used as indicators. 4) The subjective state that goes with these conditions (boredom, fatigue, sleepiness) may change at the same time, yet not be causally related to the psychomotor decrement (the drinker's conviction that he is singing well is not borne out by the song rendered). 5) Changes in psychomotor speed, both decrement and restorations, are observed at all three levels of *fine* psychomotor function here distinguished, but not necessarily equally.[23,42,76,84,88,139,149]

As a rule, changes made in the conditions under which normal subjects work are intended to disrupt the adaptive balance and to worsen performance, while changes of the conditions under which patients work are more often benevolent and intended to improve their over-all adaptive behavior—which is as it should be. Let us look for a moment at some of the effects of therapy on simple psychomotor behavior, bearing in mind that any changes observed may be the result of a basic improvement in the patients clinical condition, or may reflect only a temporary relief from disabling symptoms—a partial restoring of normal function by countering the degrading influence of an underlying psychopathology.

III. PSYCHOMOTOR SPEED AND CHANGED PSYCHIATRIC STATUS

The use of simple psychomotor tests to follow change in status by a given patient or group of patients over time is still comparatively rare—although evaluation by means of more complex perceptuomotor tests has long been known.[50,62,65,68,69,101,102,105,123,137] Most basic might be the changes recorded in *fine* psychomotor speed by patients judged to be much improved or worsened without any specific therapy, but such data are virtually nonexistent. The best approximation is found among the evaluations made of patients while they served as members of a "control group," either temporarily untreated or next in line to receive active therapy.[98] The few patients so tested who were much improved (none worsened) always significantly improved on all tests of psychomotor speed applied.[78] The identical measures administered before, during, and after an active treatment that produced, alas, disappointing therapeutic results (psychosurgery for the relief of paranoid schizophrenia) also showed no improvement in psychomotor behavior. A temporary *slowing*, in fact, was regularly observed on reaction time, tapping speed, and finger dexterity measures immediately following the operation, followed by an exact return to preoperative speed levels within two months—a result that was attributed to temporary postoperative physiological interference with the motor integrative function of the frontal brain.[63] This regular temporary reduction was found to characterize all of the surgical interventions studied (venous ligation, superior and orbital topectomy) and was of about equal magnitude among both mildly and severely disturbed chronic schizophrenic patients. It is noteworthy that a detailed evaluation of visual, auditory, and kinaesthetic-proprioceptive functions of the identical patients did not reveal concomitant losses in sensory function. More definitively, schizophrenic patients judged to be *much improved, slightly improved, unchanged* and *worsened* following a prolonged period of electric stimulation of limbic brain structures[51] were found to exhibit exactly those conditions when evaluated by their performance on tests of fine psychomotor speed: reaction time, tapping speed and finger dexterity.[81] By observing individual patient performance during active stimulation of the limbic brain and associated structures (septum, hippocampus and caudate nucleus), momentary changes could be effected in ongoing psychomotor behavior when the same brain area was excited electrically in different schizophrenic patients and when different brain areas were stimulated in the same patient.[68] Particularly striking was a dramatic increase in the speed of ongoing psychomotor movement (tapping) with excitation of the septal area, followed by an abrupt return to the baseline level on interruption of the stimulating current. This repeatable effect was obtained without change in the instruction or procedures governing performance on this well-practiced task. It was closely related in time, however, to the greater "alerting" (in terms of speech clarity and improved personal "contact" with the psychiatric interviewer) that has been reported to accompany stimulation of this brain region.[51,52]

The concomitant changes of psychiatric status and measured psychomotor speed, only suggested by these few carefully studied individual patients, have since been confirmed by experimental findings reported on far larger clinical groups treated with drugs, or by drugs combined with a variety of socially-supportive efforts in a push for rehabilitation of the chronic patient. J. H. Court (1964) has attacked the problem of identifying change in the status of the acute mental patient, using simple psychomotor measures in the longitudinal study of patients consecutively admitted to an acute ward.[32] Evaluations were made before treatment began (using tests of reaction time, finger dexterity, and others), at the halfway point of the usual hospital stay (3 weeks), and again at usual full hospital stay (6 weeks), whether or not the patient was discharged. No attempt was made to divide the patients into classes by diagnosis or treatment; the question centered only on whether any improvement manifest on psychiatric ratings would accord with indices of simple psychomotor speed. All patients were not equally disturbed on admission, of course, nor did all improve in a similar way. The obvious agreement found between the two independent estimates of status led this investigator to say in summary: that "a short battery of psychomotor tests can provide useful information concerning the mental state of a wide range of psychiatric disorders, and periodic retesting is sufficiently reliable to justify conclusions concerning changes in condition and the effects of a given therapeutic regime." The psychomotor measures were found, at times, to be even more sensitive than clinical judgment, in the sense that trends could be detected before change in over-all behavior was yet certain. "These 'early warnings' must depart from the envelope of daily or weekly variation to be of value, of course, but they have often been found in our laboratory to presage changes not yet apparent to clinical judgment or behavior ratings."[32] Court and Cameron (1963) examined the treatment of schizophrenic and manic excitement by Haloperidol and Disipal, similarly evaluated by longitudinal psychomotor technique.[33] In summary of this work they say: "The findings indicate that there is a severe impairment of psychomotor function in states of excitement, which improves with return to health. Test results are sufficiently stable to be used as indicators of the changes taking place under chemotherapy. The side-effects produced by Haloperidol do not affect all tasks equally. The improvement in performance under chemotherapy indicates that the drug does not simply have a sedative effect, but is actively antipsychotic."*

Heilizer in 1959, using much the same approach to the study of chronic schizophrenia, has reported that chlorpromazine improved the contact of his patients with the "real world," while shortening reaction time latency and reducing its variability, along with improved dexterity.[53] In a long-term, thorough study of rehabilitation of various

---

*The direct effects of neuroleptic agents such as phenothiazine or reserpine on the musculature can, of course, complicate the psychomotor evaluation of psychiatric status, but need not limit seriously its usefulness.[20,32,33,82,124,145] Reaction time is nearly normal in Parkinson's Disease[115,66,130] and seems little affected in psychosis by the side-effects of chlorpromazine[53] or trifluoperazine.[20] The problem has been confronted directly by Brooks and Weaver,[20] who have observed severely disturbed schizophrenic patients from the points of view of psychiatric status, psychomotor functioning, and muscular change that might result from drug-induced extrapyramidal dysfunction. Withdrawal from (prior) medication with placebo replacement was found to produce clear evidence of deteriorated clinical status, which continued through a period of substitution of an ineffective medication and was then reversed and the patients brought to their original status with medication by trifluoperazine (to which was later added an anti-Parkinsonian agent, usually benztropine methanesulfonate). Psychomotor tests proved to be differentially sensitive to all of these changes, reaction time and steadiness rather exactly following the time-course of change in psychiatric status (over 15 weeks), and not being affected adversely by muscular dysfunction. The dexterity measure and a test of motor learning were affected by muscular dysfunction, a finding similar to that of Court.[32] When explicitly drug-induced Parkinsonism has been studied, a close temporal linking could be observed between increased tranquilizer medication and measured extrapyramidal dysfunction, with the latter relieved by anti-Parkinsonian agents. Serial reaction time, dexterity measures, and time on a rotary target were clearly negatively affected by increased tranquilizer dosages, but immediately following anti-Parkinsonian medication all returned to their original levels.[145]

kinds of chronic psychotic patients, Weaver and Brooks have used psychomotor tests (reaction time, tapping rate, transport assembly, and others) to follow changes in the mental status of large-scale clinical samples. They report that psychomotor performance closely reflected differing grades of behavior disorganization,[144] and that these changes follow faithfully the course of clinical improvement;[146,147] but what is at first glance more surprising, they discovered that ". . . patients who were judged to have responded favorably to tranquilizing drugs did significantly better on psychomotor tests before as well as after drug administration."[146,p.70] This may be the counterpart of the ironic conclusion reached in the day of psychosurgery, that the least disturbed schizophrenic patients (who were the faster psychomotor performers) offered the best potential for improvement by the operation.[54,55,79,80] Hundreds of chronic schizophrenic patients have since been screened to put this observation to the test. A high degree of association was found between good or poor psychomotor performance and release from the hospital, with or without special rehabilitation procedure, or remaining in hospital, with and without special rehabilitation. More recently, Weaver and Brooks have extended their sample to include manic-depressive, chronic brain-syndrome, personality disorder, and mental deficiency patients—approximately 1,000 cases in all. Using tests of reaction time and serial reaction time, tapping speed, and transport assembly, they have established—by multiple regression and multiple correlation methods—a 75 per cent prediction of patient outcome.[147; also see 3,22,121]

In summary, we may say that any marked change in the clinical status of a given psychiatric patient, or group of patients, whether resulting from "spontaneous" improvement or brought about by active psychiatric therapy, is reflected faithfully in measures made of simple psychomotor efficiency throughout the treatment period. Even the mixed direct effect (on the musculature) and indirect influences (on clinical status) that are commonly observed with the use of psychoactive drugs have been separately analyzed and found to relate in systematic ways to disordered psychomotor function.

IV. PSYCHOMOTOR SPEED UNDER CHANGED EXPERIMENTAL CONDITIONS

An enormous literature describes the experimental effort to understand the nature of psychomotor response generally, in the normal subject, as it can be influenced by physical or physiological factors, knowledge of results, fatigue and rest, learning, and so on.[1,27,43,76,133,138,150,156,157] Within the narrower definition of *fine* psychomotor speed used here—that which is above the neuromotor and below the perceptuomotor—the greatest experimental effort has been directed to study of the reaction time measure alone and, where applied to psychopathology, to the question of whether the increased latency of response characteristic of schizophrenia can be reduced by altering the conditions under which it is measured. We can only suggest the sources of this work and try to define an attitude that will make its empirical findings with psychopathological subjects more easily understood. It has been apparent since the experiments of Wundt (1874) and Exner (1873) that the reaction time measure combines elements of *attention* and *action,* and that it can be made even more inclusive by the use of a disjunctive (or "choice") response to admit virtually any desired degree of cognitive or sensory appreciation.[41,160] Woodworth, in fact, includes reaction time among the psycho-physical methods—viz., the larger the sensory, perceptual or cognitive difference among the stimuli to be responded to, the shorter will be the reaction time.[155,p.426;157,p.261] It is the *action* component of this measure that will be emphasized here, however, "in which a simple perceptual experience leads to a straightforward action when the mental set for it is affirmative," as Miles has put it in describing psychomotor tests of cerebral function that are sufficiently objective to be used with confidence by other scientific disciplines.[99] Obviously, the same test method can be used also to center on attention,[57,85] or on uncertainty in time,[48,119] or intensity,[58,135] or other properties of the stimulus[2,27,106,128,157]—at the option of the investigator. The meaning of any difference in latency recorded will, then, be controlled by his choice of experimental procedure. A frequent confusion of these possibilities does little to lighten the task of synthesizing the experimental findings reported in applying the method to psychopathological patient groups. It has been given special mention here, since a concern with this fascinating but mixed index of reactivity has tended to dominate thinking about *psychomotor* functioning in behavior disorder—which it can represent only in part, and which can easily become confounded with perceptual or cognitive determinants of the response.

The influence of temporary, experimental change in "incentive" or "biological motive" on the slowed reaction latency of psychopathologic patients has been examined by pairing electric shock with the signal to respond, by rewarding faster response with praise or money or cigarettes, and by the manipulation of direct stimulus dynamisms (i.e., the intensity of the signal to respond). The trends that emerge from comparable experiments are remarkably consistent. Social praise, verbal urging, and the use of "success" or "failure" commentary brings only slight improvement in reaction time (or rudimentary choice reaction time measures) or in finger dexterity performance among schizophrenic, brain damaged, or normal control subjects. In fact, "failure" and "censure" commentary has usually produced greater improvement than has positively-toned verbal reward.[8,25,35,47,120] When the "warmth" or "rebuff" of prior social contact between the experimenter and the patients have been systematically manipulated, the attitude of "rebuff," unexpectedly, was found to be associated with improved reaction time performance.[12] The familiarity with both task and experimenter that go with repeated practice runs and spaced rest intervals are reflected in "settling down" and a limited improvement on reaction time measures (and in rudimentary choice-reaction) by normal subjects, but this "sharpening" of response is not equally evident among data collected in the same way from schizophrenic or brain-damaged patients.[64,76] It would appear that the attempted manipulation of the interpersonal element of measurement (between the examiner and the subject tested) exerts no important influence on the reaction time subfactor of *fine* psychomotor performance. Distraction also seems to be largely ineffective. Although schizophrenic patients may show considerable original retardation on tests such as reaction time, tapping, and aiming, experimental distraction has not been found to affect them adversely, as it does more complex behaviors produced by the same subjects—on tests of spot or maze tracing, and auditory and visual attention and integration.[96,97,122] Pairing an electric shock or a loud noise with the signal to respond, or the use of louder or brighter signals themselves, in contrast, regularly shortens the latency of schizophrenic response. Although performance usually remains slower than the normal,[141] there is no doubt that speeding of the reaction time may be so induced. The mechanism, in both instances, has been interpreted as a better definition of the task-relevant stimuli by these procedures, rather than an effective alteration of the subjects "need to respond."[23] This interpretation finds clear support in the data of those investigators who have chosen to vary the dimension of stimulus magnitude explicitly,[34,71,136,142] in which a systematic decrease in reaction time latency is found to accompany increased physical intensity of the signal to respond. An equal sensitivity by schizophrenic and normal subjects to change in the experimental variable has been shown, when the change in performance of each group is related to its own base-level. Systematic reduction of the intra-individual variability of response is also observed as the signal to respond grows stronger.[71] More recent evidence makes it clear, moreover, that the "strength" of the stimulus is best considered psychologically as a contrast phenomenon (change in energy), and not the direct effect of an absolute intensity. Schizophrenic subjects show approximately equal latency on measures of Incidental Serial Reaction Time,* to stimuli going off as well as on, as do normal subjects. When the responses of the normal and schizophrenic subjects are then compared in terms of the off latency alone, following tones of systematically differing loudness, it is perfectly evident that the reaction of both groups is faster to the cessation of an intense stimulus than it is to the cessation of a moderate or a weak stimulus.[77; see also 17,27,157] Lang and Buss (1965) have concluded from their analysis of all forms of psychological deficit occurring in schizophrenia—including the psychomotor—that "deficit in chronic schizophrenia is greatest for low-intensity inputs and least when stimulus intensity is high."[88,p.95] They relate this general finding to the considerable body of evidence for "set" disturbances in schizophrenia, to the greater susceptibility of such patients to "associative interference" and to the concept of (stimulus) "overinclusiveness." It would appear that, in the face of interference by competing stimuli from within, only the more dramatic cues from the environment may call forth relatively efficient response. The more severe the deficit, the greater the response to increased input.

---

*The subject presses a switch when he hears a stimulus-tone come on (in earphones) and releases it when the tone goes off, just as threshold measurements are made in clinical audiometry. His accuracy in following patterned "short," "medium," and "long" tones—with the interstimulus interval also controlled—yields objective evidence that all stimuli are above threshold. The subject's delay in response following onset of the signal-tone, and his corresponding lag in signalling its offset, are recorded by graphic traces on a moving paper strip. The "on" and "off" latencies calculated for stimuli of differing intensity and duration constitute Incidental Serial Reaction Time—called incidental, since the subject's attention (set) is directed only to accuracy in detecting the presence or absence of the tone, with no emphasis laid on the speed of response beyond the original, and routine, instruction, "When you hear the tone come on, signal that to me by pressing the hand-button; when you hear it go off, let your finger up."[77]

V. The Shape of the Problem

There has been a tendency, dating almost from its discovery, to explain away the psychomotor deficit of behavior disorder by what have been called the "easy explanations,"[10] which invoke faulty cooperation, a lack of motivation, fatigue, negativism, or underarousal to account for the slower-than-normal performance observed. These explanations have sought, typically, to account for a known by an unknown and to explain the subnormal psychomotor performance recorded by means of a construct that is itself inferred from (other) inefficient behaviors. Whether the psychomotor defect reflects (or is a part of) a primary condition or is held to be a secondary consequent of some other disturbance is, usually, related to the kind of mechanism that is endorsed. The scope and coherence of the empirical findings just reviewed should serve to make it clear, however, that the problem is a far more complex one than can readily be explained by an unenthusiastic or ideationally disturbed participation in the measurement process alone. A comprehensive overview of the many conditions and forms under which the phenomena appear should serve as a logical first-step in any search for mechanisms that may underlie psychopathological slowing of the simple psychomotor behaviors.

Whatever interpretation be proposed, it must fit a complex but stable pattern of empirical data that includes: similar rates of response acquisition by the slowed and the normal; greater temporary improvement in response by "punishment" than "reward"; a clear deficit in psychomotor speed by patients able to carry out demanding perceptual tasks; reduced speed in continuing as well as initiating action; notable stimulus dynamism effects; relatively greater loss in simple than in complex psychomotor performance; and a close quantitative correspondence with the degree of behavioral disorganization arising from the most varied causes—aging, neural damage, functional disorder, physiologic imbalance, and arrested mental development.

The choice of tests, procedures, and even the scoring methods used may contribute to how the deficit is seen. Let us continue to review, therefore, something more of the "shape" of the problem as it has emerged from the experimental work already cited, and add those bits of new evidence that may help lend form to the question of what must be taken into account by any adequate "explanation" of the psychomotor slowing that so regularly accompanies adaptive disorder.

We have seen that when an effort is made to identify independent sub-factors within the domain of the fine psychomotor ability of the normal subject, tests for all have been found to be affected adversely by severe behavior disorder, to a roughly equivalent degree, and with raised correlations among them. Certain of the factors seem more readily influenced by a specific kind of disorder; finger dexterity is reported to be affected more strongly by central-acting drugs,[20,32,33] for example, while reaction time appears more sensitive to the presence of schizophrenia or cerebral disease.[16,64] It is the *nonspecific* quantitative slowing that is the most striking effect, however, and the fact that quite different kinds of action are similarly affected by quite different kinds of psychopathological problem. An impression that both group and individual variability in psychomotor performance are dramatically increased by psychopathology derives mainly from the many measures made of reaction time or its variants. Group and individual variability are regularly found to be expanded and skewed positively (to include a greater number of very slow responses) when simple reaction time is measured among schizophrenic,[32,64,144] sleep-deprived,[154] or brain-injured subjects.[16] At the same time, group and individual variation on tests that reach other psychomotor subfactors, such as tapping speed and finger dexterity, are only moderately increased, as a rule, and may even be over-regular on occasion reflecting a stereotypy in performance.[64]

The kind of action measured and its physiologic and psychologic determinants will obviously be pertinent to the size and form of the defect recorded. A slowing of the average (or the median) reaction time and the expansion of individual response variability tend to occur together in states of behavior disorder, whether temporary or permanent, and may be regarded as related aspects of the vigor of responding.[36,61,71] Timed actions that have passed the initiating stage are also regularly found to be slowed whenever over–all adaptive behavior is disorganized, as has been shown by those tests of continuing motion and movement dexterity already cited.[73,76] In addition, it has been found that timed tests of a rudimentary action, such as a linear thrust of the arm and hand from point A to point B, reveal significant slowing in chronic schizophrenia,[74] in mental deficiency,[30] and in Parkinson's disease.[66] These slowed measures represent simple effector movements only after their recorded beginning and before the duration of the action under study has lasted half a second. They are found whether the movement is initiated on a signal from the examiner, or when executed wholly at the subject's own volition.[74] The simplest of paper-and-pencil tracing tasks, such as Trail Making (Part A) or the Limited Foreview Tracing Task, also consistently register slower completion times among brain-damaged,[109] schizophrenic,[75] and mentally deficient subjects.[127] These speed losses in relatively uncomplicated tracing times have been found to be heavily intercorrelated with the psychopathological slowing of the simple thrust (traverse) times just described; with several reaction time measures (lift, jump, and simple-choice); with tapping speed; and with measured finger dexterity.[75] These findings, which confirm results reported using a variety of psychomotor measures that center on simple actions only after their initiation,[32,70,91,144,158] make it clear that "readiness to begin response" does not suffice to account for all of the psychomotor retardation to be found among the behavior disorders. see also: [60,88]

In summary, the broad pattern of slowed simple effector action in psychopathological states reveals a pattern not unlike that of normal subject performance on the same tests when it has been degraded by deliberately induced organismic states of psychologic or physiologic imbalance. The deficit in initiating action may be restored partly, temporarily and within limits, by experimental procedures that help delimit external signals to begin action. Continuing actions, whether of simple oscillation or guided and controlled, imply a flow of internal and external subsignals to guide the movement in progress (start; brake; turnaround). When the choice of experimental procedures permits only the most limited entry of these in the movement selected for study, however, the retarded psychomotor speed characteristic of behavior disorder may still plainly be observed. That there is a systematic, quantitative change in a unitary variable whenever the adaptational balance of the organism is less than optimal is suggested by changes in the speed of ongoing action that result immediately from the stimulation of brain "alerting" centers; the subtle partial speed losses that follow the ingesting of small amounts of alcohol; the similar rates of response acquisition by markedly slowed psychotic or brain-damaged patients and normal subjects; raised intercorrelations among psychomotor performances reflecting subfactors that are known to be more independent among the normal; the orderly changes that appear in great age or with fluctuations of the psychotic state—and a host of other empirical findings. It does not follow from this that the suboptimal state must arise from a single cause, nor that it will be manifest in equal degrees no matter how it is measured. The particular factors tested or the scoring method chosen by a given investigator may be expected to be either more convenient or more valuable for the study of some special problem—such as identifying the rehabilitation potential of individual patients belonging to some larger clinical group, or sampling the form of inefficiency that may result from enforced sleep loss. These selected uses do not, of course, determine the psychophysiologic system under study, but represent, rather, empirically useful aspects of the basic psychomotor defect for some specific and usually quite practical purpose.

VI. Psychomotor Slowing in Psychopathology: A Biopsychologic View

This selective review has sought to emphasize the quantitative aspect of psychomotor retardation in psychopathology and to outline its orderly parallelism in the most varied kinds of disorder, the amounts of disorganization in each, and in concomitant changes in patient status and psychomotor speed, whether brought about by natural, therapeutic, or experimental means. By comparing directly the slowed psychomotor performance produced by physiologic imbalance, functional disorder, and defective neural structure, it becomes possible to regard the speed of accomplishment of these simple behaviors as a sensitive indicator of the integrity of the organism as a whole and as an objective estimate of the optimal, or suboptimal, state of behavioral functioning by the individual. In simplest form, the question becomes: How closely does the usual psychomotor performance resemble the maximal? Uncomplicated *fine* psychomotor performance—by the normal, rested, alert, and well-practiced subject—proves to be capable of only limited improvement, suggesting that the usual normal response is nearly optimal for the individual. The question is only slightly altered when applied to the assay of behavior disorder: How closely does the performance of the psychopathological subject resemble the normal (and optimal)? We have seen that if all conditions of measurement are kept constant—except the organismic state of the subject examined—his "usual" psychomotor response will fall to a level that reflects accurately the degree to which his organismic integrity is suboptimal at the moment tested. Is the lowered prevailing level of psychomotor reactivity a part of the disorder itself, or is it only secondary to the mental state for each condition? One aspect or another of the data surveyed would seem to bear on this question of primacy and on whether the source of the psychomotor defect observed seems to lie mainly in input, "processing," or output mechanisms. All debate of the question must recognize at the outset, however, the artificiality of any true division of the continuous sensorimotor interchange that is characteristic of all psychomotor behavior and implicit in its very name. The visual, proprioceptive, and touch-sense guiding of psychomotor action is of such obvious importance to its execution as to require no further comment. It does seem fair to ask, however: If we were to place a special emphasis on the cognitive or attentional elements of fine psychomotor performance, what will be the consequences for response—as contrasted with what can be observed when these elements are kept constant (or are made optimal) and the active components of response are brought into focus? It is altogether likely that the reception of information and the effector component of response both may be affected by some disorders, in normal aging, for example,[56,73,131] and in schizophrenia.[129] It is not at all clear that both are involved in other psychopathological conditions—in Parkinson's disease, for instance,[66,91] or in patients with electrical "spike" foci in the temporal lobes.[40]

There is no doubt that the slowing of certain psychomotor responses can be caused by a greater degree of difficulty in resolving the stimulus to initiate action. The regular increase in the latency of (normal) choice reaction time, compared with the simple reaction, makes this quite plain. Measures of the kind emphasize the stimulus component of sensorimotor response, although they typically use overall (stimulus presentation to motor response) delay as a measure. Psychological probes—based on graded problems of stimulus resolution and signaled by a simple motor response—have long found valid use in exploring the thought disorganization of behavior disorder; in the form of reaction time "set" disturbances,[118,119] for example, or in the association-motor response,[92,93] and even in certain forms of the word-association test.[31,131] The delay to first response, or to correct response, can be most informative about the ability of a subject to attend to, or to sort into classes so that he may respond to, signals reaching him from the environment. The significant deficits that can be demonstrated using this emphasis on the "input" aspect of sensorimotor response might be expected to reveal themselves equally well by other test methods, shorn of the connection with an active motor component—in the forced-choice method of sensory threshold measurement, for instance.[28,29] There are indications that they do, in part,[19,23,48,88,143] but it is notable that they are clearest when joined in a natural way with an active-response element. Psychomotor error, expressed either by a time-score or the accuracy of a response trace, has also been demonstrated to characterize the performance of psychopathological subjects on tests requiring an *intermediate* level of integration: e.g., Star-Tracing;[158] Trail Making, B;[109] Mirror-Tracing;[100] Writing Speed,[32] geometric copying,[4] drawing from recent memory,[5] and the like.[65] Here again, those problems met in receiving stimuli and deciding on the appropriate response seem to combine naturally and well with a motor "write-out," possibly because the motor recording modulates to express delicately grades of imperfect solution.

Performance on perceptuomotor tasks which require a motor expression of the solution of obviously higher-order psychological problems (that call for intelligence, memory, and reasoning) have many times over demonstrated their particular sensitivity to behavior disorder. Deficient performance on the pursuit-rotor motor learning task,[144] the reduced rate of continuous (manual) problem solving,[62] the lowered scores made on the Porteus Maze Test[104,105] or the Block Design and Object Assembly subtests of the Wechsler Intelligence Scale[148,62] and others,[65] are affected adversely by psychopathology often enough to be prized by the psychological clinician for their aid in making a differential diagnosis.[107] All of these approaches emphasizing the use of a motor "write-out" to input (perceptuo-cognitive) problems merit further study, especially when they point to variables or processes that are subject to test by independent (non-motor) methods. They have been cited here in some detail, although falling outside the main theme of this review, to make it quite clear that those mental states that limit attending, or make more difficult the selection of task-relevant cues giving rise to action can affect the timing of over-all sensorimotor response. Were this the primary or the only source of variance for the psychomotor deficit found in behavior disorder, we would expect several features to typify the empirical data collected: a greater defect accompanying increased stimulus complexity, for example; the contamination of response by stimulus-perseveration tendencies; lapses in attending (or selective focusing) that might bring about an intermittent performance with blank periods alternating with quite adequate response; those procedures that allow stimulus "pull" (intensity, centrality, movement) to coincide with stimulus "relevance" improving pathological reactivity disproportionately (compared with the normal)—and so on.

Turning once again to the active component of sensorimotor response, we may better understand now the meaning of the psychomotor slowing observed using experimental procedures that keep stimulus uncertainty and complication to a minimum and emphasize response tendencies—by measuring straightforward, well-practiced actions with positive mental "set," which sample the factorial domain of *fine* psychomotor movement at more than one level. The most different forms of behavior disorganization—in terms of either their known or suspected etiology or the mental states associated with them—have been well described by slowed active simple psychomotor responding in a way that suggests quantitative similarity across quite different conditions and that seems closely attuned to grades of disorder within each.[30,32,76,147,158] Manmade maladaptive states also regularly produce subnormal levels of psychomotor function when measured by the same test methods emphasizing the active sensorimotor component.[26,67,76,111,154] Whenever special attention has been given to the sensitivity of fine psychomotor tests to changed conditions, improved speed has always been found to accompany improved psychiatric status, however b r o u g h t about,[32,33,64,67,76,146,147] but could be little influenced by attempts to motivate the patient socially.[12,,15a,88] The rates of acquisition of simple psychomotor response are also quite similar for the slowed response of patients and for the normal—indicating the presence of similar motive states and limits on learning for each.[6,7,64,144] Distraction had no effect on these simple responses when measured among schizophrenics, although the performance of more integrative tasks could be so influenced in the same individuals.[96,97] Changes in stimulus strength, either by manipulated stimulus dynamism[49,71,142] or the pairing of noxious conditions with signals to respond, definitely decrease the latency of response initiation in schizophrenia,[87,88,112] as they do for the normal subject to an equivalent relative degree.[71] These partial, temporary restorations of active simple psychomotor responding suggest the manner in which normal performance on the same tests, degraded by psychologically or physiologically induced disequilibrium, can be reversed and improved by manipulated experimental or organismic conditions that have only limited effect on (or which may even reduce) normal psychomotor functioning.[73,76,83,84,149] The greater slowing of performance on simple psychomotor than on more complex tasks, by psychopathological subjects[16,30,50,65,76,96,97,121,126] is a mixed finding, since it may reflect both the close dependence of these simple active responses on physiological integrity[86,64,67] as well as a greater likelihood that it is the stimulus input elements that have been complicated among the more complex psychomotor tasks. What have been called the simpler tasks have, in effect, often been those sensorimotor response situations that stress stimulus simplicity—with a resultant emphasis on the active component of response.[74]

These fragmentary data and the trends that emerge from them support the idea that *fine* psychomotor reactivity is a sensitive and systematic correlate of behavior disorder—quantitative enough in its expression to be regarded as a true dimension of psychopathology. How can they be ordered, in their admittedly incomplete present form, to accord with a neurobiologic view of behavior disorder? It is possible, as I have suggested elsewhere,[73] ". . . to conceive of the organism as a whole-system, one normally 'tuned' to a state of reasonably optimal adaptibility to its environment, a state that rests upon the entirety of biologic structure, growth and balance in its physiological and psychological state. Any change of the factors that may affect the balance of this total state, then, such as damage to its communication system, the presence of prolonged emotional states or momentary physiological variation with an indirect influence on the function of the nervous system that is strong enough to produce clinically detectable changes in organized and adaptive behavior, may be seen to affect the psychomotor adequacy of the individual—not so much as the result of any given submechanism, but as an aspect of the integrity of the whole and as an important component in its continuing contact with the environment." The state of optimal fine psychomotor resiliency for an individual appears to be biological at its base and determined, in part, by age, by sex, and by body-temperature level, reflecting genic similarity and related to events in the cardiac and brain-electric cycles.[73,76] Any intrusive unbalance must necessarily either slow or make more irregular (or both) the function of a coordinating system that normally operates near its optimum. Since modifying both psychological and physiological conditions to a significant degree affects measured independent levels of active fine psychomotor function, we are reminded that this index is an organismic rather than a pathological one—which is to say that the behavior measured may more aptly be considered to represent what the organism can do with "what is left" and as an effort by the total organism to integrate its reactive behavior with the functional neural remainder. The defective human organism does not unwind slowly and progressively like a child's toy, nor is it like a new car that runs perfectly until it is out of gas—but rather like an old engine that runs, labors, falters, and then takes hold and runs again.[18] It seems likely that it is for this reason that most of the psychomotor defects appearing in psychopathology are "smooth" or gradual ones, rather than presenting the sharper step-like changes that might be expected to result from the pathology of specific submechanisms. It may also explain the ready reversibility of psychomotor deficit, whether observed in restoring the performance of a normal subject temporarily degraded by imposing counter-conditions, or seen in the restoration of psychomotor speed that has been shown to be the consistent concomitant of improved psychopathological status.

Over-all sensorimotor slowing in behavior disorder can be traced to changed attentional or stimulus-focusing abilities in some instances, and in others just as clearly to errors in the central integration of response. There is no essential conflict in these views, although there has often been confusion. Reactivity implies both stimulus and response, and an analytic emphasis placed on either component may bring out more explicitly its contribution to the over-all variance of behavior. A low state of psychophysiologic arousal and states of strong hyperarousal are both known to reduce fine psychomotor speed in the normal subject.[11,24,46,73,95,139] As what is called "arousal" continues to be the subject of debate and is obviously dependent on the autonomic criteria and the time-relationships favored in its definition,[37,39,94,114,132] the utility of the concept as it relates to psychopathological disorder remains unsettled.[103,140,141] Several clusters of psychomotor evidence make it seem at least promising. Skeletomuscular "inner-tensiveness," measured by the electromyogram and other methods, is reported to be higher in old age, among mental defectives, and in depressive and brain-damaged patients.[38,73,151,159] Schizophrenics classed as "process" patients also show elevated muscular tensive response under conditions of rest as well as stress, more so than the "reactive" patient—and both are significantly elevated above normal levels.[110] It might be expected, then, that relaxing and sedating drugs that slow the fine psychomotor performance of normal subjects—would paradoxically improve, say, schizophrenics' instructed movement, which is just what they seem to do.[32,53,89,121,146] Whether or not "arousal" theory proves to refer to a unitary characteristic of the individual and to be useful as a unifying concept in the study of psychopathology, it does appear that most states of disorganized behavior can be described as exhibiting some form of "hyper-regulation from within." Although this state may arise from quite different initial causes—pervasive fear, severe sleep loss, brain damage, or mental subnormality—all may find ultimate expression by a similar basic neural mechanism, such as a gradual "whittling down" of the control of integrative organismic reactivity to the lower brain centers. It may matter little whether this is achieved by the gradual structural changes in aging or cortical agenesis or is brought about by the "functional decortication" of exhaustion, unrelieved pain, or overwhelming fear. As the balance of normal organismic reactivity is struck between stimuli arising from within (biologic, physiologic, psychologic) and without (physical, interpersonal, social), any decided tipping of the scale toward greater innerregulation would be expected to influence all subsequent reactivity to stimuli arriving from without—to the extent that the kind of reactivity used as assay is basic. More intensive stimuli may force a momentary rebalance by differentially weighting signals of external origin. It is suggested that the active fine psychomotor behaviors may serve as basic reactions in just this way. Not much controlled by learning or intelligence, nor subject to social influence, they appear to sample the available active response tendencies of the organism as a whole at a given moment—reflecting in their speed its vigor and resilience. Whatever can be established firmly about abnormal inner hyper-regulation by independent biological methods would be expected—by this hypothesis—to relate systematically and quantitatively to psychomotility as a basic dimension of behavior disorder.

REFERENCES

1. Adams, J.: Motor skills. Ann. Rev. Psychol. 15:181-202, 1964.

2. Avakyan, R., Vardapetyan, G., and Gershuni, G.: Reaction time as a function of duration and intensity of acoustic stimuli. Zh. Vysshei Ner. Dey. 16:1037, 1966.

3. Balinsky, B.: Factors in the vocational adjustment of schizophrenics after mental hospital discharge. J. Clin. Psychol. 3:341-349, 1947.

4. Bender, L.: A visual motor Gestalt Test and its clinical use. Amer. Orthopsychiat. Res. Monogr. 3:1-176, 1938.

5. Benton, A.: A Visual Retention Test for Clinical Use. New York, Psychological Corp., 1963.

6. Benton, A., and Blackburn, H.: Practice effects in reaction-time tasks in brain-injured patients. J. abnorm. Soc. Psychol. 54:109-113, 1957.

7. ——: Effects of motivating instructions on reaction-time in mental defectives. J. Ment. Subnormality 9:81-83, 1963.

8. Benton, A., Jentsch, R., and Wahler, H.: Effects of motivating instructions on reaction time in schizophrenia. J. Nerv. Ment. Dis. 130:26-29, 1960.

9. Benton, A., and Joynt, R.: Reaction time in unilateral cerebral disease. Confin. Neurol. 19:247-256, 1959.

10. Benton, A., Sutton, S., Kennedy, J., and Brokaw, J.: The crossmodal retardation in reaction time of patients with cerebral disease. J. Nerv. Ment. Dis. 135:413-418,1962.

11. Bergum, B.: A taxonomic analysis of continuous performance. Percept. Mot. Skills 23:47-54, 1966.

12. Berkowitz, H.: Effects of prior experimenter-subject relationships on reinforced reaction time of schizophrenics and normals. J. Abnorm. Soc. Psychol. 69:522-530, 1964.

13. Berkson, G.: An analysis of reaction time in normal and mentally deficient young men. I. Duration threshold experiments. J. Ment. Defic. Res. 4:51-58, 1960.

14. Berkson, G.: An analysis of reaction time in normal and mentally deficient young men. II. Variation of complexity in reaction time task. J. Ment. Defic. Res. 4:59-67, 1960.

15. ——: An analysis of reaction time in normal and mentally deficient young men. III. Variation of stimulus and of response complexity. J. Ment. Defic. Res. 4:69-77, 1960.

15a. Blackburn, H.: Effects of motivating instructions on reaction time in cerebral disease. J. Abnorm. Psychol. 56:359-366, 1958.

16. Blackburn, H. and Benton, A.: Simple and choice reaction time in cerebral disease. Confin. Neurol. 15:327-338, 1955.

17. Bragiel, R. and Perkins, C.: Conditioned stimulus intensity and response speed. J. Exp. Psychol. 47:437-441, 1954.

18. Broadbent, D.: Variations in performance arising from continuous work. In Conference on Individual Efficiency in Industry. Cambridge, England, Medical Research Council, 1955.

19. Broen, W.: Response disorganization and breadth of observation in schizophrenia. Psychol. Rev., 73:579-585, 1966.

20. Brooks, G. and Weaver, L.: Some relations between psychiatric and psychomotor behavior changes associated with tranquilizing medications. Compr. Psychiat. 2:203-210, 1961.

21. Brožek, J., and Taylor, H.: Tests of motor functions in investigations on fitness. Amer. J. Psychol. 67:590-611, 1954.

22. Burstein, A., Asher, S., Gillespie, H., and Haase, M.: Prediction of hospital discharge of mental patients by psychomotor performance: partial replication of Brooks and Weaver. Percept. Motor Skills 24:127-134, 1967.

23. Buss, A. H. and Lang, P.: Psychological deficit in schizophrenia. I. Affect, reinforcement, and concept attainment. J. Abnorm. Psychol. 70:2-24, 1965.

24. Catalano, J., and Whalen, P.: Factors in recovery from performance decrement: activation, inhibition and warm-up. Percept. Motor Skills, 24:1223-1231, 1967.

25. Cavanagh, D., Cohen, W., and Lang, P.: The effect of "social censure" and

"social approval" on the psychomotor performance of schizophrenics. J. Abnorm. Soc. Psychol. 60:213-218, 1960.

26. Chase, R., Harvey, S., Standfast, S., Rapin, I., and Sutton, S.: Comparison of the effects of delayed auditory feedback on speech and key tapping. Science 129:903-904, 1959.

27. Chocholle, R.: Les temps de réaction. Ch. VI in Traité de Psychologie Experimentale. II: Sensation et Motricité. Fraisse, P. and Piaget, J. (Eds.). Paris: Presses Universitaires, 1963.

28. Clark, W. C.: The psyche in psychophysics. Psychol. Bull. 65:358-366, 1966.

29. Clark, W., Brown, J., and Rutschmann, J.: Flicker sensitivity and response bias in psychiatric patients and normal subjects. J. Abnorm. Psychol. 72:35-42, 1967.

30. Clausen, J.: Ability Structure and Subgroups in Mental Retardation. Washington, Spartan, 1966.

31. Corrigan, R.: Visual, verbal, and motor responses as indicators of personal values in perception. Unpublished dissertation, Tulane University, 1954.

32. Court, J.: A longitudinal study of psychomotor functioning in acute psychiatric patients. Brit. J. Med. Psychol. 37:167-173, 1964.

33. Court, J. and Cameron, I.: Psychomotor assessment of the effects of Haloperidol. Percept. Mot. Skills 17:168-170, 1963.

34. Crider, A., Maher, B., and Grinspoon, L.: The effect of sensory input on the reaction time of schizophrenic patients of good and poor premorbid history. Psychonomic Science 2:47-48, 1965.

35. D'Alessio, G. and Spence, J.: Schizophrenic deficit and its relation to social motivation. J. Abnorm. Soc. Psychol. 66:390-393, 1963.

36. Dey, M.: Latency gradient of stimulus generalization with voluntary reactions. J. Gen. Psychol. 74:289-298, 1966.

37. Eason, R. and White, C.: Relationship between muscular tension and performance during rotary pursuit. Percept. Mot. Skills, 10:199-210, 1960.

38. Edwards, A.: Finger tremor, finger tremor waves, and brain waves in normal and abnormal cases. J. Gen. Psychol. 56:229-232, 1957.

39. Edwards, A., and Hill, R.: The effect of data characteristics on theoretical conclusions concerning the physiology of emotions. Psychosom. Med. 29:303-311, 1967.

40. Ervin, F., Epstein, A., and King, H. E.: Behavior of epileptic and non-epileptic patients with "temporal spikes". A.M.A. Arch. Neurol. Psychiat. 74:488-497, 1955.

41. Exner, S.: Experimentelle Untersuchung der einfachsten psychischen Processe. Pflug. Arch. Ges. Physiol. 7:601-660, 1873.

42. Eysenck, H., and Trouton, D.: The effect of drugs on behavior. In: Eysenck, H. (Ed.) Handbook of Abnormal Psychology. New York, Basic Books, 1961, Chap. 17.

43. Fitts, P.: The information capacity of the human motor system in controlling the amplitude of movement. J. Exp. Psychol. 47:381-391, 1954.

44. Fleishman, E.: Dimensional analysis of psychomotor abilities. J. Exp. Psychol. 48:437-454, 1954.

45. Freeman, G. L.: Mental activity and the muscular processes. Psychol. Rev. 38:428-447, 1931.

46. ——: The relation between performance level and bodily activity level. J. Exp. Psychol. 26:602-608, 1940.

47. Goodstein, L., Guertin, W., and Blackburn, H.: Effects of social motivational variables on choice reaction time in schizophrenics. J. Abnorm. Soc. Psychol. 62:24-27, 1961.

48. Grim, P.: A sustained attention comparison of children and adults using reaction time set and the GSR. J. Exp. Child Psychol., 5:26-38, 1967.

49. Grisell, J. and Rosenbaum, G.: Effects of auditory intensity on simple reaction time of schizophrenics. Percept. Mot. Skills, 18:396, 1964.

50. Halstead, W.: Brain and Intelligence. Chicago, University of Chicago Press, 1947.

51. Heath, R. (Ed.): Studies in Schizophrenia. Cambridge, Harvard University Press, 1954.

52. ——: Correlations between levels of psychological awareness and physiological activity in the central nervous system. Psychosom. Med. 17:383-395, 1955.

53. Heilizer, F.: The effects of chlorpromazine upon psychomotor and psychiatric behavior of chronic schizophrenic patients. J. Nerv. Ment. Dis. 128:358-364, 1959.

54. Hoch, P., Cattell, J., and Pennes, H.: Report of the psychiatric discipline. In: F. A. Mettler (Ed.): Psychosurgical problems. New York, Blakiston, 1952, Chap. 15.

55. Hoch, P., Cattell, J., Pennes, H., and Glaser, G.: Psychiatric effects. In: Lewis, N., Landis, C. and King, H. E. (Eds.): Studies in Topectomy. New York: Grune & Stratton, 1956, Chap. 11.

56. Hurwitz, L. and Allison, R.: Factors influencing performance in psychological testing of the aged. In: Welford, A. and Birren, J. (Eds.): Behavior, Aging and the Nervous System. Springfield, Charles C Thomas, 1965, Chap. 24.

57. Huston, P. and Senf, R.: Psychopathology of schizophrenia and depression. I. Effects of Amytal and Amphetamine Sulfate on level and maintenance of attention. Amer. J. Psychiat. 109:131-138, 1952.

58. Jarl, V.: Method of stimulus presentation as antecedent variable in reaction time experiments. Nordisk Psykologi, 9:167-183, 1957.

59. Jellinek, E. and McFarland, R.: Analysis of psychological experiments on the effects of alcohol. Quart. J. Stud. Alcohol 1:272-371, 1940.

60. Johannsen, W.: Motivation in schizophrenic performance: A review. Psychol. Rep. 15:839-870, 1964.

61. Karpovitch, P., and Ikai, M.: Relation between reflex and reaction time. Fed. Proc. 19:300, 1960.

62. King, H. E.: Intellectual function. In: Mettler, F. (Ed.), Selective Partial Ablation of the Frontal Cortex. New York, Hoeber, 1949, Chap. 14.

63. ——: Psychomotor aspects of the orbitofrontal cortex. Fed. Proc. 9:70, 1950.

64. ——: Psychomotor Aspects of Mental Disease. Cambridge, Harvard University Press, 1954.

65. ——: Psychomotor tests. In: Zubin, J. (Ed.): Experimental Abnormal Psychology, New York: Columbia University Bookstore, 1957, Chap. 13.

66. ——: Defective psychomotor movement in Parkinson's disease: exploratory observations, Percept. Mot. Skills 9:326, 1959.

67. ——: Some explorations in psychomotility. Psychiat. Res. Rep. 14:62-86, 1961.

68. ——: Psychological effects of excitation in the limbic system. In: Sheer, D. (Ed.): Electrical Stimulation of the Brain. Austin: University of Texas Press, 1961, Chap. 33.

69. ——: Repeated measurement of the status of the psychiatric patient. In: Zubin, J. (Ed.): Experimental Abnormal Psychology. New York: Columbia University Bookstore, 1961, Chap. 16.

70. ——: Anticipatory behavior: Temporal matching by normal and psychotic subjects. J. Psychol. 53:425-440, 1962.

71. ——: Reaction-time as a function of stimulus intensity among normal and psychotic subjects. J. Psychol. 54:299-307, 1962.

72. ——: Psychomotor indicators of behavior disorder arising from neurologic trauma and disease. Psychiat. Comm., 5:31-35, 1962.

73. ——: Psychomotor changes with age, psychopathology and brain damage. In: Welford, A. and Birren, J. (Eds.): Behavior, Aging and the Nervous System. Springfield: Charles C Thomas, 1965, Chap. 25.

74. ——: Reaction time and speed of voluntary movement by normal and psychotic subjects. J. Psychol. 59:219-227, 1965.

75. ——: Trail-making performance related to: psychotic state, age, intelligence, education and fine psychomotor ability. Percept. Motor Skills, 25:649-658, 1967.

76: ——: Psychomotor correlates of behavior disorder. Objective Indicators of Psychopathology. Biometrics Research Workshop, 1968, (to be published).

77. King, H. E.: Auditory on-off stimulus dynamism effects for normal and schizophrenic subjects. Unpublished manuscript, 1968.

78. ——: Psychomotor evaluation of change in psychiatric status—without active therapy. Unpublished manuscript, 1968.

79. King, H. E. and Clausen, J.: Psychophysiology. In: Mettler, F. (Ed.): Psychosurgical Problems. Philadelphia: Blakiston, 1952, Chap. 13.

80. ——: Psychophysiology. In: Lewis, N., Landis, C. and King, H. E. (Eds.): Studies in Topectomy. New York: Grune & Stratton, 1956, Chap. 9.

81. King, H. E., Young, K., Corrigan, R., and Bersadsky, L.: Psychological observations before and after stimulation. In: Heath, R. (Ed.): Studies in Schizophrenia. Cambridge: Harvard University Press, 1954, Chap. 16.

82. Klugman, S.: Differential effects of various tranquilizing drugs on speed of tapping. J. Clin. Psychol. 18:89-92, 1962.

83. Kornetsky, C.: Effects of meprobamate, phenobarbital and dextroamphetamine on reaction time and learning in man. J. Pharmacol. Exp. Ther. 123:216-219, 1958.

84. Kornetsky, C., Mirsky, A., Kessler, E., and Dorff, J.: The effects of dextroamphetamine on behavioral deficits produced by sleep loss in humans. J. Pharmacol. Exp. Ther. 127:46-50, 1959.

85. Kristofferson, M.: Shifting attention between modalities: A comparison of schizophrenics and normals. J. Abnorm. Psychol., 72:388-394, 1967.

86. Landis, C.: Discussion. In: Heath, R. G. (Ed.), Studies in Schizophrenia. Cambridge: Harvard University Press, 1954, 519-524.

87. Lang, P.: The effect of aversive stimuli on reaction time in schizophrenia. J. Abnorm. Soc. Psychol. 59:263-268, 1959.

88. Lang, P. and Buss, A.: Psychological deficit in schizophrenia. II. Interference and activation. J. Abnorm. Psychol. 70:77-106, 1965.

89. Layman, J.: A quantitative study of certain changes in schizophrenic patients under influence of sodium amytal. J. Gen. Psychol. 22:67-86, 1940.

90. Lazarus, R., Deese, J., and Osler, S.: The effects of psychological stress upon performance. Psychol. Bull. 49:293-317, 1952.

91. Lifschitz, W. and Melzer, Mlle.: Étude de l'initiative psychomotrice volontaire dans les maladies mentales et neurologiques, Rev. Neurol. (Paris), 86:353-354, 1952.

92. Luria, A.: The Nature of Human Conflicts. Gantt, W. (trans.). New York: Liveright, 1932.

93. Malmo, R., Shagass, C., Bélanger, D., and Smith, A.: Motor control in psychiatric patients under experimental stress. J. Abnorm. Soc. Psychol. 46:539-547, 1951.

94. McBain, W.: Noise, the "arousal hypothesis" and monotonous work. J. Appl. Psychol. 45:309-317, 1961.

95. McCormack, P.: A two-factor theory of vigilance. Brit. J. Psychol. 53:357-363, 1962.

96. McGhie, A., Chapman, J., and Lawson, J.: The effect of distraction on schizophrenic performance: I. Perception and immediate memory. Brit. J. Psychiat. 111:383-390, 1965.

97. ——: The effect of distraction on schizophrenic performance: II. Psychomotor ability. Brit. J. Psychiat. 111:391-398, 1965.

98. Mettler, F. (Ed.): Psychosurgical Problems. Philadelphia: Blakiston, 1952.

99. Miles, W. (Ed.): Selected psychomotor measurement methods. Methods in Medical Research, 3:142-218, 1950.

100. Peters, H.: The mirror tracing test as a measure of social maladaption. J. Abnorm. Soc. Psychol. 41:437-448, 1946.

101. Peters, H. and Jones, F.: Evaluation of group psychotherapy by means of performance tests. J. Consult. Psychol. 15:363-367, 1951.

102. Petrie, A.: Personality and the Frontal Lobes. New York: Blakiston, 1952.

103. Pfeiffer, C., Beck, B., Goldstein, L., and Neiss, E.: Etiology of the stimulant nature of the schizophrenias. In: Recent advances in biological psychiatry, 9:241-249, Chap. 16, 1967.

104. Porteus, S.: Porteus Maze Tests: Fifty Years of Application. Palo Alto: Pacific Books, 1965.

105. Porteus, S. and Peters, H.: Maze test validation and psychosurgery. Genet. Psychol. Monogr. 36:3-86, 1947.

106. Posner, M. and Mitchell, R.: Chronometric analysis of classification. Psychol. Rev. 74:392-409, 1967.

107. Rapaport, D.: Diagnostic Psychological Testing, Vol. 1. Chicago: Year Book Publ., 1946.

108. Reitan, R.: Investigation of the validity of Halstead's measures of biological intelligence. A.M.A. Arch. Neurol. Psychiat. 73:28-35, 1955.

109. ——: Validity of the Trail Making test as an indicator of organic brain damage. Percept. Mot. Skills 8:271-276, 1958.

110. Reynolds, D. J.: An investigation of the somatic response system in chronic schizophrenia. Dissert. Abstr., 23:(12, pt. 1), 1963.

111. Rhule, W. and Smith, K.: Effects of inversion of the visual field on human motions. J. Exp. Psychol. 57:338-343, 1959.

112. Rosenbaum, G.: Reaction time indices of schizophrenic motivation: A cross-cultural replication. Brit. J. Psychiat. 113:537-541, 1967.

113. Rosenbaum, G., Cohen, B., Luby, E., Gottlieb, J., and Yelen, D.: Comparison of sernyl with other drugs. Arch. Gen. Psychiat. 1:651-656, 1959.

114. Schlosberg, H. and Kling, J.: The relationship between "tension" and efficiency. Percept. Mot. Skills 9:395-397, 1959.

115. Schwab, R., Chafetz, M., and Walker, S.: Control of the simultaneous voluntary motor acts in normals and in Parkinsonism. Arch. Neurol. Psychiat. 72:591-598, 1954.

116. Seashore, R.: Work and motor performance. In: Stevens, S. (Ed.): Handbook of experimental psychology. New York, Wiley, 1951, Chap. 36.

117. Seashore, R., Buxton, C., and McCullom, I.: Multiple factorial analysis of fine motor skills. Amer. J. Psychol. 53:251-259, 1940.

118. Shakow, D.: Psychological deficit in schizophrenia. Behav. Sci., 8:275-305, 1963.

119. ——: Segmental set. A.M.A. Arch. Gen. Psychiat. 6:1-17, 1962.

120. Shankweiler, D.: Effects of success and failure instructions on reaction time in brain-injured patients. J. Comp. Physiol. Psychol. 52:546-549, 1959.

121. Shapiro, M. and Nelson, E.: An investigation of the nature of cognitive impairment in cooperative psychiatric patients. Brit. J. Med. Psychol. 28:239-256, 1955.

122. Shapiro, M., Kesell, R., and Maxwell, A.: Speed and quality of psychomotor performance in psychiatric patients. J. Clin. Psychol. 16:266-271, 1960.

123. Sheer, D.: Psychometric studies. In: Lewis, N., Landis, C. and King, H. E. (Eds.): Studies in Topectomy. New York: Grune and Stratton, 1956, Chap. 6.

124. Simon, S.: Effect of tranquilizers on the Trail Making test with chronic schizophrenics. J. Consult. Psychol. 31:322-323, 1967.

125. Smith, K.: The functions of the intercortical neurones in sensorimotor coordination and thinking in man. Science 105:234-235, 1947.

126. ——: Bilateral integrative action of the cerebral cortex in man in verbal association and sensorimotor coordination. J. Exp. Psychol., 37:367-376, 1947.

127. Smith, T.: Relation of the Trail Making test to mental retardation. Percept. Mot. Skills 17:719-722, 1963.

128. Snodgrass, J., Luce, R., and Galanter, E.: Some experiments on simple and choice reaction time. J. Exp. Psychol. 75:1-17, 1967.

129. Sutton, S. and Zubin, J.: Effect of sequence on reaction time in schizophrenia. In: Welford, A. and Birren, J. (Eds.): Behavior, Aging and the Nervous System. Springfield: Charles C Thomas, 1965, Chap. 27.

130. Talland, G.: Manual skill in Parkinson's disease. Geriatrics 18:613-620, 1963.

131. ——: Initiation of response, and reaction time in aging, and with brain damage. In: Welford, A. and Birren, J. (Eds.): Behavior, Aging and the Nervous System. Springfield: Charles C Thomas, 1965, Chap. 26.

132. Taylor, S. and Epstein, S.: The measurement of autonomic arousal. Psychosom. Med. 29:514-525, 1967.

133. Teichner, W.: Recent studies of simple reaction time. Psychol. Bull. 51: 128-149, 1954.

134. ———: Reaction time in the cold. J. Appl. Psychol. 42:54-59, 1958.

135. Thrane, V.: Sensory and preparatory factors in response latency. Scand. J. Psychol. 3:1-15, 1962.

136. Tizard, J. and Venables, P.: The influence of extraneous stimulation on the reaction time of schizophrenics, Brit. J. Psychol. 48:299-305, 1957.

137. Tow, P.: Personality Changes Following Frontal Leucotomy. London: Oxford University Press, 1955.

138. Tufts College Institute of Applied Experimental Psychology: Handbook of Human Engineering Data, Part VI. Motor Responses. Port Washington, New York, U.S. Naval Training Service Center, 1951.

139. Tufts College Institute of Applied Experimental Psychology: Handbook of Human Engineering Data, Part VII. Physiological conditions as determinants of efficiency. Port Washington, New York: U.S. Naval Training Center, 1951.

140. Venables, P.: Performance and level of activation in schizophrenics and normals. Brit. J. Psychol. 55:207-218, 1964.

141. ———: Slowness in schizophrenia. In: Welford, A. and Birren, J. (Eds.): Behavior, Aging and the Nervous System. Springfield: Charles C Thomas, 1965, Chap. 28.

142. Venables, P. and Tizard, J.: The effect of auditory stimulus intensity on the reaction time of schizophrenics. J. Ment. Sci. 104:1160-1164, 1958.

143. Wachtel, P.: Conceptions of broad and narrow attention. Psychol. Bull. 68:417-429, 1967.

144. Weaver, L.: Psychomotor performance of clinically differentiated schizophrenics. Percept. Mot. Skills 12:27-33, 1961.

145. Weaver, L. and Brooks, G.: The effects of drug-induced Parkinsonism on the psychomotor performance of chronic schizophrenics. J. Nerv. Ment. Dis. 133: 148-154, 1961.

146. ———: The use of psychomotor tests in predicting the potential of chronic schizophrenics. J. Neuropsychiat. 5:170-180, 1964.

147. ———: The prediction of release from a mental hospital from psychomotor test performance. J. Gen. Psychol. 76:207-229, 1967.

148. Wechsler, D.: The Measurement of Adult Intelligence. 4th edition. Baltimore: Williams and Wilkins, 1958.

149. Weiss, B. and Laties, V.: Enhancement of human performance by caffeine and the amphetamines. Pharmacol. Rev. 14:1-36, 1962.

150. Welford, A.: Psychomotor performance, In: Birren, J. (Ed.): Handbook of Aging and the Individual. Chicago: University of Chicago Press, 1961, Chap. 17.

151. Whatmore, G. and Ellis, R.: Some neurophysiologic aspects of depressed states: An electromyographic study. A.M.A. Arch. Gen. Psychiat. 1:70-80, 1959.

152. Wilkinson, R.: After effect of sleep deprivation. J. Exp. Psychol. 66:439-444, 1963.

153. ———: Effects of up to 60 hours of sleep deprivation on different types of work. Ergonomics 7:175-186, 1964.

154. Williams, H., Lubin, A., and Goodnow, J.: Impaired performance with acute sleep loss. Psychol. Monogr., 73:(No. 484), 1-26, 1959.

155. Woodworth, R.: Experimental Psychology. New York: Holt, 1938, Chap. 14.

156. ——: Dynamics of behavior. New York: Holt, 1958.

157. Woodworth, R. and Schlosberg, H.: Reaction time. In: Experimental Psychology. Revised edition. New York: Holt, 1954, Chap. 2.

158. Wulfeck, W.: Motor function in the mentally disordered. I. A comparative investigation of motor function in psychotics, psychoneurotics and normals. Psychol. Rec., 4:271-323, 1941.

159. ——: Motor function in the mentally disordered: II. The relation of muscle tension to the performance of motor tasks. Psychol. Rec. 4:326-348, 1941.

160. Wundt, W.: Grundzüge der physiologischen Psychologie. Leipzig: Engelmann, 1874.

Discussion of Dr. King's Paper

by LELON A. WEAVER, JR., Ph.D.

University of Vermont

A CRITICAL appraisal of Dr. King's paper is rather difficult for the writer because of the long-standing similarity of our views on the utility and significance of psychomotor behavior in the study of mental patients. At the Vermont State Hospital, we have investigated the psychomotor performance of mental patients under a variety of non-optimal conditions as well as under the 'normal' conditions for hospitalized mental patients. Within the limits imposed by commonality of measurement techniques and objectives, we have repeatedly confirmed his research findings. We are quite convinced that psychomotor test performance is directly related to the state of the central nervous system and reflects it more clearly than any other techniques.

In the latter portion of his paper, Dr. King addresses himself to a consideration of some evidence regarding the locus of the observed deficits in psychomotor performance. I would like to add a footnote to this discussion based on a re-evaluation of some previously published data.

It is generally considered that the deficit occurs in all three aspects of psychomotor behavior—i.e., the sensory input, the "data processing," and the motor response, since all three are centrally mediated. It has been clearly established that increasing the complexity of the stimulus increases the latency of response, that increasing stimulus intensity (contrast) decreases latency, and that in schizophrenia the rate of movement in a simple act is slowed even when freed completely from the stimulus-response element. Yet the evidence is not quite unequivocal. The data to be reported below may be interpreted differently.

Some years ago we did a study[1] concerned with the effects of drug-induced Parkinsonism on psychomotor test performance. Parkinsonism was induced in a group of chronic schizophrenics by replacing the anti-Parkinsonism medication with placebo. At the end of the study period, the effect was reversed by restoration of the active agent. Clinical ratings of the extent of motor impairment were made by a psychiatrist.

129

The psychomotor test battery, described elsewhere[1] in detail, had five tests. The rate of tapping, reaction time to light, and three-speed pursuit rotor tests were essentially standard in type. Further, a serial reaction time test had five brass target plates, each with an associated stimulus lamp. The task of S was to tap with a wand on the plate indicated by the lamp. A sequence of 20 such self-paced responses constituted one trial. The last test was a grooved peg-board in which 25 pegs had to be properly oriented, inserted against light spring pressure, and rotated slightly to retain them. The pegs were supplied from a magazine placed 18 inches away from the board. The circuitry was so arranged that the time spent placing pegs, grasping pegs, and transporting in both directions, could be measured separately.

The battery can be divided into two categories on the basis of the amount of eye–hand coordination involved. The reaction time, serial reaction time, peg-placement, and the pursuit rotor tests are primarily visually coordinated actions. The tapping, the two transport elements, and the peg-grasp at the magazine are not coordinated by reference to external stimuli.

It is also important to note that condition of the subjects was distinctly unfavorable for optimum motor performance. In addition to being chronic schizophrenics, most of them had clinically manifest drug-induced Parkinsonism. This condition is not known to affect perception, but it does have a marked effect on motor performance. Thus the expectation would be that all test performance would be adversely affected, but that there should be no differential effect between the two test categories as outlined above.

Since the detailed results of the study have already been published, they will not be repeated here. The results, as they have implication for the current problem, are summarized below.

1. The four tests with the visual coordination aspects showed either marked deficits in performance or, in the case of the pursuit rotor, a pronounced interference with an otherwise orderly learning curve. These effects were in close temporal accord with the clinical ratings of the severity of motor impairment.
2. The remaining tests, which do not depend on visual coordination, showed either negligible interference or, in the case of the transports, an actual improvement.

In view of the fact that the situation was markedly unfavorable for the motor aspect due to the presence of drug-induced Parkinsonism (characterized by absence of automatic associated movements and cogwheel rigidity in response to passive flexion), these results are interpreted as indicating deficits in the input and/or processing aspects. The fact that, despite the handicap, the patients were able to resist deterioration and even to improve performance indicates that the motor aspect was affected least.

In evaluating the unexpected part of these results, the patients were questioned about the apparent paradox. Their replies indicated that, since they had performance-level expectations from the preliminary testing experience, they were disturbed by the deterioration in their peg-placement performance and tried to compensate by reaching faster. This position is supported by the fact that, as medication was restored and Parkinsonism controlled, the peg-placement performance recovered and the transport declined to its former level.

These results do not appear to conflict with previous experimental findings. King[2] found that the rate of movement in a simple thrust response already under way when measurement was initiated was significantly slower in schizophrenics. The paradoxical improvement reported here could readily be superimposed on the decreased level of performance and does not necessarily constitute a conflict of results.

On the basis of these results, it is suggested that a large portion of the observed decrement in psychomotor performance associated with schizophrenia is accounted for by deficits in the sensory input and/or central processing aspects.

REFERENCES

1. Weaver, L. A., Jr., and Brooks, G. W.: The effects of drug-induced parkinsonism on the psychomotor performance of chronic schizophrenics. J. Nerv. Dis. 133:148-154, 1961.

2. King, H. E.: Reaction time and speed of voluntary movement by normal and psychotic subjects. J. Psychol. 59:219-227, 1965.

7

SENSORY ASPECTS OF PSYCHOPATHOLOGY

by PETER H. VENABLES, Ph.D.*

I Introduction

THERE has until recently been comparatively little work on the role of sensory factors in psychopathology. Such work as there is is sparse and scattered and may not appear to be particularly concerned with sensory processes unless examined more closely. An example of such a study is that of Wells and Kelley in 1922[40] whose work on "the simple reaction in psychosis" showed that a reaction to a sound stimulus was relatively lengthened with respect to that of a light stimulus in a group of dementia praecox patients as compared to a normal group.

This example can be used as a starting point to illustrate one of a number of possible approaches to the study of sensory factors, one of the major difficulties of the field, and some of the difficulties of interpretation. As a means of studying sensory factors, the reaction time procedure is one of the most straightforward. If the type of response is kept constant then there is some justification in thinking that, other things being equal, changes in latency may reflect changes due to presentation of different kinds of sensory input. The "other things" being kept equal are such factors as set, expectancy, information content, and the like. There is, of course, abundant evidence that sensory input is modified by attentional processes, and the likelihood that attention is less successfully controllable in patients than in normals.

A particular methodological difficulty which is exemplified by the Wells and Kelley study is that of matching the quantities of different modalities of sensation. This is a major problem in the case of intensity, although solutions are presented by Stevens, for instance.[27] The problem may, however, be insoluble in the case of factors such as hue and saturation, pitch and timbre, which are unique to particular modalities.

The third point that arises from the consideration of the use of reac-

---

*Birkbeck College, University of London.

tion time in this context is concerned with the dual role of sensation as input to the central nervous system. First, sensory input acts as a signal bearing information carried by the classical sensory pathways and having major or direct influence at the cortex. Second, it functions as input via collaterals to the reticular, diffuse thalamic, and limbic systems, exerting influence on the motivational state of the organism.

The multiple effects of input through peripheral organs blur the distinction between sensation and perception that were once perhaps discriminable notions to earlier workers. Now, however, this distinction is difficult, although there is a tendency, particularly among those workers whose concepts are influenced by communication and information engineering models, to consider a signal as pre-perceptual or still in a sensory mode when no processing has been carried out upon it. It is not proposed at this time to try and maintain a clear distinction between sensation and perception; emphasis will, however, be given to studies where the meaningful content of the input to the organism is at a minimal level. Two classes of experiment will be considered. One is mainly concerned with reaction time to simple stimuli, where the cue and arousal function of a stimulus may be interlinked and where the effect of sensory influences is shown by a simple response measure. The second is concerned with temporal resolution of two sensory signals in the cortex, where time relations are such that it seems likely that only the cue functions of the stimuli are involved. The response in this instance is a report by the patient on his perception, and as such is subject to a wide range of influences.

II STIMULUS INTENSITY

In considering the response of patients to stimuli of high intensity, the Pavlovian construct of protective inhibition is relevant. It is suggested[19] that the schizophrenic possesses a "weak nervous system." The features of this type of nervous system are summarized by Gray as follows:

The weak nervous system is more sensitive than the strong: it begins to respond to signals at stimulus intensities which are ineffective for the strong nervous system; throughout the stimulus intensity continuum its responses are closer to its maximum level of responding than the responses of the strong nervous system and it displays its maximum response, *or the response decrement which follows this maximum* at lower intensities than the strong nervous system. (Emphasis added.)[5]

In the weak nervous system protective inhibition is developed at an early stage and leads to a "breaking of the law of strength" so that strong stimuli elicit weak responses of the same magnitude as weak stimuli.[15] In a reaction time experiment by Venables and Tizard, visual stimuli ranging in intensity from 16 to 1500 foot-candles were presented to chronic, non-paranoid schizophrenic patients. It was shown that, on the first occasion of testing, maximum response speed was achieved with stimuli of moderate intensity and that there was a decrease in speed with stimuli of the maximum intensities used.[37] The Pavlovian notion of the disruption of the law of strength was thus confirmed. On the second occasion of testing there was an over-all slowness of response, but no indication of the "paradoxical" reversal of the "law of strength." Gray has re-interpreted the strength of the nervous system in terms of arousal concepts, and suggests that the weak nervous system displays high arousability.[6] The suggestion which was put forward by Venables and Tizard to explain the lack of paradoxical effect on the second occasion of testing would appear to be fully in accord with Gray's interpretation.

On the first occasion in an unfamiliar situation subjects were apprehensive and in a state of considerable emotional excitation. The excitation resulting from the stimulus lights superimposed on this general excitation became "ultra-marginal" in strength and resulted in the paradox observed. On the second occasion of testing the subjects were more familiar with the situation and the total excitation did not reach ultra-marginal strength.[37]

In an experiment on the reactions of schizophrenic patients to a range of auditory stimuli up to 115 db in intensity, and of frequencies of 200 Hz and 1000 Hz and also white noise, there was no evidence on any occasion of a paradoxical reversal of the law of strength, although a marked degree of slowness which was greater than that shown in the visual modality was evident throughout (Venables and Tizard, 1958).[38]

Parallels between the Pavlovian idea of protective inhibition developing in persons having a weak nervous system and the distinction between "reducers" and "augmenters" proposed by Petrie[20,21] have been drawn by Silverman[25] and Buchsbaum and Silverman.[4] Division of a group into those persons showing reduction or augmentation responses is made on the basis of the kinaesthetic figural after-effect.[12] Petrie reports augmenters to be those persons who show heightened sensitivity to pain, in contrast to reducers, who tolerate pain well. Buchsbaum and Silverman provide evidence in this framework that is directly relevant to the 1956 Venables and Tizard study. They show that amplitude of the late components of the averaged evoked response to visual stimuli is markedly reduced as a function of increased stimulus intensity, in a group of male schizophrenics who are selected on the basis of the kinaesthetic figural after-effect as being "reducers." Previously Silverman had reported that non-paranoid, long-term, poor premorbid schizophrenics tended to be "reducers" in contrast to short-term, paranoid patients, who showed augmentation responsiveness.[25] There was thus evidence for an actual reduction in the amplitude of the evoked potentials at the cortex in response to high intensity visual stimulation in the patients, of the same type as those tested by Venables and Tizard.[37]

No evidence so far seems available to extend these sorts of consideration to the auditory modality. When these data are available they may enable us to answer the question of whether or not the general slowness to a wide range of auditory stimuli is a product of general "reduction" of the amplitude of evoked potentials, possibly by the mechanism of protective inhibition.

Additional evidence of modality differences in susceptibility to the development of protective inhibition is provided by the findings of Rozhdestvenskaya et al. (quoted by Gray[5]) which point to a modality difference in the factor of strength. In a factor analytic study, visual sensitivity was loaded 0.76 and auditory sensitivity 0.49 on the strength factor—a finding in line with suggestions put forward earlier. The independence of visual and auditory systems in their likelihood to exhibit protective inhibition is also suggested by the work of Nebylitsin[18] (quoted by Gray[5]), who shows a correlation of only 0.26 between the sensitivity (and hence the strength) of the two systems.

III STIMULUS MODALITY

In the previous section, the generally slower response to auditory than to visual stimuli by non-paranoid chronic schizophrenic patients was reported. This was in contrast to the widely accepted finding of faster auditory than visual reaction times in normal persons.[32] This finding was repeated with visual and auditory stimuli of fixed intensity, but with a wider range of schizophrenic patients.[36] It was shown that intact paranoid schizophrenics behaved in a way very similar to normal subjects, showing faster reactions to auditory than to visual stimuli. On the other hand, all non-paranoid patients and withdrawn paranoid patients showed slower reactions to auditory than to visual stimuli. These find-ings essentially confirm those of Wells and Kelley (1922) mentioned in the introduction. The stimuli used in these studies were in the moderate range of intensity and did not, therefore, involve the paradoxical effects of the previous section. A similar pattern of reversal of modality ef-fectiveness in reaction time was provided by data in a study by Sutton, Hakerem, Zubin and Portnoy.[29] In later studies reviewed by Sutton and Zubin,[30] the reactions of schizophrenic subjects to sound stimuli were impaired if the previous trial or trials involved visual reactions, whereas reactions to light stimuli were not significantly impaired if the previous stimuli were sounds.

An indirect but possible explanation of these findings may be sug-gested. Bryant (1961) has shown that non-paranoid schizophrenics tend to be characterized as field dependent rather than field independent[2] (a finding that in itself might be used to argue for the continuing ef-fectiveness of the visual modality in schizophrenics when pitted against the somaesthetic modality in the rod and frame test). Work by Pillsbury, Meyerowitz, Saltzman and Satran has shown that the *initial* alpha desynchronization response of field dependent subjects to an auditory stimulus tends to be smaller than that of field independent sub-jects.[22] Later responses tend to show the reverse effects, and the whole pattern of findings is completely reversed for stimuli in the visual modality. It might therefore be expected that, in schizophrenic subjects who tend to be field dependent, an auditory stimulus coming unex-pectedly after a visual stimulus would produce a smaller arousal response and hence possibly a slower reaction time than a visual stimulus following an auditory reaction time. If, as in some of Sutton's and Zubin's experiments, several stimuli in the visual modality preceded the auditory stimulus, each visual stimulus after the first would tend to lower EEG arousal in the field dependent subjects and hence exaggerate the effect.

Any explanation such as this, however, requires direct ex-perimentation before it can have any standing. Another piece of work that adds confirmation to the modality pattern shown in the previous studies is that of Spain,[26] who showed better eyelid conditioning to a visual CS than to an auditory CS in schizophrenics, and the reverse in normals. More recently it has been possible to show that insofar as the schizophrenic patient is rated as deteriorated so he tends to have a relatively higher two-click threshold in relation to two-flash threshold.[34]

This finding is of interest in that there is evidence that the visual stimulus intensity does not affect threshold over a reasonably wide range of intensities,[8] and preliminary evidence suggests that this may be the same in the auditory modality. The finding of alteration of normal modality order in schizophrenics therefore stands on a slightly firmer footing methodologically. Studies showing independence of two-flash and two-click threshold from intensity in a patient population are, however, clearly required. Alteration of the normal modality order is by no means confined to schizophrenics; experiments similar to those reported here on visual and auditory reaction time have been carried out by Talland,[31] who showed a longer reaction to sound stimuli than to light stimuli in older persons.

In a review of early infantile autism, Schopler[24] provides evidence for a preference for "near-receptor dominance" and an apparent lack of development of visual and auditory usage. This report is partially in agreement with the findings of Hermelin and O'Connor,[7] who, when pitting visual, auditory and tactile modalities of stimulation against each other in pairs, found that both autistic and IQ–matched retarded children tended to respond to visual stimuli most strongly; but when visual stimuli were not used tactual stimuli tended to be dominant in autistic children and auditory stimuli tended to be dominant in subnormal controls. These few examples show a variety of fields in which there appears to be a disturbance of normal sensory dominance. In considering extension of this work it is perhaps taking too narrow a view to restrict attention to sensory modality. Rather, we ought to examine the effect of alterations in analyzers[28,41,16] and also to examine how far distorted patterns that are found are acquired as a result of the disease or may be part of the fundamental disease process itself.

It was said earlier that in trying to examine sensory processes only primary and early state functions could be considered. It is, however, necessary to mention in passing the work of McGhie, Chapman and Lawson[17] and Lawson, McGhie and Chapman.[13] These workers showed impaired short-term memory for visually presented materials as compared to auditory material, but they also showed less effect of visual distraction on short-term memory tasks. They suggested that the absence of the distraction effect in the visual modality may well be the consequence of a deficit at the input stage of visual short-term memory. What has already been said about the apparent effectiveness of protective inhibition in the visual modality in schizophrenic patients may have relevance here as a mechanism which reduces the effective intensity of visual signals as distractors and also as to-be-remembered information.

IV Two-Pulse Thresholds

An experiment[34] comparing two-flash and two-click thresholds has already been described as providing evidence for a reversal of the normal modality order in schizophrenics. The findings using two-pulse techniques on schizophrenic populations taken as a whole in general show no mean difference in threshold between patients and normals.[11,33,14] Data are available, however, to show that if the patient group is subdivided, then two-flash and two-click thresholds bear relationship to these subdivisions. Venables and Wing showed that the more withdrawn the non-medicated, non-paranoid schizophrenic patient, the lower his threshold tended to be.[39] This was confirmed in a later study,[35] where the findings with two-flash threshold were also shown when using two-click threshold. Among coherent paranoid patients, however, the relation between both two-flash and two-click threshold and withdrawal was reversed, and more recent unpublished evidence suggests that phenothiazine medication upsets the earlier reported relation in non-paranoid patients. The click threshold used in this experiment was a mean value derived from two measurements taken on each ear. When the threshold for each ear was examined separately there was evidence for a finding of considerable potential interest. In normal subjects unpublished data has been obtained for a lower threshold in the left ear than in the right. There is evidence that this laterality is reversed in schizophrenics, the extent of the reversal being related to the degree of incoherence of speech shown by the patient. As the lateral differences found are small in magnitude, it is difficult to feel confident about the differences in threshold so far obtained, and another method has been employed that gives hope of producing more satisfactory evidence. Work at present being carried on suggests that signal detection procedures may be satisfactorily applied to this problem, and values of d' may be obtained that appear to confirm the lateral difference already found in normals using other methods. The ability to derive a measure of confidence, β, from the signal detection procedure enables factors of set and expectancy, which may differ in patients and normal subjects, to be taken into consideration. The finding of superiority of the left ear for two-click threshold in normal subjects is consonant with other evidence.

Kimura[10] reported the superiority of the left ear in a dichotic listening task using melodies as stimuli for recall. She found a similar laterality effect in a task requiring perception of the number of clicks presented dichotically. The superiority of the left ear for non-verbal material is contrasted with the finding of superiority of the right ear when verbal material is used,[1,3,9] and its consequent association with the well-established data on the role of the left hemisphere in dealing with verbal material. If the work described continues satisfactorily it offers the possibility of probing, by the use of simple sensory procedures, the functioning of the two hemispheres in patient populations, and of using this method to investigate the factors underlying the malfunctioning of verbal processing mechanisms without using verbal material.

V SUMMARY

The interest of sensory processes in the study of psychopathology is not so much in the sensory processes themselves, but in the light which they are able to throw on the malfunctioning of more central processes. It may be that in the work which has been outlined too little attention has been paid to possible deficiencies in the peripheral factors. However, even here it is difficult to draw hard boundaries in view of the present knowledge of the efferent control of sensory input by central systems. It seems more worthwhile to treat a sensory event as a signal introduced by a fairly well defined route into a system. This system is then watched by the most appropriate techniques and methods that are available, so that the extent of adequate functioning of the system may be determined. By the use of simple sensory input we are perhaps only able to see the most gross types of malfunction. However, adequate mapping of the disturbance of even coarse mechanisms may be preferred to the less well-controlled examination of more complex functions.

REFERENCES

1. Broadbent, D. E. and Gregory, M.: Accuracy of recognition for speech presented to the right and left ears. Quart. J. Exp. Psychol. 16:359-360, 1964.

2. Bryant, A. R. P.: An investigation of process-reactive schizophrenia with relation to perception of visual space. Unpublished Ph.D. thesis, University of Utah, 1961.

3. Bryden, M. P.: Ear preference in auditory perception. J. Exp. Psychol. 65:103-105, 1963.

4. Buchsbaum, M. and Silverman. J.: Stimulus intensity control and the cortical evoked response. Psychosom. Med. 30:12-22, 1968.

5. Gray, J. A.: Pavlov's Typology. Oxford, Pergamon Press, 1964.

6. ———: Strength of the nervous system, introversion-extraversion, condition-ability and arousal. Behav. Res. Ther. 5:151-169, 1967.

7. Hermelin, B. M. and O'Connor, N.: Effects of sensory input and sensory dominance on severely disturbed, autistic children and on sub-normal controls. Brit. J. Psychol. 55:201-206, 1964.

8. Kietzman, M. L.: Two pulse measures of temporal resolution as a function of stimulus energy. J. Opt. Soc. Amer. 57:809-813, 1967.

9. Kimura, D.: Cerebral dominance and the perception of verbal stimuli. Canada. J. Psychol. 15:166-171, 1961.

10. ———: Left-right differences in the perception of melodies. Quart. J. Exp. Psychol. 16:355-358, 1964.

11. King, H. E.: Two-flash and flicker fusion thresholds for normal and schizophrenic subjects. Percept. Motor Skills 14:517-518, 1962.

12. Köhler, W. and Dinnerstein, D.: Figural after-effect in kinaesthesis. In: Michotte, A. (Ed.): Miscellaneas Louvain, 1947, pp. 196-220.

13. Lawson, J. S., McGhie, A. and Chapman, J.: Distractibility in schizophrenic and organic arterial diseases. Brit. J. Psychiat. 113:527-535, 1967.

14. Lykken, D. T. and Maley, M.: Autonomic versus cortical arousal in schizo-phrenics and non-psychotics. J. Psychiat. Res., in press, 1968.

15. Lynn, R.: Attention, Arousal and the Orientation Reaction. Oxford, Perga-mon Press, 1966.

16. Mackintosh, N. W.: Selective attention in animal discrimination learning. Psychol. Bull. 64:124-150, 1965.

17. McGhie, A., Chapman, J. and Lawson, J. S.: The effect of distraction on schizophrenic performance. T. Perception and immediate memory. Brit. J. Psychol. 111:383-390, 1965.

18. Nebylitsyn, V. D.: Individual differences in the strength and sensitivity of both visual and auditory analysers. Vop. Psikhol, 4:153-169, 1957.

19. Pavlov, I. P.: Conditioned Reflexes and Psychiatry. (Trans. W. H. Gantt). London, Lawrence and Wishart, 1941.

20. Petrie, A.: Some psychological aspects of pain and the relief of suffering. Ann. N.Y. Acad. Sci. 86:13-27, 1960.

21. ———, Holland, T. and Wolk, I.: Sensory stimulation causing subdued ex-perience: audio analgesia and perceptual augmentation and reduction. J. Nerv. Ment. Dis. 137:312-321, 1963.

22. Pillsbury, J. A., Meyerowitz, S., Salzman, L. F. and Satran, R.: Electroen-cephalographic correlates of perceptual style: field orientation. Psychosom. Med. 29:441-449, 1967.

23. Rozhdestvenskaya, V. I., Nebylitsyn, V. D., Borisova, M. N. and Yermolayeva-Tomina, L. B.: A comparative study of various indices of strength of the nervous system of man. Vop. Psikhol. 5:41-56, 1960.

24. Schopler, E.: Early infantile autism and receptor processes. Arch. Gen. Psychiat. 13:327-335, 1965.

25. Silverman, J.: Variations in cognitive control and psychophysiological de-fense in the schizophrenias. Psychosom. Med., in press, 1967.

26. Spain, B.: Eyelid conditioning and arousal in schizophrenic and normal subjects. J. Abnorm. Psychol. 71:260-266, 1966.

27. Stevens, S. S.: Decibels of light and sound. Physics Today 8:12-17, 1955.

28. Sutherland, N. S.: Stimulus analysis mechanisms. In: Proceedings of a Symposium on the Mechanization of Thought Processes. Vol. 2. London, H.M.S.O., 1959.

29. Sutton, S., Hakerem, G., Zubin, J. and Portnoy, M.: The effect of shift of sensory modality on serial reaction time: a comparison of schizophrenics and normals. Amer. J. Psychol. 74:224-232, 1961.

30. —— and Zubin, J.: Effect of sequence on reaction time in schizophrenia. In: Welford, A. T. and Birren, J. E. (Eds.): Behavior, Aging and the Nervous System. Springfield, Ill., Charles C Thomas, 1965.

31. Talland, G. A.: Initiation of response and reaction time in aging and with brain damage. In: Welford, A. T. and Birren, J. E. (Eds.): Behavior, Aging and the Nervous System. Springfield, Ill., Charles C Thomas, 1965.

32. Teichner, W. H.: Recent studies of simple reaction time. Psychol. Bull. 51: 128-149, 1954.

33. Venables, P. H.: The relationship between level of skin potential and fusion of paired light flashes in schizophrenic and normal subjects. J. Psychiat. Res. 1:279-287, 1963.

34. ——: A comparison of two flash and two click thresholds in schizophrenic and normal subjects. Quart. J. Exp. Psychol. 18:371-373, 1966.

35. ——: The relation of two flash and two click thresholds to withdrawal in paranoid and non-paranoid schizophrenics. Brit. J. Soc. Clin. Psychol. 6:60-62, 1967.

36. —— and O'Connor, N.: Reaction times to auditory and visual stimulation in schizophrenic and normal subjects. Quart. J. Exp. Psychol. 11:175-179, 1959.

37. —— and Tizard, J.: Paradoxical effects in the reaction time of schizophrenics. J. Abn. Soc. Psychol. 53:220-224, 1956.

38. —— and Tizard, J.: The effect of auditory stimulus intensity on the reaction time of schizophrenics. J. Ment. Sci. 104:1160-1164, 1958.

39. —— and Wing, J. K.: Level of arousal and the sub-classification of schizophrenia. Arch. Gen. Psychiat. 7:114-119, 1962.

40. Wells, F. L. and Kelley, C. M.: The simple reaction in psychosis. Amer. J. Psychiat. 2:53-59, 1922.

41. Zeaman, D. and House, B. J.: The role of attention in retardate discrimination learning. In: Ellis, N. R. (Ed.): Handbook in Mental Deficiency: Psychological Theory and Research. New York, McGraw Hill, 1963.

Discussion of Dr. Venable's Paper

by ENOCH CALLAWAY, M.D.

Langley Porter Neuropsychiatric Institute, San Francisco

DR. VENABLES' very interesting paper calls our attention to two classes of sensory phenomena that are relevant for an understanding of psychopathology. The first class involves non-monotonic input-output relationships. That is to say, increasing stimulus intensity may, at some point, actually reduce the amplitude of the subject's response. The second group of phenomena involves variations in modality and laterality effects that are encountered in psychopathology. In particular, Dr. Venables calls attention to the peculiar deficiencies and irregularities of auditory perception in the nonparanoid withdrawn schizophrenics.

I would like to add a few data that may shed some light on the first class of phenomena, so I will return to that in a moment. The second class of phenomena is more puzzling. Certainly, there is something odd about the auditory channel in schizophrenics. Why this should be seems to be quite an open question, and I would like to hazard one somewhat wild speculation. I think it is profitable to view schizophrenia as a disorder of Plans. Miller, Galanter, and Pribram used the word *Plan* for the human analog of the program in a computer. Plans, in this sense, are considered as test-operate-test-exit units with integral feedback systems. Plans are purposive units and deal not so much with input or output as with the discrepancy between what is and what is planned for. Schizophrenics, in particular, seem to have a disorder in the highest level of Plans that monitor and mediate among the simultaneous Plans that a person is likely to have in operation at any time. Now, it is of interest that these highest-level Plans are frequently stored in the form of language, and they are available to the individual as though they existed in some sort of audio storage. Does the schizophrenic have some difficulty with auditory information because of his disordered monitor Plans, or are his Plans disordered because of some defect in his handling of auditory data? This would seem to be a fruitful area for investigation.

Returning to the first point, a considerable amount of evidence is accumulating from a number of sources on the peculiar non-monotonic

142

response of individuals to sensory input. Of course it is well known that the hair cells of the ear show a non-monotonic response to auditory stimuli with the maximum of the inverted "u" at about 80 db. Following the work of Buchsbaum and Silverman and of Petrie, to which Dr. Venables has already referred, Dr. Spilker has examined the averaged evoked response to sinewave-modulated light. Here it is easy to demonstrate a reduction in the amplitude of the evoked response, in certain subjects, when the depth of modulation of the stimulating light has increased past a certain point. We calculate the slope of the evoked response amplitude as a function of depth of modulation. Even though these functions are frequently not monotonic, such a simple linear slope does provide an index of the degree to which evoked response amplitude continues to increase as depth of modulation is increased.

In a group of 29 subjects, a correlation between slope and performance to a kinesthetic figural aftereffect test similar to that used by Petrie, was 0.67. On the other hand, in 6 out of 6 subjects, the instillation of neosynephrine into the eye caused the slope of this input—AER output curve to become steeper. In other words, dilating the pupils caused all of the subjects to "augment" more in Petrie's terms. This would indicate that so-called "reducing" behavior involves pupillary mechanisms, but although peripheral mechanisms are involved in the control of sensory input, still the correlation between visual and kinesthetic performance is very high.

I wonder if we don't make things hard for ourselves when we consider such observations under the heading of sensory phenomena. This implies a linear stimulus→response model with a little black box called cognition hidden somewhere between the S and the R. Rather, let's consider that some people have a kind of program or sub-routine for keeping input within certain limits. This program (or Plan) is called up in a variety of situations—and utilizes a variety of devices to accomplish its purpose. If this Plan is stored in unverbalized form, then we must puzzle it out by psychophysiological procedures. We can then hope to see precisely what the Plan is, and what the conditions are that call it into operation.

8

PERCEPTUAL ASPECTS OF PSYCHOPATHOLOGY

by PHILIP S. HOLZMAN, Ph.D.*

INVESTIGATORS have taken two general approaches to perception–psychopathology relationships. One approach regards perception as an independent variable and directs attention to the effects of disordered perception on personality development. These studies tend to be careful analyses of single cases, like those of blind or deaf children. A second approach regards psychopathological conditions as independent variables and studies the perceptual behavior as outcomes or effects. Each approach has its methodological difficulties. Each will yield its own kind of data. To discuss both approaches overreaches my task assignment and I will therefore focus on the second approach, one which investigators have more frequently followed. Even this literature is galactic in proportion and I must be selective in what I discuss, often at the risk of bypassing many important contributions.

I shall discuss four areas. First, I shall discuss the nature of perception in order to establish its status as a complex multiprocess act. Second, I shall examine the nature of the independent variable, psychopathology, in order to fix more precisely what it is we are attempting to study. Third, I shall list several methodological difficulties investigators must encounter in studying the perceptual aspects of psychopathology. Finally, with specific reference to schizophrenia I shall explore some empirical findings and attempt to assess their significance for the perceptual behavior of schizophrenic patients. In this endeavor I shall examine the adequacy of the concept of perceptual and cognitive deficit and suggest alternative conceptualizations of some of the empirical findings. The alternatives involve 1) stylistic, personological variables as explanations for one group of findings, and 2) a suggestion that the locus of perceptual defect in schizophrenia is to

---

*University of Chicago.

be sought not in input or registration stages of perception but in perceptual feedback, the effectiveness of which depends upon intact proprioceptive, autonomic and vestibular functions.

PERCEPTION

Perception properly refers to a perceptual act that transforms a physical stimulus into psychological information. This transformation involves complex processes that include at least four stages: reception of the stimulus, registration, the processing of the registered information, and the checking of the information against the continued input. Sensory, cognitive, conceptual, conative, affective and motor processes are linked with each other in any perceptual act.

The crucial significance of perception has been recognized by most psychologists and psychiatrists. Freud, for example, relegated to perceptual acts a central role in the development of those modulatory and controlling structures he called the ego, for the perceptual act reflects the psychological point of contact between a person and his external and internal milieu. Its principal function is to convey information from this ambience for integration with other psychological functions such as memory, judgment, and anticipation. But it also receives and carries information about the nature and consequences of the perceiver's actions. Perception is thus a central ingredient in effective adaptation, in the "fitting in" process between the person and his environment. I shall examine the four stages of the perceptual act in order later to bring them into relation with the diverse studies of perception and psychopathology.

Reception and registration

It makes sense to separate conceptually the processes of reception and registration, and also to be cognizant of the possibility that registration of a percept can occur with or without awareness. Many factors influence the reception phase, such as the context in which the object is imbedded and the nature of the medium—such as fog or distorting lenses—transmitting the object. Heider has provided a cogent examination of the differentiation between an object and the transmitting medium.[43] The input of a white chair bathed in red light, for example, differs from that of a white chair bathed in white light. And, of course, the nature of the receiving organ obviously influences reception. But perception, as many psychologists have carefully pointed out, is not a passive process of intake. The physical stimulus is organized and transformed even at the point of reception and of registration. The gestalt laws like the law of Prägnanz and the law of good continuity describe the organizing and selecting process of perception at this phase of the perceptual act. That the gestalt laws express relatively durable and almost inviolable regularities indicates their relative autonomy from potentially disruptive influences from within the organism, such as motives and drives.

Physical stimuli are transmitted through and via media. But from the vantage point of the perceptual act it is the physical medium that comes into direct contact with the receptors. Properties of an object are conveyed across space to the perceiver by the medium of air or through a fog, and under varying conditions of illumination. With certain task sets, however, the mediation itself may become the object of a perceptual act.

Objects are arrangements of spatial, temporal and surface properties, such as movements, physiognomic properties, brightness, contours, and textures, among other characteristics. Objectness—such as that of "tableness" or "faceness"—is conveyed by organizations of these properties. Like physical media, these properties, too, may become objects of the perceptual act. Indeed most psychological perception experiments study the perception of these object properties, such as brightness, slant, figure-ground arrangements, apparent and real movement, and size constancy. As Heider[43] points out, arrangements of these properties can be either "loose" or "tight." Tightly organized properties tied to particular objects, like those transmitting the impression of "bookness"—in contrast to the mediational properties of a Rorschach card, for example—provide less ambiguity and more stability. Thus, the physical arrangements of object properties and the firmness of the relationship of objects to their mediational properties are crucial determinants of where and to what extent percepts can be altered and distorted.

The Processing of Sense Data

After registration, the sense data are subject to further transformations as cognitive, affective and conative processes enter the perceptual act. For example learning and experience shape the engram. Ivo Kohler's compelling demonstration of the learned reorganization of the perceptual field, distorted by the wearing inverting prisms, is a case in point.[57] The development with chronological age of size, shape and brightness constancies that inform us of the actual nature of the object, rather than its sensed quality, is another example. A more subtle but not less cogent influence is the cumulative effects of one's past experience on selection and organization of stimulation. The musicologist who hears in the performance of a Beethoven quartet the intricate development of themes, the untrained listener who hears waves of beautiful music as a global impression, and the performer who hears that his intonation may be a bit off—all are organizing and selecting from the same sensory events on the basis of their own personal histories.

Every perceptual act is primed by several intentions. Many times, particularly in laboratory experiments, there is an externally imposed task set, such as an instruction to hear or see something. In addition, there is always a personal motive to hear or see something, to look for something or to avoid something. These task intentions can narrow or expand the registration and processing activities. They too function to make perception selective and directed. Both the task set and the personal motives prepare and point the person towards the object that is to be perceived. The hungry man searches for food, and food for a hungry man is different from food for a satiated man. In this formulation intention and drive, as George Klein has pointed out,[55] are steering and directing rather than push factors. Intention thus primes a person for the appearance of a relevant class of objects. Even at the level of drive involvement, the perceptual act includes cognitive elements in the form of the interchangeable relevance of objects called for by drives. "Conceptual activity," Klein wrote, "can be said to have a *recruiting* or *priming* effect on behavior, whereby the activated concepts and memories reinforce certain sensory stimuli and not others, predisposing thought and behavior toward or away from particular objects and events. . . Since any object is actually a complex arrangement, only certain impingements become stimuli and only certain properties of an object are experienced as such . . . Perception is indispensable to this selective adjustment; . . . percepts reflect the relevance of objects to drives."[55]

But the remarkable accomplishment of perception is that drives, motives, and intentions do not for the most part override the reality attunement of the perceptual act. Most of the time perception is remarkably efficient, even in the context of strong drive pressures. Indeed, motivated perception is *not* necessarily distorted perception, and studies demonstrating the role of motivation in perception do not generally demonstrate distortion, but simply influence, an influence that generally does not contravene effective reality attunement.[86] Where distortions occur they are often quickly corrected, once feedback information is provided. True enough, the medium of transmission, as Heider has shown, can affect the coordination of the percept with the real object, such that in a poorly transmitting medium there do occur distortions contributed either by the medium itself—as in a foggy night—or by the strength of the motives. Some objects provoke the perceiver's personal reactions more than others, but these reactions are most frequently subsequent to the perception, and do not interfere with reality appraisal. Thus the structure of objects and the intact perceptual act restrain the effects of drives and motives, thus preventing behavioral solipsism. The cogwheeling of structuring processes and intentions results in perceptual acts that are neither photographic duplicates of objects nor plastic projections of drive-molded objects.

The accomplishment of effective veridicality requires not only the perceptual structuring processes that occur at input and registration, but steering and modulating structures that affect the entire perceptual act. These structures, studied by Klein,[55] Gardner,[35] Witkin,[111] Schlesinger[97] and myself,[45] we call cognitive controls. Cognitive controls pertain not to *what* is perceived, but *how* objects are perceived. We referred to them as styles of reality contact, or ways of organizing sense data. Like intentions and motives they are purposive in that they serve a class of the perceiver's intentions, but these intentions are not necessarily with respect to consummatory objects. They consequently express the differences among people in the way the perceiver registers and works over aspects of objects. Thus differences in thresholds, organizing time, figure-ground distinctions, all reflect differences in cognitive controls. Where some people seem to heighten figure-ground distinctions, others tend to blur them. Where some tend to focus attention sharply on particular stimulus attributes, others typically deploy their attention in a less focused way.

In our studies of cognitive controls we postulated that they may facilitate, inhibit or modulate the influence of drives on behavior. For example, in a study by Klein, thirst was the motivational variable.[54] The effects of thirst on size estimation of disks with thirst-relevant content, however, differed among subjects. Inasmuch as being thirsty was irrelevant to the task of judging the size of disks regardless of their content, the effect of thirst was minimal for those subjects whose cognitive control geared them to keep irrelevant stimuli isolated from the task performance. Those subjects whose cognitive control was not so geared showed significant influence of being thirsty on their size judgments.

Several cognitive controls have been described and studied: among these are leveling–sharpening,[45] scanning,[36,46,87] field articulation,[46,111] and equivalence range.[35] The activation of a particular cognitive control depends upon the requirements of intentions and tasks. Leveling–sharpening, for example, is activated in situations requiring temporal arrangements of stimuli. It refers to degrees of differentiation in memory organization as a function of the extent to which successively appearing stimuli assimilate to each other. Levelers show relatively undifferentiated memory organizations; sharpeners are able to maintain discrete impressions of successive stimuli, and thus show highly differentiated memory organization.

The cognitive control of scanning refers to variations in the intensity and extensity of attention deployed onto objects. At one extreme there is acute and broad awareness of object properties; and at the other extreme there is attenuated attention deployment. It is apparent that cognitive controls exert their effects at several points in the perceptual act—at registration and after registration. Cognitive controls seem to be relatively stable characteristics of the perceiver, and the arrangement of cognitive controls within the person we have called *cognitive style*. It is part of the enduring qualities of a person that form his character. Thus, motivational variables can enter at various points and exert various effects in the perceptual act.

Perceptual Feedback

An often neglected phase of the perceptual act is a motor component referred to as feedback, or accommodation. I described how set or intention, whether implicit or explicit, is always involved in perception. Percepts transmit information about the relevance of objects to those intentions or motives. The activity of set itself is a motor adjustment including postural adjustments that provide a readiness to do something to or with objects. This pre-perceptual set prepares the perceiver to select one group of inputs rather than another. Things are thus action-valent. The perceptual world is not merely geometric; it is populated by motivationally relevant objects which have action-encouraging properties. When we are tired, as Werner wrote, "the chair exhibits a 'sitting tone' . . . which encourages us to sit down. Any stump in the woods may become a chair so far as its signal-quality (temporarily created by our need) is concerned."[107] More properly, it is the percept *chair* which exhibits the sitting tone.

The relevance of objects to our intentions requires a constant testing out. This clearly is contributed by postural adjustments as well as by autonomic and proprioceptive consequences of the sensory input. These aspects of perception result in accommodative responses and inform the perceiver whether the object is the one sought for. Thus, exteroceptive stimuli, registered with the help of motor adjustments, themselves trigger motor responses which in turn are perceived and act as signals for the acceptance of an intention-relevant object. This "accommodation by backlash," as Freeman referred to it,[28] is basic to the apprehension of meaning in a percept.

A variety of experiments show the critical role of such motor feedback at various stages of the perceptual act. Ivo Kohler[57] demonstrated the postural adjustments in reversing and righting the visual field; Werner and Wapner showed the effect of body movement and muscular involvement on the perceived upright, on movement perception, and on visual sensitivity.[e.g.68] Interferences with feedback produce dramatic distorting effects. Our own experiments on hearing one's own voice[44] and those of Klein and Wolitsky,[56] for example, provide evidence that interfering with the feedback monitoring of one's own voice as one speaks produces noticeable effects on control and modulation of ideas and affects. Valins[97] has shown that providing inaccurate feedback information to a subject about his own heart rate while he is viewing pictures of nude females influenced the attractiveness of those photographs. Increasing environmental feedback, on the other hand, results in greater attunement to one's environment and control over one's acts, as Chase[14] has shown. A recent study by Hardyck, Petrinovich and Ellsworth,[42] for example, showed how providing auditory feedback of laryngeal muscle activity while subjects read silently resulted in sudden and long-lasting extinction of subvocalization, thus eliminating a barrier to more rapid reading.

There seems to be good reason to assign to the feedback phase of perception a principal role in reality attunement. Even so basic a function in reality contact as distinguishing an idea from a percept requires perception of one's own motor accommodations. This is one of the issues Freud tried to deal with in his *Project for a Scientific*

Psychology, and later in Chapter VII of *The Interpretation of Dreams.* As he wrote, one knows that one has in reality perceived the object one wishes to perceive through the aid of proprioceptive and enteroceptive discharges. "The perceptual excitation leads to a perceptual *discharge,* and a report of this (as of all other kinds of discharge) reaches the [psychological integrating system]."[32] The feedback stage of perception involves not only reports from muscles and peripheral organs, but also, according to Gellhorn, the cerebellum and sensorimotor cortex.[39] Vestibular functions and the autonomic nervous system are also involved in the complex processing of sense data at this stage.

The perceptual act is clearly complex, involving as it does sensory, motor, cognitive and motivational processes. The resultant—the percept—is available only in the interactions of the part processes of perception. In studying perception one may choose as a unit of analysis one or more of the part processes, depending upon the purposes and interests of the investigator. But the study of single elements of the perceptual act may require an artificial interference with other aspects of the perceptual act, by excluding or restricting their activity. We thus have an application of the indeterminancy principle in psychology. A possible outcome of this state of affairs in studies of psychopathology may be that part processes may show no effects of psychopathology, for the component variables considered separately may function effectively. Perhaps only in their ensemble will the influence of psychopathology be seen. Although focusing on one or another aspect of the perceptual act may be convenient for experimental purposes, it would seem that one cannot build up a picture of perceptual dysfunctions merely from a study of part processes.

PSYCHOPATHOLOGY

The nature of psychopathology is extraordinarily complex. There is a large range of conditions labeled "psychopathological," extending from conditions whose etiology is well delimited (general paresis for example), to those of unknown or uncertain etiology (schizophrenia and obsessive-compulsive neurosis, for example). The range shifts and expands with changing social and scientific positions, for what one chooses to call psychopathological many times reflects what one is able to do or claims one can do about the condition. Thus chronic alcoholism and certain antisocial behaviors are called psychopathological, depending upon technological considerations.

Many psychopathologists tend to reify the names of abnormal psychological conditions and thus to assume their reality as entities. A more consistent clinical view regards diagnoses as names given to sets of extreme variations of different kinds of behavior. The behaviors subsumed under a diagnostic category are not describable as unitary. It is not the diagnoses which have a reality reference but the behavioral variations that the diagnoses describe. In any class of behavior one will see extremes, and the laws that describe those extremes are the same as those that describe the nonpathological functioning. This would seem to be the meaning of the idea of continuity between normal and abnormal.

A further complication is the fact that no one behavior is unique to a diagnostic category; therefore individual symptoms are not reliable indications of membership in a psychopathological grouping. Where, however, precise and definite etiological factors have been isolated and the pathogenesis is well understood, the disease entity itself surely may be used to define a population; correlations with psychological functions may then be undertaken following the medical model, a model Teuber,[95] Luria[61] and others have used to explore the functions of the nervous system from a study of neurologically impaired patients. This is a rational application of the Virchow principle. Most studies on psychopathological conditions without definite etiology or pathogenic factors, however, lack such focus; and the consequent results of those psychological studies are not clear.

Methodological Problems

The usual experimental procedure for tracing the perceptual aspects of psychopathology is to test specific groups of patients—e.g., schizophrenics—in one or more perceptual tasks. The patients' scores are then compared with those of another group of subjects. With a few noteworthy exceptions, results have been ambiguous. The ambiguity can in large measure be traced to a number of methodological flaws. I shall point to six major methodological difficulties an investigator must encounter in any investigation of the perceptual aspects of psychopathology and in particular of schizophrenic patients, difficulties that published studies have not adequately met. The six difficulties are: 1) establishing the validity of the diagnosis in order to make sure what psychopathological group we are studying; 2) establishing the reliability of the diagnosis; 3) meeting the problem of complications produced by drug therapy; 4) providing an adequate number of patients in the study; 5) gearing the results to the logical requirements of interpretation; and 6) studying appropriate comparison groups. I shall discuss these points with particular reference to the study of schizophrenic patients.

The validity of the diagnosis. In any study of schizophrenic pathology one confronts the question of the nature of the condition. Even Kraepelin repeatedly revised his classification of the schizophrenias in eight revisions of his textbook, a fact that attests to his own dissatisfaction with his description and classification efforts. For Kraepelin the validity of the diagnosis was in many instances determined by the outcome of the case, whether, for example, there was deterioration or remission. Today, the difficulty in making a valid diagnosis continues to reflect the poor agreement among experienced psychiatrists about what constitutes the central aspect and range of schizophrenia. It is therefore quite important to get expert agreement on what behaviors are being subsumed under the diagnostic rubric as well as on the severity of the condition. The researcher should know the basis for the diagnosis of his subjects, whether on the basis of specific symptoms, personality traits, groups of reactions, or subtle assessments of thought organization. Ideally the observational basis for the diagnosis should be specified so that the results can be compared with those of other investigators. The usual pragmatic solution to the problem of diagnostic validity has been to accept as "schizophrenic" what psychiatrists agree is "schizophrenic." This may be the most useful practical solution, but the construction of standard metrics of specified phenomena would do much to relieve the confusion about whether psychopathological subjects in one study are similar to those in another.

It would be a distinct contribution to include the inference process which led to the diagnosis. Too often we are presented with the end product of a diagnostic reasoning process, in which the basic observations may not at all buttress the conclusions. Perhaps, in addition to interviews, ward observations, or other techniques, the psychological test protocols, which record objective evidence of the kind of thought disorder, could be systematically used to establish the validity of the diagnosis. In this way, the congruence of two different methods—in the manner recommended by Campbell and Fiske[10] in another context—would increase the certainty of the investigator's knowledge and the composition of his subject group.

The reliability of the diagnosis. Establishing the reliability of the diagnostic appraisal is often neglected in experimental studies. It is rare to see specified in any published report who the person is who has made the diagnostic determination, what his training and experience have been, the length of his contact with the patient, and the nature of his contact with the patient—that is, on the basis of what instruments he has reached his conclusions. Further, there is often no effort to get a second independent confirmation of the diagnostic appraisal.

My colleagues, Herbert Spohn, Paul Thetford, and Robert Cancro have addressed themselves to this troublesome area by having the case records of the patient subjects reviewed by two psychiatrists in addition to the one who originally made the diagnosis, and only patients about whose diagnosis all psychiatrists agree are included in their study.

The drug problem. The use of psychotropic drugs, particularly the phenothiazines, has been a welcome adjunct to the treatment of psychotic patients, but it has altered the field of investigation in significant ways, the extent of which is not even yet known. It is obvious, however, that patients receiving drugs perform differently from those not receiving drugs. Indeed, investigation of the drug state itself has occupied the attention of many investigators. The confounding of drug state with psychopathology in many studies of perceptual aspects of psychopathology makes results uninterpretable. When investigators recognize the need to control the drug state, it is often difficult to get patients removed from drugs, many times for obvious and good therapeutic reasons. When patients are removed from drugs, testing may unfortunately be instituted before the effects of the drugs is completely gone, a period that can range up to many weeks and even months, particularly when MAO inhibitors are used.

A related difficulty in most psychological experiments is in the choice of patients. Many times we see reports describing the patients as cooperative, or with the phrase "only patients able to cooperate were used." This choice of only cooperative subjects limits the representativeness of the sample and therefore restricts the generalizability of conclusions to the realm of cooperative patients, whatever they may be. A study by Klein and Spohn[33] showed that there are indeed important significant differences between cooperative and uncooperative patients, and that a better understanding of the perceptual aspects of psychopathology requires inclusion of this latter group of patients. Further, L. Chapman[13] has shown that there are significant differences in thought organization between patients who do and do not profit from tranquilizing medication. The reliance on standard laboratory tests for which cooperativeness is a prerequisite may have to be abandoned, at least in some instances, in favor of more imaginative and probably more revealing measures that do not require the cooperation of the subject.

The size of subject groups. In perception-psychopathology studies it is rare to find studies with 100 or more subjects. Indeed, the typical size of subject groups in these reports is under 25. Replication by the investigator of his own work is also a rarity. Generally such cross-validation is left to another investigator, whose procedures may be different and whose subjects may also differ in important respects. When disparate results are reported it is difficult to untangle the source of the disparity, particularly since the response range of schizophrenic subjects is typically wide.

Silverman[93] attributes the failures to get replicated results to the heterogeneity of schizophrenic subgroups. This may indeed be the case in many studies, if indeed schizophrenia is not a unitary entity, but is instead, as Bleuler[4] has argued, a group of reactions. The present solution to this dilemma has been to increase the homogeneity of subject groups by dichotomizing the subjects along each of three dimensions: process-reactive schizophrenia, acute-chronic schizophrenia, and paranoid-nonparanoid schizophrenia. Silverman[93] argues that only the use of the three classificatory variables will insure interpretable results and create the conditions for replicability. Such dichotomization—with sufficient subjects in each category—surely is worth trying, and to my knowledge only the Spohn-Thetford studies have employed all three variables in classifying subjects. It remains, however, not to reify even these classifications but to study the psychological essence of the process-reactive, acute-chronic and paranoid-nonparanoid dimensions. My hunch is that these classes consist in differences in personality structure which define the path of psychotic disruption. I will have more to say about this later.

Jacob Cohen reviewed samples of studies published in the *Journal of Abnormal and Social Psychology*.[20] Cohen was interested in the statistical limits placed on interpretations of the results by small numbers of subjects. Where slight differences between small groups of subjects existed there was a probability of only .18 of rejecting a false null hypothesis. When the group differences were moderate the probability rose to .48 and for large differences the probability was .83 of rejecting a false difference. As Schooler and Feldman[88] comment, "the notoriously high variances which plague studies of schizophrenics makes the likelihood of rejecting false null hypotheses in this area even slimmer than suggested by Doctor Cohen's survey which includes studies of far more homogeneous populations." Thus it would seem that unless one studies *large* numbers of subjects, or—where small numbers are used—unless one analyzes intensively the response behavior of *each subject*, the findings in a psychological experiment based on small groups where the differences are small or moderate tend to promulgate errors of the first type described above.

Interpretation of results. The fifth difficulty, conceptual rather than procedural, lies in the interpretative requirements of results. Most studies are cast in the correlational mold. When psychological deficits are found to be associated with psychopathology, does one conclude that the relationship is a causal one, and if so, what are the causal chains? Does schizophrenic disorganization cause the score deficit, or does the perceptual variation play a causal role in the development of the psychopathology? Or do both the psychopathology and the perceptual variation reflect the effects of a third process? Or is the perceptual variation an artifact of the testing situation, and does it reflect principally motivational, attentional, and judgmental variables or misunderstandings? Without careful control and understanding of the context of the experiment the meaning of the results cannot be ascertained. I remember a colleague who served as a subject in a study of the perceptual and cognitive effects of mescaline. The situation represented in size estimation tests, object constancy and threshold experiments seemed so uninteresting and unimportant to him while in the drug state—although he was otherwise deeply interested in perceptual problems—that he could not be induced to finish any experimental task. An outstanding merit of Rodnick and Garmezy's program of experimentation is their attempt to test patients within a context of relevance.[82] Although their choice of situation relevance may be incorrect, the experimental paradigm is a compelling one.

Control groups. The sixth difficulty is in the choice of comparison groups. One evaluates experimental results only with respect to comparative performances. In the psychopathological literature comparison groups are generally characterized as "normal." Many times the groups are hospital personnel, and sometimes college students. Rarely is the normal group matched with the psychopathological group on critical variables. When such obvious variables as age, education and socioeconomic status are matched, generally the crucial factor of patienthood is not considered. Thus the effects of mere illness or of hospitalization is not tagged in the variance. At this point in our scientific development it is not sufficient to know that schizophrenics differ from normals. We must know the specificity of the result for schizophrenia, or whatever psychopathological group is under study. Therefore comparison groups consisting of patients with a different psychopathology from that of the experimental group as well as nonpsychiatric patients must be included in the study. A study by Eysenck in 1952 highlights this requirement. Vandenberg[98] reworked Eysenck's data and uncovered many differences between schizophrenics and normals and between depressed patients and normals. But when the schizophrenic patients were compared with depressed patients no differences were statistically significant. The failure to use comparison groups of other psychopathological patients vitiates the information yielded by the experiment and dulls the specificity of the experimental findings.

Further, there is sufficient evidence now to indicate that within a psychopathological group men and women perform differently and indeed may even manifest their symptoms differently. It therefore seems crucial that subject groups consist of equal numbers of men and women, and their results evaluated separately.

If one tests the experimental literature on the perception-psychopathology relationships by these six requirements, one is left with no studies that fulfill all of these requirements for placing confidence in results. In reviewing the empirical studies, therefore, one must remember that conclusions based on the data are tentative and require retesting.

PERCEPTUAL ASPECTS OF PSYCHOPATHOLOGY

What with all the methodological difficulties that lie in the way of the investigator of perception-psychopathology relationships, with the terrifying complexity of the area of psychopathology itself, and the multivariate nature of perceptual experiences, perhaps only the foolhardy dare tread where the pure psychonom would choose not to. There are nevertheless many empirical studies—995 of them since 1950 in the area of schizophrenia alone, according to the abstracts, incomplete at that, by Schooler and Feldman.[88] I shall turn now to that empirical literature. To simplify my presentation I shall restrict my survey to the perceptual aspects of schizophrenia.

There are two classes of studies of the perceptual aspects of schizophrenia. One is a pure empirical approach in which schizophrenic patients are tested in a variety of experimental tests without regard to the testing of a theory about the disorder—and even stopping short of theoretical generalization. The second is a deductive approach in which aspects of a theory of schizophrenia are subjected to experimental tests.

The Empirical Approach

The pure empirical approach has implicitly searched for the presence of perceptual deficit in schizophrenic patients. This approach assumes an equation between psychological deficit and perceptual deficit, and therefore an expectation that perceptual or cognitive deficit is present in groups of schizophrenic patients. The term "psychological deficit" was first promulgated in the review by Hunt and Cofer in 1944 to characterize the poorer performance of psychopathological patients on psychological tests when compared with that of normals. Since that time there have been many hundreds of studies whose purpose has been to search for disordered perception or cognition in psychopathological subjects—that is, to look for perceptual and cognitive deficits in such psychiatric patients. Differences found between groups of schizophrenic patients and normals, for example, have typically been interpreted in terms of impairments, defects, or loss of efficiency. The term "psychological deficit" was adopted by Hunt and Cofer because it seemed to be a neutral term, a term free of the theoretical fetters of "dementia," "deterioration" or "regression." In the more than two decades since their review, the term, which served usefully as a guide, has itself become a restraint on empirical search, for it has directed attention to reduced, disordered and deficient performance and thus forced a neglect of differences that may not be interpretable as deficits. The idea of non-disordered perception among schizophrenic patient seems less interesting to empirical investigators than does that of perceptual or performance loss.

Most of the studies in this empiricist tradition have made use of standard laboratory procedures and employed psychopathological subjects instead of or in addition to nonpathological subjects. Much of this work has lacked relevance for the practicing clinician and the clinical theoretician. The situation has been much like that of the drunkard who dropped his doorkey as he was trying to open his door and searches for it down the street because, as A. Kaplan describes the drunkard's reasoning, the light is better there.[52] True, the psychological tests are there, but they do not seem to be in the realm of relevance circumscribed by the disorder.

These laboratory tests—like size estimation, size constancy, and apparent motion—are clearly recommended by their availability. As I previously pointed out, when one looks at the results of numerous studies of schizophrenic patients one finds, as Silverman[93] has shown graphically, a wider range of response by schizophrenic than by nonschizophrenic subjects, and this fact of high inter-subject variability has lowered the probability of replicable findings of schizophrenia-perception relationships. Efforts to reduce this variance by subclassifications has helped somewhat, but the study of subclasses of schizophrenia has not solved the problem of high variability and therefore stability of results.

Even with the high variability of schizophrenic subjects in these tasks, the results have not been so extreme or bizarre as to cast doubt upon the general efficiency of judgments. The relevance of high overestimation of disks or low brightness constancy for actual, active, adaptive perceiving has not been established. Therefore it seems procrustean to fit the results of schizophrenic subjects in these tasks to the bed of *deficit* performance. Variable, yes. But deficient, not proven. The tasks we are talking about require optimum performance from a subject. The experimenter tells the subject to gear his attention to the task, and to exclude distractions; he makes him comfortable and takes considerable time to establish a working relationship between him and his subject. These tasks thus bring out the best in the subjects; and under these circumstances they do not bring out what can be called *operational effectiveness*.[26] The extraction of optimum performance is aided by the fact that testing sessions are limited in time so as not to overtax the subject; thus the testing sessions may end before impairments can show themselves. This could be one explanation for the differences found between schizophrenics and nonschizophrenics in time estimation studies done under naturalistic conditions, and the ambiguous results of studies using psychophysical judgments of time.

Let us quickly glance at some of the major findings of size estimation and size and distance constancy in schizophrenic patients. Some experiments—like those of Cooper,[22] Reynolds,[81] and Weckowitz[103, 104,106]—show that chronic schizophrenics are less constant than a normal control group. Others like Johannesen et al.[50] show a "restitutive effect" for extreme chronic schizophrenics. With acute patients and with early paranoid schizophrenics the typical finding is of no difference from normals, and some studies such as that of Raush[79,80] show the paranoids to be *over*-constant, that is, to be above average in their functioning. But even where schizophrenic performance is significantly less constant than that of nonschizophrenic subjects, the extent of the differences is not large in absolute terms and the range of results not extreme.

When one then considers that brightnesses or real size judgments are generally not objects of perception, but are object mediators, one is not convinced that the perceptual experiences of patients are necessarily deficient. Performance differences of mediators of things may not necessarily result in defective perception of the *thing*. Studies of the organization and integration of mediators are scarce, yet it is the integration of these qualities into patterns that is the object of perceptions. It would therefore seem that it is in the whole perceptual act that important differences and meaningful deficit performances should be sought.

The use of these tasks seems geared to assessing not perception-psychopathology relationships, but the enduring cognitive-perceptual response dispositions of subjects—the style and form of reality attunement which we have called cognitive controls. These studies, then, highlight variations in the stable regulatory strategies of subjects, strategies that are relevant to the experience of perception but which themselves are not to be considered as the perceptual act.

Freed from the constraints of viewing patients' responses in these tasks as deficits, one can view them as forms of reality contact, styles of organizing sense data that probably antedate the patient's psychopathology. For, if there is an entity like schizophrenia, it is surely not unitary. Kraepelin's great achievement was to discern some unifying principle in the diverse forms of psychotic disorganization; but he never assumed that psychotic disorganization made all of its victims alike in all respects. It is the person who becomes disorganized, and the person's style of perceiving and cognizing will show itself even in states of disorganization, although the styles may appear exaggerated or extreme, as David Rapaport has stated.[78] Thus the individuality of a person's perceptual organization will show itself uniquely in disease. Such disease processes may exaggerate or minimize a person's characteristic perceptual functioning. Conversely, the style of perceptual and cognitive functioning may determine the *nature* of the psychopathological organization—not *whether* disorganization will occur, but if it does occur, for whatever reason, the form it takes will be determined by perceptual and cognitive strategies of the person. Thus, the subclasses of schizophrenia themselves may reflect these stable personality dispositions. The hyperalertness to detail and the litigious orientation of the paranoid schizophrenic are characteristic not of the psychopathological condition but of the person, exaggerated by the decompensation of trends previously existing in the individual. The meticulous, intellectualizing hair-splitter, were he to develop neurotic symptoms, would likely show compulsive and obsessive symptoms and not hysterical ones.

The body of data represented by these laboratory studies may be reinterpreted as shedding some light on the choice of symptoms in psychopathology. Thus Witkin[109] finds that process schizophrenics tend to be field dependent and undifferentiated, while the active schizophrenics tend to be field independent and differentiated subjects,[7] although Cancro[11] did not confirm these results. Voth and Mayman[101] report a correlation between response to the autokinetic phenomenon—that is, whether subjects tend to see much movement or little movement—and psychopathological symptoms. Silverman[92] reports that paranoid schizophrenic subjects tend to underestimate the sizes of disks and to scan the field intensively—that is, to be scanners—while nonparanoid schizophrenics tend not to be scanners. Gardner et al.[36] demonstrated that subjects who rely on isolation as a principal mechanism of defense tend predominantly to be scanners. Holzman and Gardner[47] showed that those subjects relying principally on repression, the dominant defense mechanism in hysteria, tend to level successively appearing stimulus differences, that is, to show a preference for the leveling cognitive control.

Another cognitive control, less well studied and in need of replication and careful delineation, is Petrie's augmenter-reducer dimension.[76] This dimension refers to the amplification or reduction of intensities of stimulus input, from whatever the source, whether painful tactual stimulation or the kinesthetic after-effect which is the criterion task. Extreme augmenting appears to be typical of paranoid-reactive early schizophrenic patients. But extreme reducing seems typical of non-paranoid schizophrenics. These observations are consistent with reports that schizophrenic subjects are quite tolerant of pain.

Although extreme forms of cognitive controls are consistent with certain forms of psychopathology, they are not specific to any one form of psychopathology. Witkin's studies,[109] for example, exemplify the nonspecificity of psychopathology in respect to the dimension of psychological differentiation. He notes that extreme performances at both ends of the dimension occur in many different psychopathological groups. It is true that there is evidence that psychopathological subjects tend to give extreme scores, whatever the dimension, but psychopathology manifests itself differently at the two extremes. "The kinds of pathology that have been found at each extreme may be conceived as having the form which impaired integration is likely to take when more differentiated or less differentiated personalities break down."[109,p.324] Thus, alcoholic patients, obese patients, catatonic schizophrenics, hysterical patients, those with certain character disorders, and those nonpatients with prominent dependency problems all tend to have high field dependent scores. Field independent scores are likely to be found among paranoid patients and obsessional patients.

These findings suggest directions for future research. Cognitive controls have a developmental dimension. They are discernible in early childhood and their continuity and stability have been studied in the empirical work of Witkin[109] and Gardner.[37] Witkin, for example, reports evidence of field dependence–field independence as early as the third year, and correlates of this dimension have been discovered in the looking behavior of three-month-old infants. These two factors—their stability over time and their appearance early in childhood—permit a prospective developmental study of psychopathology such as that suggested by Norman Garmezy in his paper at the 1967 Rochester Conference on Schizophrenia.[38] Garmezy addressed himself to our inadequate knowledge about the etiology of schizophrenia, and directed cogent criticism at the method of retrospective reconstruction. He advocated systematic longitudinal studies, and cited Mednick's method of choosing subjects with a high risk rate of schizophrenia. Continued surveillance of matched triads of subjects—two from a high-risk population and one from a low-risk population—and persistent studies of a number of dimensions of personality development in the subjects would,

I agree, contribute much to our understanding of the development of schizophrenic disorganization and the forms it takes. Included in the variables to be studied would be a number of cognitive controls. Garmezy's proposal has the important merit of systematically scrutinizing cognitive and perceptual development prior to the clear emergence of psychopathological disruption. It would seem reasonable that investigation of cognitive control variables should enter the nomological search at this stage, and in this developmental manner, rather than as they have been, as *post hoc* cross-sectional studies without full awareness by the investigators of the nature of the variables studied. The longitudinal search may illuminate whether in certain high-risk people aspects of perception may be disordered early in development, but with training and experience the child has learned to compensate for an earlier deficit.

The Deductive Approach

The allegation of perceptual deficit in schizophrenia is not as clearly supported as it is in some organic conditions or toxic states. Even the principal clinical theorists have not agreed about the perceptual aspects of this disorder. Bleuler,[4] for example, explicitly denied that in schizophrenia there is a primary disturbance of perception. "Sensory response," he wrote, "to external stimulus is quite normal. To be sure, the patients will complain that everything appears to be different, and frequently we can observe the absence of the 'feeling of familiarity' with known things. However, this strangeness is usually attributable to a deficit in customary associations and particularly to an alteration of emotional emphasis, not to disturbances of sensation. Even the normal person may, under special circumstances, feel that all of a sudden certain percepts are different from the usual. We know the feeling of the 'world having turned gray' from the melancholics. Very often it is assumed that the sensations derived from the bodily organs are altered in these patients. Any number of complicated symptoms have been explained by this alteration. It is possible to distinguish the patient's sensations from his hallucinations and illusions to which certainly many, if not all, of these paresthesias properly belong. In any event, one is able to show quite frequently that such sensations are a consequence of affectively charged concepts, while a true primary disturbance of sensation has not yet been demonstrated with certainty."[4, pp. 56-57] C. G. Jung agreed with Bleuler's point of view. If indeed there is a perceptual disorder in schizophrenia, Jung argued, it would be a reflection of an attentional disturbance rather than a primary perceptual disturbance. Thus Jung (1936) quotes René Masselon's clinical study of dementia praecox to the effect that "perception of external objects, perception of our own personality, judgment, the feelings of rapport, the belief and certitude disappear when the power of attention disappears."[51]

For most of these classical clinical systematists the primary deficit lay in associational and attentional processes, a view concurred in by many empirical investigators. Thus the compelling studies of Shakow[91] and of Sutton and Zubin on reaction time[94] give support to the presumption of primary attentional disturbances in schizophrenia. Where attention is a principal variable in a perceptual act one can expect deviations in perception in those subjects in whom attention is disturbed.

Paul Federn, however, claimed for schizophrenia a primary perceptual disturbance. In schizophrenia, Federn maintained, there is a fundamental failure to differentiate the psychological and physical experience of selfness from the outside. This failure manifests itself in inadequate and nonveridical distinctions between a real object and its thought representation, between an anticipation of an action and the actual action. Federn's term for this phenomenon is a "breakdown in ego boundaries," and it expresses itself perceptually in the deadness and coldness of sensory experiences, in the unfamiliarity and lifelessness of external impressions. "Mere loss of interest and attentional deficit do not suffice to explain the effects for many estranged objects remain in the field of interest."[25,p.257] Freeman, Cameron and McGhie[30] agree with Federn's formulation and therefore with his relegation of perceptual disturbance to a primary role in schizophrenia. They add that "one result of the weakened ego function and consequent lack of sensory organization is seen in the schizophrenic's susceptibility to environmental stimuli, which he is unable to perceive in their proper order and context . . . the schizophrenic's reduced capacity to experience himself as a separate and distinct entity, with a personal identity, leads to similar difficulties in locating and organizing perceptions arising from external stimuli."[30]

For Freud, the primary role of reality testing consisted in distinguishing a thought from a percept, and reality from an idea. In schizophrenia and some other psychopathological conditions the capacity to make such distinctions is disrupted.

Meehl[70] described a number of clinical symptoms, subtle behaviors and traits that he uses in identifying "schizotypic" individuals—that is, those who might be classified as preschizophrenic, pseudoneurotic schizophrenic, or borderline cases. He is presently investigating the clinical utility of these signs. There are some 25 major signs and 20 special signs that he lists. Of these, six seem to implicate perceptual experience: a) body image distortions, b) sensory input compulsions, c) noise oversensitivity, d) touch aversion, e) photophobia, and f) spatial-motoric-kinesthetic defect—a characterological clumsiness. Hilde Bruch has assigned a significant role in schizophrenic pathology[5] and in anorexia nervosa[6] to inappropriate recognition of bodily sensations. This misrecognition, which develops early in the schizophrenic patient's life, leads to distorted ideas about the body and about self-experience in general.

The clinical literature thus suggests a number of studies of perceptual aspects of schizophrenia. Unfortunately, there are extremely few studies which pursue deductions from the clinical insights on schizophrenia. The deductive approach begins with a perusal of the classical clinical literature or of a major theory of schizophrenia and studies the clinical manifestations of expected phenomena and then subjects them to experimental test. The results would be placed within the context of components in the perceptual act—whether input, registration, processing, style, or feedback. Thus, for schizophrenia, one might study deductively at least five areas: the distinction between a percept and an idea, time perception, pain perception, person perception, and the sensory input anomalies including the spatial-kinesthetic defects that seem to implicate the perceptual feedback phase of perception.

Percept or an idea. There are no studies from which one could draw valid conclusions about the distinction in schizophrenic patients between a percept and an idea. Naturalistic clinical observations would be called for first, supplemented by skillful inquiry. Experimentation could also be undertaken perhaps following the model of the Perkey experiment[75] in which subjects are asked to imagine an object and to describe it while the experimenter simultaneously projects a similar object on to a screen. The fusing of percept, image, and idea can then be examined.

Schizophrenic subjects typically produce what has been called perceptual distortions on psychological tests of the projective type. For example on the TAT, objects are misidentified or shadows become substantial objects. Intensive inquiry and testing of the limits could help determine the perceptual status of these responses. Likewise intensive studies of hallucinating patients would seem to be another area to which one could direct investigations. Curiously, there are still no published experiments testing schizophrenic patients on standard illusions.

Time perception. In studies of the effects of certain drugs like LSD, mescaline, and psilocybin on performance, phenomenological reports and performance on simple tasks dramatize time distortions. For most subjects time misperceptions are clearly demonstrable. Laboratory tests with schizophrenic subjects, however, are equivocal. For example, Lhamon and Goldstein[60] showed that schizophrenic subjects were significantly poorer than college students in estimating one-second intervals. Orme,[71] on the other hand, found no differences between schizophrenic subjects and other clinical groups. A later study by Orme[72] found that paranoid schizophrenics, hysterics, manics, and psychopaths gave longer time estimations than did nonparanoid and depressed patients. Pearl and Berg,[74] too, found that schizophrenic subjects overestimated the time that conflict-related pictures were exposed. But these errors in time estimation do not approach those found in many drug studies. Warm, Morris and Kew[102] in a psychophysical time estimation study report no differences between schizophrenics and normals. The general finding is that schizophrenic subjects do show mild deviations in time estimations; but the more the technique of observation relies on experimental manipulation and psychophysical methods and less on naturalistic techniques, the less apparent are the differences between the psychopathological groups and normals.

Pain perception. The clinical literature reports several instances of massive coronary attacks in schizophrenics apparently unfelt by the victims, or severe burns without any apparent pain response. The studies, however, are insufficient to establish with any definiteness whether there is a pain threshold anomaly, or a pain response deficit. Hall and Stride[41] report that schizophrenic subjects have raised thresholds to thermal pain. May,[66] using pupillary responses as an indicator, found diminished pain reaction. Malmo and Shagass[64] report similar hyporesponsivity to pain in chronic schizophrenics, but hyperresponsivity in acute patients. The probability is that schizophrenics' response to pain is neither a threshold nor a response phenomenon, but reflects a defect in perceptual feedback, an issue we will talk about later. Clearly, more systematic studies are called for before generalizations can be made.

Person perception. It would seem that person perception is another potentially rich area to be studied on the basis of the clinical data. Some studies like that of Cleveland[15] indicate that the schizophrenic patient is less precise than nonschizophrenic patients in judging body size. Cleveland et al.[16] for example, attribute this difference to a loss of "body definiteness," thus supporting the descriptions of Federn. But whereas their subjects overestimated body size, the subjects in a study by Weckowicz and Sommer[105] underestimated their body parts. The person perception literature for the most part is concerned not with perceptual effects, but rather with judgments and descriptions by verbal report. A recent study, however, reported that when subjects had to adjust a distorting mirror to approximate acceptable reflections of their own bodies, chronic schizophrenic subjects showed a wider range than normals of acceptable reflections.[96] But the same differences between schizophrenics and normals obtained when subjects had to adjust a rectangular frame. This study strongly suggests that distorted perception of own body by schizophrenic patients is not specific to body-image perception.

The perceptual feedback phase. There is mounting evidence that focusses on the central role of this stage more than that of the others in the perceptual aspects of many psychopathological conditions and particularly of schizophrenia. The evidence here is more compelling than in the other four areas. Consider the following findings:

1. Several investigators report a state of high psychophysiological arousal in schizophrenic subjects. Malmo and Shagass[63] and Malmo et al.,[65] for example, found high base-line electromyographs, with the highest resting levels being characteristic of the most withdrawn patients. These findings of high base-line muscle tonus have subsequently been replicated by many other investigators, for example by Reynolds[81] and by Peturrson.[77] The high level of resting muscle potential is coupled with the discovery of faster heart rates and higher systolic blood pressure among schizophrenics than among nonschizophrenics. Further, Funkenstein et al.[33] reported reduction in systolic blood pressure basal level with improvement in or treatment of the psychosis. Venables and his associates, pursuing the findings of Malmo and Shagass, linked psychological withdrawal with heightened basal arousal levels.[99] It would seem that high muscle tone, with other evidence of a high basal arousal state, would influence reactivity, stimulus input and stimulus integration.

2. There is consistent evidence of *underreaction* to specific stimuli in schizophrenic patients. Pain thresholds are raised, as reported by Hall and Stride[41] and by Petrie;[76] King,, in a carefully done study,[52a] reported deficient reactivity in chronic schizophrenics, and May[66] reported diminished pupillary response to pain and exercise. A complementary finding is that suggested by DeVault's report[23] of cardiac deceleration in chronic process schizophrenics when viewing stimuli connoting psychological threat. The expected response to threatening stimuli is cardiac acceleration, which indeed occurred in normal subjects and in reactive chronic schizophrenics. Lacey[58] has interpreted the cardiac acceleration response as a physiological aspect of control and modulation of stimulus input; the cardiac deceleration response as the concomitant of the failure of such post-input modulation and restraint. The deceleration response is part of the preparation the perceiver makes for further input; Graham and Clifton[40] couple the cardiac deceleration response with the orienting reflex, interpreted as facilitating reception of new percepts. The acceleration response, on the other hand, is part of the working over of the percepts, with the gating of new inputs and thus has been interpreted as part of a defensive response.[58] Parallel work on the OR (orienting reflex) confirms these trends. Gamburg,[34] for example, found schizophrenic patients to be impaired in both the motor and autonomic components of the OR to sound only. Four of 42 schizophrenics showed the OR, compared with 29 of 34 normals.

3. Poor performances in process and chronic schizophrenics improve when stimulus backgrounds are simple and underarousing. Indeed under conditions of sensory isolation there seems to be minimal adverse effects.[18,85] Conversely, when stimulus input is intense, standing out as unambiguous figure, impairment in performance is also lessened. These findings suggest that a condition of stimulus overload occurs in the context of too much input or where figure and ground of the stimulus input are not clearly separable. It is as if the perceptual system has too much to process, is unable to work over the input as required for effective perception, and therefore response is indiscriminate.

4. The extraordinary series of reaction time studies by King,[52a] by Shakow,[91] and by Sutton and Zubin[94] show that schizophrenic subjects are always slower than nonschizophrenic subjects, irrespective of the interval between signal and stimulus. Even when uncertainty is removed, as in a shifting modality experiment by telling the subjects what modality the stimuli will be presented in, slower reaction times

continue to appear in schizophrenic subjects. This is due not to incorrect anticipation by schizophrenic subjects—that is, not to *pre*-perceptual factors—for even where patients' anticipations are correct they still show longer reaction times, although the most retarded effects occur when the patients are wrong in their guesses. Shakow explains these results as reflecting a "segmental set" in schizophrenic patients. Callaway and Dembo[8] link the response decrements with narrowed attention and suggest that high arousal levels lead to narrow attentional focus and tend to "information overload." That attentional processes are involved here seems almost incontestable, and my colleagues Spohn, Thetford and Cancro are presently carrying on a major study of the form varieties of attention and attention defect in schizophrenia. These studies do not demonstrate that attention defects are to be considered the causal factor in slowed reaction times. It is equally possible that attention and set are impaired by other factors such as the proprioceptive and autonomic adjustments involved in perceptual feedback. The import of the formulations by Shakow, by Sutton and Zubin, and by Callaway is that restraining internal modulating processes are at fault, resulting in indiscriminate unselective responses, particularly when the field is complex and without clear figure ground differentiation.

The studies of CEP (cortical evoked potentials), too, indicate differences in reactivity between schizophrenics and nonschizophrenics. Shagass and Schwartz,[89] for example, report that CEPs to the second of two successively appearing shocks were considerably attenuated in schizophrenic patients and not in nonschizophrenic subjects. However, CEP to uncomplicated stimuli is clearly stronger in schizophrenics than in nonschizophrenics. Callaway, Jones and Layne[9] report similar findings.

5. Drug studies, particularly of the anesthetic Serynl (phencyclidine hydrochloride), are highly suggestive. This drug seems to mimic the aforementioned effects: heightened basal arousal levels, increased muscle tonus with accompanying thought disorganization, feelings of estrangement and attention impairments, slowed reaction times to cognitive stimuli, but not to direct shock stimulation. The important work done by Rosenbaum and his colleagues at the Lafayette Clinic[17,19,20,83,84,85] points to the action of Sernyl as depressing the integration of sense data at a post-input stage by interfering with proprioceptive feedback, and hence with the reperception phase of the perceptual act. The drug seems to exacerbate schizophrenic symptoms in

schizophrenic patients and to induce them in nonschizophrenic subjects. Chlorpromazine, which reduces muscle tone, diminishes these effects.

6. A number of studies directly link vestibular dysfunction with schizophrenia. Angyal and Blackman[2] and Angyal and Sherman,[3] for example, reported that schizophrenic patients showed less nystagmus than normals after the subjects' external auditory meatus was irrigated with water at 20° C. or after the subjects were revolved ten times in a chair. Freeman and Rodnick's 1942 studies showed that schizophrenic patients were considerably less unsteady than controls following rotation.[29] Indeed, Hoskins (1946) underscores the finding of vestibular impairment as the most reliable of his studies on the biology of schizophrenia.[48] Paul Schilder, commenting on these and other essentially confirmatory findings, attributed the results to a defect in the vestibular apparatus.

Thus the most stable finding of the Worcester studies[48] is the diminished *reactivity* of schizophrenics in respect to vestibular functions which govern balance and postural adjustments. These processes are crucial for effective and adaptive integration of stimulus inputs. The defects suggest diminished reactivity to perceptual stimuli at the post-input phase of perception. This diminished reactivity is apparently not a result of perseverative sets or undue influence of previous stimuli or responses, for diminished postural reactivity occurs even without previous response sets, as Freeman and Rodnick[29] have shown.

More recently Colbert et al.[21] have shown that in schizophrenic children nystagmus following rotation was significantly reduced in duration. Ornitz and Ritvo[3] comment that findings such as those of Colbert et al. are consistent with clinical reports of the tendency of autistic children to whirl and spin themselves and to be fascinated by spinning objects as if, these authors speculate, they are thereby trying to increase their diminished vestibular stimulation.

Another interesting and related fact is provided by Ornitz et al. who, studying the auditory average evoked response (AER), found that in autistic children the amplitude of the N_2 wave during REMP sleep—particularly during actual eye movements—was significantly greater relative to REM than that found in normal children. That is, the usual reduction or inhibition of AER during REMP is not present in autistic children. Rather there is an augmentation of amplitude in REMP over NREMP. Ornitz et al.[73] argue that the normally expected reduction in AER during bursts of REM is independent of peripheral input and is centrally regulated, probably by the vestibular apparatus. Here again, it is not the integrity of sensory input pathways that are in question, but rather the working over of the imput, mediated by feedback processes provided by vestibular functions; for the phasic dampening of response during REM sleep is, in normals, controlled by vestibular nuclei. It is the failure of this dampening process that is apparent in the studies of AER in autistic children during sleep.

While awaiting replication of these findings in improved methodological contexts that would strengthen their verisimilitude, we can venture a formulation that encompasses their apparent diversity. It seems plausible that the defects discovered in schizophrenics by laboratory testing in this series of studies relate to the feedback stage of perception. In this regard Lang and Buss comment on the findings of high muscle tension among schizophrenics: "a number of authors have proposed that this directly accounts for schizophrenic symptoms. Angyal suggested that the disturbances of muscle tension may be the perceptual basis of somatic delusions in schizophrenia . . . Furthermore diffuse neuromuscular activity may contribute to deficit in psychomotor or perceptual tasks by interfering directly with coordinated behavior."[59]

It would seem that the combination of high basal levels of activation and diminished reactivity reflect the psychological concomitants of the statistical facts of Wilder's law of initial values. It reflects an organismic response cut-off via interferences in reperception. Input function would not be affected. Passive attention would not be involved. Response to the already registered stimuli however is involved. Silverman proposes a similar explanation. Noting that cardiac deceleration accompanies alerting by novel and significant stimuli, he links the sympathetic nervous system response with cortical activity in the form of a feedback relationship to the central nervous system and the cardiovascular system. Thus cardiac deceleration permits attention to be focused on the sensory input and away from the cognitive-connotative significance of the stimulus. This situation obtains during periods of stress and during periods of "information overload." "Under extreme stress conditions, hyperresponsiveness to sensory inputs becomes pronounced and attention is focused almost solely on sensory attributes; connotative attributes of stimuli are partially or even completely dissociated from their sensory configuration. Objects and people may then appear as unfamiliar, unreal, unintegrated."[93] These assumptions have plausibility, although they have not yet been tested as an integrated theory of perceptual defect in schizophrenia. The data, however, suggest that more than an attention defect is involved in the perceptual patterns detailed above. This something more would be the dysfunctioning of the perceptual feedback stage, involving proprioceptive and autonomic factors.

In postulating that the perceptual defect in schizophrenia involves the feedback stage and not input or storage, I am neither implicating specific anatomical locations, nor neurological mechanisms, nor am I bypassing motivational considerations. I am, however, pointing to the most plausible site of perceptual aspects of schizophrenic psychopathology, on the basis of available clinical and experimental evidence. There is a congruence between this formulation of perceptual defect involving the feedback phase and MacReynolds' idea that the perceptual defect in schizophrenia occurs in the assimilation of percepts,[62] and also Meehl's postulation of an "integrative neural defect."[69] Meehl believes—and I cannot see anything but heuristic merit in his formulation, particularly in the light of the reports by Rosenbaum and his group—that this defect is responsible for the ubiquitous schizophrenic thought disorder: inadequate integration at the neural synaptic level disrupts the reality attunement of thinking and perceiving, particularly in the context of motivational factors. Meehl's formulation imparts cause to the neural defect. My own preference is not to go beyond the relational network presented here and to seek carefully controlled replications of these studies, with additions suggested in this paper. We could then with greater confidence tag the defective aspect of the perceptual act and go on to trace causal links.

SUMMARY

I have examined the methodological difficulties facing the investigator of the perceptual aspects of psychopathology. After discussing the multivariate nature of perception and the complex nature of psychopathology, I perused the experimental literature on the perceptual aspects of schizophrenia. I tried to show that the purely empirical approach, assuming *a priori* a perceptual deficit and choosing tasks that require response to thing mediators, contributes knowledge about perceptual and cognitive controls in schizophrenia. Studies deduced from the major clinical studies are sparse. The major findings of a group of studies point to defects in the feedback or reperception phase of the perceptual act. These studies should be replicated with careful attention to the methodological requirements outlined.

ACKNOWLEDGMENTS

The author expresses his appreciation to a number of colleagues who offered helpful criticism. Among them are W. Grant Dahlstrom, Paul Thetford, Herbert Spohn, Robert Cancro, Gardner Murphy, and Elmer Green.

REFERENCES

1. Aronson, B. S.: Hypnosis, depth perception and schizophrenia. Paper presented at the Eastern Psychological Association meeting, Philadelphia, Pennsylvania, 1964.

2. Angyal, A. and Blackman, N.: Vestibular reactivity in schizophrenia. Arch. Neurol. Psychiat. 44:611-620, 1940.

3. ——, and Sherman, M. A.: Postural reactions to vestibular stimulation in schizophrenic and normal subjects. Am. J. Psychiat. 98:857-862, 1942.

4. Bleuler, E.: Dementia Praecox or The Group of Schizophrenias. New York, International Universities Press, 1950.

5. Bruch, Hilde: Falsification of bodily needs and body concept in schizophrenia. Arch. Gen. Psychiat. 6:18-24, 1962.

6. ——: Anorexia nervosa and its differential diagnosis. J. Nerv. Ment. Dis. 141:555-566, 1966.

7. Bryant, A. R.: An investigation of process-reactive schizophrenia with relation to perception of visual space. Unpublished doctoral dissertation, University of Utah, 1961.

8. Calloway, E., III, and Dembo, D.: Narrowed attention. Arch. Neurol. Psychiat. 79:74-90, 1958.

9. ——, Jones, R. T. and Layne, R. S.: Evoked responses and segmental set of schizophrenia. Arch. Gen. Psychiat. 12:83-89, 1965.

10. Campbell, D. T. and Fiske, D. W.: Convergent and discriminant validation by the multitrait-multimethod matrix. Psychol. Bull. 56:81-105, 1959.

11. Cancro, R.: A comparison of process and reactive schizophrenia. Unpublished doctoral dissertation, Downstate Medical Center, State University of New York, 1962.

13. Chapman, L. J.: The problem of selecting drug-free schizophrenics for research. J. Consult. Psychol. 27:540-542, 1963.

14. Chase, R. A., Sutton, S. and Rapin, I.: Sensory feedback influences on motor performance. J. Auditory Res. 3:212-223, 1961.

15. Cleveland, S. E.: Judgments of body size in a schizophrenic and normal control group. Psychol. Reports, 7:304, 1960.

16. ——, Fisher, S., Reitman, E. E., Rothaus, P.: Perception of body size in schizophrenia. Arch. Gen. Psychiat., 7:277-285, 1962.

17. Cohen, B. D., Luby, E. D., Rosenbaum, G., and Gottlieb, J. S.: Combined Sernyl and sensory deprivation. Comp. Psychiat., 1:345-348, 1960.

18. ——, Rosenbaum, G., Dobie, Shirley I. and Gottlieb, J. S.: Sensory isolation: hallucinogenic effects of a brief procedure. J. Nerv. & Ment. Disease, 129:486-491, 1959.

19. ——, Rosenbaum, G., Luby, E. D. and Gottlieb, J. S.: Comparison of phencyclidine hydrochloride (Sernyl) with other drugs. Arch. Gen. Psychiat. 6:395-401, 1962.

20. Cohen, J.: The statistical power of abnormal-social psychological research. J. Abnorm. Soc. Psychol. 65:145-153, 1962.

21. Colbert, E. G., Koegler, R. R. and Markham, C. H.: Vestibular dysfunction in childhood schizophrenia. Arch. Gen. Psychiat. 1:600-617, 1959.

22. Cooper, Ruth: Objective measures of perception in schizophrenics and normals. J. Consult. Psychol. 24:209-214, 1960.

23. De Vault, S. H.: Physiological responsiveness in reactive and process schizophrenia. Dissertation Abstracts 17:1387, 1957.

24. Eysenck, H. J.: The Scientific Study of Personality. London, Routledge and Kegan, Paul, 1952.

25. Federn, P.: In: E. Weiss (Ed.): Egopsychology and the Psychoses. New York, Basic Books, 1952.

26. Fiske, D. W.: Why do we use situational performance tests. Personnel Psychol. 7:#4, 464-469, 1954.

27. ——: Effects of monotonous and restricted stimulation. In: Fiske, D. W., and Maddi, S. R. (Eds.): Functions of Varied Experience. Homewood, Illinois, Dorsey Press, 1961.

28. Freeman, G. L.: The Energetics of Human Behavior. Ithaca, Cornell University Press, 1948.

29. Freeman, H. and Rodnick, E. H.: Effect of rotation on postural steadiness in normal and in schizophrenic subjects. Arch. Neurol. Psychiat. 48:47-53, 1942.

30. Freeman, T., Cameron, J. L. and McGhie, A.: Chronic Schizophrenia. New York, International Universities Press, 1958.

31. Freud, S.: The Interpretation of Dreams. In: The Standard Edition of the Complete Psychological Works of Sigmund Freud, Vol. V (first published 1900). London, Hogarth Press, 1953.

32. ——: Project for a Scientific Psychology. In: The Standard Edition of the Complete Psychological Works of Sigmund Freud, Vol. I. London, Hogarth Press, 1967.

33. Funkenstein, D. H., Greenblatt, M., and Solomon, H. C.: Autonomic changes paralleling psychologic changes in mentally ill patients. J. Nerv. Ment. Dis. 114: 1-118, 1951.

34. Gamburg, A. L.: Orienting and defensive reactions in simple and paranoid forms of schizophrenia. In: Voronin, L. G., Leontiev, A. N., Luria, A. R., Sokolov, E. N. & Vinogradova, O. S. (Eds.): Orienting Reflex and Exploratory Behavior. Washington, D.C., American Institute of Biological Science, pp. 351-359, 1965.

35. Gardner, R. W.: Cognitive styles in categorizing behavior. J. Personality 22:214-233, 1953.

36. ——, Holzman, P. S., Klein, G. S., Linton, H. and Spence, D. P.: Cognitive Control. Psychological Issues, No. 4. New York, International Universities Press, 1959.

37. ——, and Moriarty, Alice: Personality Development at Preadolescence: Explorations of Structure Formation. Seattle, University of Washington Press, 1968.

38. Garmezy, N.: Contributions of experimental psychology to understanding

the origins of schizophrenia. In: Romano, J. (Ed.): Origins of Schizophrenia. Amsterdam, Excerpta Medica Foundation, 1967.

39. Gellhorn, E.: Motion and emotion: the role of proprioception in the physiology and pathology of the emotions. Psychol. Rev. 71:457-472, 1964.

40. Graham, Frances K. and Clifton, Rachel K.: Heart-rate change as a component of the orienting response. Psychol. Bull. 65:305-320, 1966.

41. Hall, K. R. L. and Stride, E.: The varying response to pain in psychiatric disorders: study in abnormal psychology. Brit. J. Med Psychol. 27:48-60, 1954.

42. Hardyk, C. D., Petrinovitch, L. F. and Ellsworth, D. W.: Feedback of speech muscle activity during silent reading; rapid extinction. Science 154:1467-1468, 16 December, 1966.

43. Heider, F.: On Perception, Event Structure, and the Psychological Environment. Psychological Issues, Vol. I, No. 3. New York, International Universities Press, 1959.

44. Holmes, C. and Holzman, P. S.: Effect of white noise on disinhibition of verbal expression. Percept. Motor Skills 23:1039-1042, 1966.

45. Holzman, P. S.: The relation of assimilation tendencies in visual, auditory, and kinesthetic time-error to cognitive attitudes of leveling and sharpening. J. Personality 22:375-394, 1954.

46. ———: Scanning; a principle of reality contact. Percept. Motor Skills 23: 835-844, 1966.

47. ——— and Gardner, R. W.: Leveling and repression. J. Abnorm. Soc. Psychol., 59:151-155, 1959.

48. Hoskins, R. G.: The Biology of Schizophrenia. New York, W. W. Norton, 1946.

49. Hunt, J. McV. and Cofer, C.: Psychological deficit. In: Hunt, J. McV. (Ed.): Personality and the Behavior Disorders. New York, Ronald Press, 1944, pp. 971-1032.

50. Johannsen, W. J., Friedman, and Liccione, J. V.: Perception as a function of chronicity in schizophrenia. Amer. Psychol. 18:364-365 (Abstract), 1963.

51. Jung, C. G.: The Psychology of Dementia Praecox. New York, Nervous and Mental Disease Monograph, 1936.

52. Kaplan, A.: A philosophical discussion of normality. Arch. Gen. Psychiat. 17:325-330, 1967.

52a. King, H. E.: Psychomotor aspects of mental disease. Cambridge, Mass., Harvard University Press, 1954.

53. Klein, E. B. and Spohn, H. E.: Further comments on characteristics of untestable chronic schizophrenics. J. Abnorm. Soc. Psychol. 68:355-358, 1964.

54. Klein, G. S.: Need and regulation. In: Jones, M. R. (Ed.): Nebraska Symposium on Motivation. Lincoln, Neb., University of Nebraska Press, 1954, pp. 224-274.

55. ———: Cognitive control and motivation. In: Lindzey, G. (Ed.): Assessment of Human Motives. New York, Rinehart and Co., 1958, pp. 87-118.

56. ———: On hearing one's own voice: an aspect of cognitive control in spoken thought. In: Schur, M. (Ed.): Drives, Affects, Behavior. New York, International Universities Press, 1965.

57. Kohler, I.: The formation and transformation of the perceptual world. Psychol. Issues, Vol. III, No. 4, Monograph 12, 1964.

58. Lacey, J. I.: Psychophysiological approaches to the evaluation of psychotherapeutic process and outcome. In: Rubinstein, E. A. and Parloff, M. B. (Eds.): Research in Psychotherapy. American Psychological Association, 1959, pp. 160-208.

59. Lang, P. J. and Buss, A. H.: Psychological deficit in schizophrenia. II. Interference and activation. J. Abnorm. Psychol. 70: 77-106, 1965.

60. Lhamon, W. T. and Goldstone, S.: The time sense; estimation of one second durations by schizophrenic patients. Arch. Neurol. Psychiat. 76:625-629, 1956.

61. Luria, A. R.: Human Brain and Psychological Processes (trans. B. Haigh). New York, Harper and Row, 1966.

62. MacReynolds, P.: Anxiety, perception and schizophrenia. In: Jackson, D. (Ed.): The Etiology of Schizophrenia. New York, Basic Books, 1960, pp. 248-292.

63. Malmo, R. B. and Shagass, C.: Physiologic studies of reaction to stress in anxiety states and early schizophrenia. Psychosom. Med. 11:9-24, 1949.

64. —— and ——: Studies of blood pressure in psychiatric patients under stress. Psychosom. Med. 14:82-93, 1952.

65. ——, —— and Smith, A. A.: Responsiveness in chronic schizophrenia. J. Personality 19:359-375, 1951.

66. May, P. R. A.: Pupillary abnormalities in schizophrenia and during muscular effort. J. Ment. Science 94:89-98, 1948.

67. Mayman, M. and Voth, H. M.: Reality closeness, phantasy and autokinesis: a dimension of cognitive style. J. Personality Soc. Psychol. (in press, 1968).

68. McFarland, J. H., Werner, H. and Wapner, S.: The effects of muscular involvement on sensitivity: asymmetrical convergence on the distribution of visual sensitivity. Amer. J. Psychol., 73:523-534, 1960.

69. Meehl, P. E.: Psychopathology and Purpose. In: Hoch, P. and Zubin, J. (Eds.): The Future of Psychiatry, Chapter 6. New York, Grune & Stratton, 1962.

70. ——: Schizotaxia, schizotypy, schizophrenia. Amer. Psychol. 17: 823-838, 1962.

71. Orme, J. E.: Time estimation and personality. J. Ment. Sci. 108:213-216, 1962.

72. ——: Time estimation and the nosology of schizophrenia. Brit. J. Psychiat. 112:37-39, 1966.

73. Ornitz, E. M., Ritvo, E. R., Panmaw, L. N., Lee, Y. H., Carr, E. M. and Walter, R. D.: The auditory evoked response in normal and autistic children during sleep. Electroenceph. Clin. Neurophysiol. in press, 1968.

74. Pearl, D. and Berg, P. S.: Time perception and conflict arousal in schizophrenia. J. Abnorm. Soc. Psychol. 66:332-338, 1963.

75. Perky, C. W.: An experimental study of imagination. Amer. J. Psychol. 21:422-452, 1910.

76. Petrie, A.: Individuality in Pain and Suffering. Chicago, University of Chicago Press, 1967.

77. Petursson, E.: Electromyographic studies of muscular tension in psychiatric patients. Compr. Psychiat. 3:29-36, 1962.

78. Rapaport, D.: The theoretical implications of diagnostic testing procedures.

In: Knight, R. P. and Friedman, C. R. (Eds.): Psychoanalytic Psychiatry and Psychology. New York, International Universities Press, 1954, pp. 173-195. Reprinted in Gill, M. M. (Ed.): Collected Papers of David Rapaport. New York, Basic Books, 1967, pp. 334-356.

79. Raush, H. L.: Perceptual constancy in schizophrenia: size constancy. J. Personality 21: 176-187, 1952.

80. ——: Object constancy in schizophrenia: the enhancement of symbolic objects and conceptual stability. J. Abnorm. Soc. Psychol. 52:231-234, 1956.

81. Reynolds, G. A.: Perceptual constancy in schizophrenics and "normals." Dissertation Abstracts, 14:1000-1001, 1954.

82. Rodnick, E. H., and Garmezy, N.: An experimental approach to the study of motivation in schizophrenia. In: Jones, M. R. (Ed.): Nebraska Symposium on Motivation. Lincoln, Neb., University of Nebraska Press, 1957, pp. 109-190.

83. Rosenbaum, G.: Feedback mechanisms in schizophrenia. In Tourney, G., and Gottlieb, J. S. (Eds.): Lafayette Clinic Studies in Schizophrenia. Detroit, Mich., Wayne State University Press, 1968 (in press).

84. ——, Cohen, B. D., Luby, E. D., Gottlieb, J. S., and Yellen, D.: Comparison of Sernyl with other drugs: simulation of schizophrenic performance with Sernyl, LSD-25, and amobarbital (amytal) sodium. I. Attention, motor function and proprioception. Arch. Gen. Psychiat. 1:651-656, 1959.

85. ——, Dobie, Shirley, I., and Cohen, B. D.: Visual recognition thresholds following sensory deprivation. Amer. J. Psychol. 72:429-433, 1959.

86. Schafer, R., and Murphy, G.: The role of autism in a visual figure-ground relationship. J. Exp. Psychol. 32:335-343, 1943.

87. Schlesinger, H. J.: Cognitive attitudes in relation to susceptibility to interference. J. Personality 22:354-374, 1954.

88. Schooler, C., and Feldman, S. E.: Experimental Studies of Schizophrenia. Goleta, Calif., Psychonomic Press, 1967.

89. Shagass, C., and Schwartz, M.: Reactivity cycle of somatosensory cortex in humans with and without psychiatric disorder. Science 134:1757-1759, 1961.

90. ——, and ——: Cerebral responsiveness in psychiatric patients. Arch. Gen. Psychiat. 8:177-189, 1963.

91. Shakow, D.: Psychological deficit in schizophrenia. Behav. Sci. 8:275-305, 1963.

92. Silverman, J.: Scanning-control mechanism and "cognitive filtering" in paranoid and nonparanoid schizophrenia. J. Consult. Psychol. 28:385-393, 1964.

93. ——: Variations in cognitive control and psychophysiological defense in the schizophrenias. Psychosom. Med. 29:225-251, 1967.

94. Sutton, S., and Zubin, J.: Effect of sequence on reaction time in schizophrenia. In: Welford, A. T., and Birren, J. E. (Eds.): Behavior, Aging and the Nervous System. Springfield, Ill., Charles C Thomas, 1965.

95. Teuber, H. L.: Space perception and its disturbance after brain injury in man, Neuropsychologia 1:47-57, 1963.

96. Traub, A. C., Olson, R., Orbach, J., Cardone, S.S.: Psychophysical studies of body-image, III. Initial studies of disturbance in a chronic schizophrenic group. Arch. Gen. Psychiat. 17:664-670, 1967.

97. Valins, S.: Cognitive effects of false heart-rate feedback. J. Personality Soc. Psychol. 4:400-408, 1966.

98. Vandenberg, S. G.: Behavioral methods for assessing neuroses and psychoses. In: Uhr, L., and Miller, J. G. (Eds.) : Drugs and Behavior. New York, Wiley, 1960.

99. Venables, P. H., and Wing, J. K.: Level of arousal and the subclassification of schizophrenia. Arch. Gen. Psychiat. 7:114-119, 1962.

100. Voth, H. M.: Choice of illness. Arch. Gen. Psychiat. 6:149-156, 1962.

101. ——, and Mayman, M.: Diagnostic and treatment implications of ego closeness-ego distance: autokinesis as a diagnostic instrument. Compr., Psychiat. 8:203-216, 1967.

102. Warm, J. S., Morris, J. R., and Kew, J. K.: Temporal judgment as a function of nosological classification and experimental method. J. Psychol. 55:287-297, 1963.

103. Weckowicz, T. E.: Size constancy in schizophrenic patients. J. Ment. Sci. 103:475-486, 1957.

104. ——: Shape constancy in schizophrenic patients. J. Abnorm. Soc. Psychol. 68:177-183, 1964.

105. ——, and Sommer, R.: Body image and self-concept in schizophrenia. J. Ment. Sci. 106: 17-39, 1960.

106. ——, Sommer, R., and Hall, R.: Distance constancy in schizophrenic patients. J. Ment. Sci. 104:1174-1182, 1958.

107. Werner, H.: Comparative Psychology of Mental Development. New York, Harper, 1940.

108. Wilder, J.: Modern psychophysiology and the law of initial value. Amer. J. Psychotherapy 12:199-221, 1958.

109. Witkin, H. A.: Psychological differentiation and forms of pathology. J. Abnorm. Psychol. 70:317-336, 1965.

110: ——: Studies in psychological differentiation. Progress Report, NIMH Grant MH 00628, 1967.

111. ——: Lewis, H. B., Hertzman, M., Machover, K., Meissner, P. B., and Wapner, S.: Personality Through Perception. New York, Harper, 1954.

Discussion of Dr. Holzman's Paper

by CHARLES SHAGASS, M.D.

Temple University Medical Center

DR. HOLZMAN has given us a scholarly exposition of the perceptual aspects of psychopathology. He has covered a large and difficult field in a thorough and incisive manner and, in the process, has made it hard for his discussant to add to what he has said or to disagree with him. This is particularly true of the first part of his paper, which is devoted to an outline of methodologic problems.

Dr. Holzman's emphasis on the fact that drives, motives and intentions do not usually over-ride the reality attunement of the perceptual act seems very important to me. We often confuse the factors which modulate perception with changed perception, whereas in general the perceptual apparatus fulfills its function of keeping the person in touch with the world.

In discussing the empirical approach to perception–psychopathology relationships, Holzman argues persuasively that the available evidence on schizophrenic subjects adds up to deviance, but not to deficiency. If I understand his argument correctly, it may be reduced to the idea that among people who develop schizophrenia there is an over-representation of the extremes in styles of cognitive control and that these styles antedate the development of illness. I am reminded of Albee and Lane's findings that, in grade school, future schizophrenic patients had lower IQ scores than their peers who were not destined for schizophrenic breakdown.[1] Although intelligence tests are not perceptual tests, the many factors that affect perceptual functioning are also capable of influencing performance on tests of cognitive ability. The lower IQs of future schizophrenic patients may reflect difficulties in learning under usual conditions in children with deviant cognitive styles.

In discussing the various approaches to study of the perceptual aspects of schizophrenia, Dr. Holzman concludes that the deductive literature is quite bare, with conflicting results being the rule rather than the exception. He suggests that there is mounting evidence to implicate

Research supported (in part) by Grant MH12507 from the National Institute of Mental Health, U.S.P.H.S.

the feedback–reperception stage more than other aspects of the perceptual act, particularly in schizophrenia. He draws upon evidence of high basal arousal state, as reflected in increased muscle tone and elevated systolic blood pressure level, and sees this as the background leading to reduced or paradoxical reactions to specific stimuli in schizophrenic patients. The argument is supported by evidence that increasing the contrast between a stimulus and its background improves performance in schizophrenics. The interpretation of attention defects in schizophrenia as resulting from faulty restraining internal modulating processes is also in accord with it.

Dr. Holzman's emphasis on the feedback–reperception stage in schizophrenia appears merited on the basis of the evidence cited by him. This emphasis is not incompatible with the one that I favor—namely, that schizophrenia involves altered functioning of one or more central regulatory mechanisms that control the inter-relationships of various

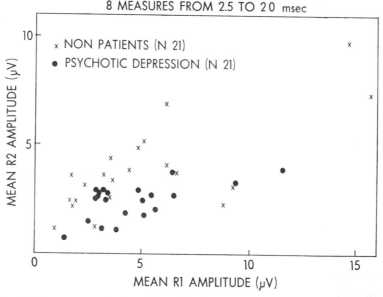

SOMATO SENSORY RECOVERY-PEAK 4

8 MEASURES FROM 2.5 TO 20 msec

FIG 1.—Scattergram showing relationship between mean amplitudes of first (R1) and second R2) response to paired median nerve stimuli over 8 interstimulus intervals from 2.5 to 20 msec. Measurements were from base line to peak 4, first positive peak after each stimulus. Note that nonpatients generally had greater R2 values for any given R1 amplitude than depressive patients.

brain functions. One example of altered relationships of this kind comes from the work of Claridge[2] and of Krishnamoorti in my laboratory[4] on the relationship between the amobarbital sedation threshold and the duration of the Archimedes spiral after-image. We verified Claridge's finding that these two measures are positively intercorrelated in non-psychotic subjects. However, we found that the relation tended to be negative in schizophrenic patients, and Claridge later confirmed and extended this finding. Furthermore, Claridge was able to show that, with remission of symptoms, the correlation tended to become positive. This kind of finding not only suggests disordered operation of some regulator, but is also a nice example of pathology being associated with a different relationship between two functions rather than with consistent deviance in one or the other.

A different kind of example comes from our work with cortical evoked potentials. We have found our most consistent differences in the recovery functions, which essentially involve measuring the interactions between two stimuli separated by varying time intervals. Figure 1 illustrates this for somatosensory evoked response data from 21 patients with psychotic depressions and an equal number of controls of the same age and sex. For the group as a whole, there was a high correlation between the mean amplitudes of response to the first and second of paired stimuli administered over eight interstimulus intervals from 2.5 to 20 msec. However, the slope of the regression was considerably steeper for the control subjects than for the patients, so that for any given R1 value, the R2 tended to be greater amongst the controls. This finding is different from the one relating the sedation threshold to Archimedes spiral in that the interaction is within the same responding system. We can offer a few suggestions as to possible mechanisms for the recovery differences, since we know that experimental alteration of functioning in such regulatory systems as the mesencephalic reticular formation or septal region can produce marked changes in recovery.[5] The relationship between two responses evoked in rapid succession thus differs in psychosis, and this shift may be experimentally produced by stimulating certain subcortical areas.

In my own presentation at this meeting, I have mentioned that we are paying much attention to the interrelationships between EEG and evoked response variables. We already have rather exciting data indicating that, in normal subjects, the nature of these electrophysiological relationships differs with respect to perceptual discriminative performance.

Data are also available from the work of Fedio et al.[3] to indicate that reaction time responding bears a different relationship to the state of electrocortical activity in schizophrenia than in normals. These investigators demonstrated that, in normals, when the alerting stimulus caused alpha blocking, quicker reaction times followed an imperative stimulus. In contrast, although schizophrenic patients blocked no less than the normals, their EEG changes were not accompanied by faster reaction times.

Finally, I should like to draw attention again to Dr. Ervin's demonstration that amazingly great behavioral changes can be produced by small brain lesions. This suggests the possibility that psychopathology may reflect relatively small shifts in the total complex of central regulatory activities.

The evidence that I have cited suggests to me that our useful indicators will come at least in pairs. It may be that one member of the pair should be physiological, since my examples go that way. With respect to schizophrenia, Bleuler told us that these were a unique group of disorders. One implication of his definition is that the organization of functions along various dimensions should be very different in the schizophrenias. We seem to have been too interested in finding single deviant dimensions to pay enough attention to the possibilities of deviant interrelationships. Dr. Holzman has ably made the point that perception by itself may not be altered in schizophrenia, but that the interplay between perceptual and other kinds of functioning may be markedly altered. It is to be hoped that future experimentation will reflect this conception.

REFERENCES

1. Albee, C. W., Lane, E. A., and Reuter, J. M.: Childhood intelligence of the future schizophrenics and neighborhood peers. J. Psychol. 58:141-144, 1964.

2. Claridge, G. S.: Personality and Arousal. A. A Psychophysiological Study of Psychiatric Disorder. London, Pergamon Press, 1967.

3. Fedio, P., Mirsky, A. F., Smith, W. J., and Parry, D.: Reaction time and EEG activation in normal and schizophrenic subjects. Electroenceph. Clin. Neurophysiol. 13:923-926, 1961.

4. Krishnamoorti, S., and Shagass, C.: Some psychological test correlates of sedation threshold. In: Wortis, J. (Ed.): Recent Advances in Biological Psychiatry, Vol. VI. New York, Plenum Press, 1964, pp. 256-266.

5. Schwartz, M., and Shagass, C.: Reticular modification of somatosensory cortical recovery function. Electroenceph. Clin. Neurophysiol. 15:265-271, 1963.

9

ALTERATIONS IN STATES OF CONSCIOUSNESS ASSOCIATED WITH CHRONIC INGESTION OF ALCOHOL

by NANCY K. MELLO, Ph.D. and JACK H. MENDELSON, M.D.*

ALCOHOL is used almost universally to induce changes in states of consciousness, and the behavioral correlates of alcohol intoxication have been well documented in the literature and art of every culture. The effects of alcohol are varied and complex, and even the most casual observer of drinking behavior can construct a dose-response gradient ranging from mild euphoria to maudlin reminiscence; expansive *camaraderie* to belligerence or withdrawal; articulate speech to slurring; release of motor tension to staggering gait and eventual immobile semistupor. These behavioral polarities are consistent with the pharmacological concept of alcohol as a drug with a biphasic effect both at a neurocellular and behavioral level.[22] Alcohol acts as a stimulant at low doses and a depressant only at higher doses.[61,51] Alcohol is usually categorized with the central nervous system depressants—i.e., the general anesthesias, sedatives, hypnotics, analgesics and tranquilizers.[74] However, little is known of the pharmacological mechanism of action of alcohol.[61]

The alcohol addict differs from the moderate or heavy drinker in that either the presence *or* the abrupt removal of alcohol can produce dramatic alterations in behavior and perception. The alcohol withdrawal syndrome is one of the major pharmacological criteria of addiction—i.e., dependence upon alcohol. The critical determinants in the development of alcohol addiction are unknown; beyond the obvious requirement of ingestion of sufficient quantities of alcohol over a long enough period of time, the nature of the addictive process remains a matter of conjecture.

*National Center for the Prevention and Control of Alcoholism, National Institute of Mental Health.

The differences in the effects of alcohol on the moderate or heavy drinker and the alcohol addict during inebriation are considerable, and have only recently been subject to systematic study.[55] Some of the behavioral differences observed reflect the phenomenon of *tolerance* for alcohol, which is the second major pharmacological criterion of addiction.

This paper will focus upon a description of the effects of experimentally induced intoxication and withdrawal in the alcohol addict. These observations have been drawn from studies in which alcoholics were given alcohol in programmed dosage or on a free choice basis for periods of 7 to 30 days in a clinical research ward setting.[52,55,58,60,63,65] A review of the relevant clinical research on alcoholic patients will also be included.

BEHAVIORAL AND BIOLOGICAL CORRELATES OF INEBRIATION

Tolerance

a) Behavioral tolerance. The fact that more alcohol is required to produce the same behavioral effect in the alcohol addict than in the heavy drinker, and that prolonged drinking may produce qualitatively as well as quantitatively different effects in the alcohol addict are two aspects of the behavioral indices of tolerance. One of the earliest studies of behavioral tolerance for alcohol involved a comparison of alcoholic and nonalcoholic subjects given equivalent doses of alcohol and rated by observers on a global scale of intoxication.[35] It was found that the percentage of alcoholics rated as "intoxicated" according to these criteria was dramatically lower than the percentage of normal drinkers that were rated as intoxicated.

One of the first comprehensive series of studies comparing the effects of alcohol on performance in alcoholics and nonalcoholics were performed by Goldberg in 1943.[20] Evidence for behavioral tolerance in alcoholics obtained in these studies has been confirmed in several laboratories. Most recently, Talland and his associates have examined the effects of a period of sustained inebriation on tasks involving attention and motor skills in chronic alcoholics.[82,83,84] Simple manual dexterity tasks were virtually unaffected by blood alcohol levels as high as 200 mg./100 ml.[82] Similarly, on vigilance and reaction tasks in which an alcoholic subject was required to respond by pressing a button whenever he detected the occurrence of a visual[83] or an auditory signal,[15] no significant decrement in performance occurred despite blood alcohol levels approaching 200 mg./100 ml. Even in a complex attention task in which subjects were required to identify sequences of 3 consecutive odd or 3 consecutive even numbers, acute doses of alcohol ranging between 0.5 and 1.0 grams per kilograms produced no serious disruption of performance.[84] Data illustrating behavioral tolerance for alcohol in an alcoholic subject during chronic alcohol intoxication are shown in Fig. 1.

Although our laboratory program has focused upon the assessment of drinking patterns of chronic alcoholics rather than the effects of alcohol on any specified index of behavior, our impressionistic observations of

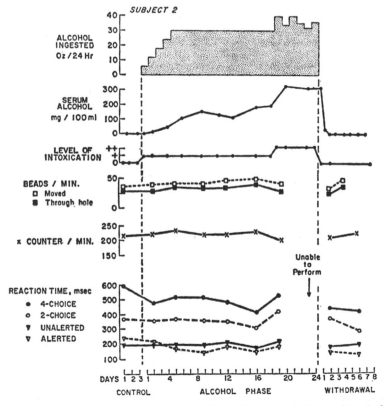

FIG. 1.—Performance scores of an alcoholic subject in relation to his alcohol ingestion and intoxication levels. "Alcohol ingested" equals ounces of 86-proof whiskey ingested per 24 hours. (From Talland, G. A. et al.[82])

approximately 30 alcoholic subjects during periods of experimental intoxication ranging between 7 and 30 days have been consistent with the notion of a global behavioral tolerance for alcohol.[52,83,63,65] Our subjects

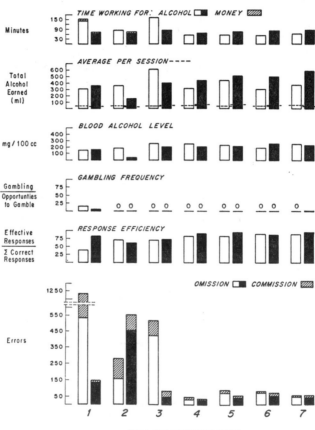

FIG. 2.—Behavioral data are presented for an individual subject. The time spent each day working for alcohol or money is shown in the first row. In the second row, the total amount of alcohol earned is shown for each experimental day. The average amount earned per session was computed by dividing the total amount of alcohol earned by the total number of glass removals during that period. Blood alcohol levels were assessed by a breathalyzer instrument. Gambling frequency, response efficiency and the types of errors made are indicated in the last three rows. (From Mello et al.[52])

have shown surprisingly little disruption of verbal, motor or social behavior despite sustained blood alcohol levels ranging between 150 and 300 mg./100 ml. For the most part, the usual signs of intoxication and/or gross inebriation have been minimal. Specifically, in a study in which alcoholic subjects were required to make a specified number of consecutive correct responses on a simple visual vigilance task in order to obtain alcohol, response efficiency was not correlated with blood alcohol levels. Moreover, response efficiency tended to improve in 9 of the 14 subjects studied during the course of the experiment. Errors were defined as a failure to respond when a light appeared on a response key, or a response when no light was present. Either type of error resulted in the loss of all previously accumulated points towards alcohol reinforcement. There was considerable variability in error rate between subjects. However, the error rate appeared to be unrelated to the blood alcohol levels and most subjects made fewer errors as the experiment progressed. This general trend is illustrated by Fig. 2.[52]

Data shown in Figs. 1 and 2 clearly demonstrate that the classical pharmacology textbook descriptions of the behavioral effects associated with blood alcohol levels of 100, 200, 300 and 400 mg./100 ml are valid only for the *non*alcoholic individual.

Consistent with the pharmacological definition of tolerance, the alcohol addict requires progressively more alcohol to produce either an objective behavioral impairment or a subjective effect. Examples of tolerance as reflected by low blood alcohol values during a period of sustained high alcohol intake are shown in Figs. 3 and 4. We have observed that subjects often try to avoid eating while maintaining a consistent pattern of alcohol consumption, and report that this is a deliberate effort to obtain more effect from the alcohol.[63] An illustration of the effect produced on blood alcohol levels by not eating is shown in Figure 3. On day 16, this subject announced that he wanted to "get high" so he would "cut down" his food intake. He spent considerably more time sleeping and lost about 3 pounds over the next two days. There was a concomitant dramatic elevation in his blood alcohol levels as compared with days 10 through 13 when he was consuming more alcohol but eating normally. By day 20, the staff successfully encouraged the subject to resume eating large quantities of food. Subsequently, the subject showed mild tremulousness and by day 21 had developed withdrawal signs of tremulousness, profuse perspiration and general irritability despite an average blood alcohol level of 120

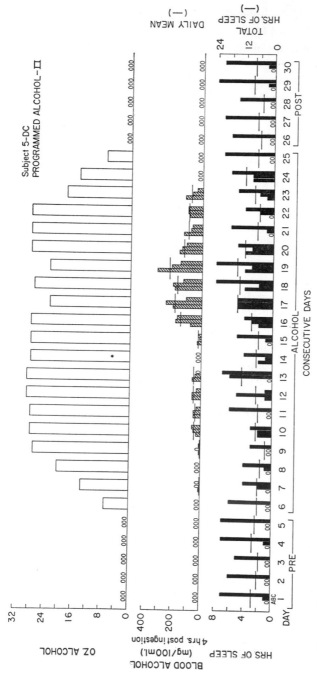

Fig. 3.—Programmed alcohol intake, blood alcohol levels as assessed by a breathalyzer instrument, and total hours of sleep each day are shown for a single subject over a twenty-day period of experimentally induced intoxication. Alcohol (86-proof bourbon) was administered in divided doses, once every four hours, around the clock. A, B and C indicate successive eight-hour periods, beginning at 8 a.m., 4 p.m., and 12 midnight. Breathalyzer readings were taken two hours following alcohol administration. The * on day 14 indicates a dilution of the alcohol, which accounts for the low blood alcohol levels observed. (From Mendelson, J. H., and Mello, N. K.[63])

mg./100 ml. These data show that a relative drop in blood alcohol level may precipitate withdrawal signs.

The occurrence of gastritis in subjects who continue to drink also correlates with relatively high blood alcohol levels. Fig. 4 shows that despite a sustained high alcohol intake, serum alcohol values were relatively low except for those periods when the subject was suffering from gastritis. There was a striking concordance between serum alcohol values and subjective ratings of intoxication made by the nursing staff. Also tremulousness was associated with the *falling* phase of each gastritis-related blood alcohol elevation.

b) *Metabolic aspects of tolerance.* The several indications of behavioral tolerance are consistent with the relatively low blood alcohol levels usually observed in alcoholics even when they are ingesting up to

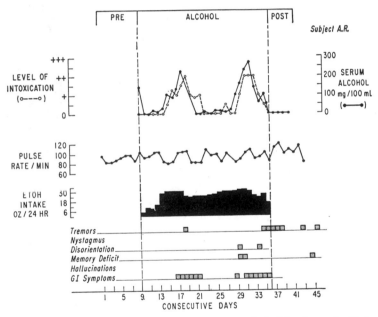

FIG. 4.—Blood alcohol levels, intoxication ratings, alcohol intake and withdrawal signs are presented for a single alcoholic subject maintained on programmed alcohol intake averaging approximately one fifth per day for 27 consecutive days. Alcohol (86-proof bourbon) was given in divided dosage every 4 hours day and night. Peak blood alcohol values and subjective assessment of increased levels of intoxication occurred when this subject developed GI symptoms (gastritis). At these times, food intake decreased markedly, but ethanol ingestion remained relatively constant.

30 ounces of whiskey per day.[55] Consequently, it is tempting to postulate that tolerance could be accounted for by differences in the rate of alcohol metabolism between alcohol addicts and heavy drinkers. However, the available data argue strongly against such an explanation. It has been found in studies of the metabolism of ^{14}C-labeled ethanol that, although administration of alcohol per se induces an increased rate of alcohol metabolism in *both* normal and alcoholic subjects, the overall rate of metabolism does *not* differentiate the two groups.[58,62] These data are shown in Figs. 5 and 6.

Although the mechanisms of physiological adaptation subserving tolerance are unknown, these data suggest that the adaptive processes may occur in the central nervous system rather than at a metabolic level. In this connection, it is of interest that although some as yet unspecified change in central nervous system processes may underlie the phenomenon of addiction, alcohol is not metabolized by brain.[92] Equally perplexing is the mechanism of cross tolerance. Alcohol addicts require relatively large doses of barbiturates in order to produce surgical levels of anesthesia.[6,42] Moreover, alcoholics show tolerance for many toxic alcohols and are able to ingest these in quantities that would be fatal for nonalcoholics.[54] Since alcoholics show cross tolerance to many other CNS depressants which involve diverse metabolic pathways, this

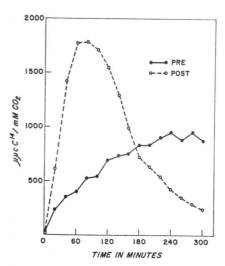

FIG. 5.—Specific activity (U.U.C. [14]C[M]NCO₂) as a function of time following IV administration of ^{14}C ethanol. (From Mendelson, J. H. et al.[58])

phenomenon further suggests that the adaptive processes subserving addiction occur in the central nervous system.

Dissociative Phenomena

Two types of dissociative reactions are commonly reported to occur in
alcoholics during periods of inebriation. The more dramatic dissociative
reaction is the "blackout," in which the patient professes total amnesia
for a series of events which culminate in "finding himself" in an unexpected or unfamiliar situation. Information concerning this type of
dissociative phenomenon is based totally upon retrospective reports obtained during periods of relative sobriety. Frequently these dissociative
reactions are not accompaniments of unacceptable behavior, although
the occurrence of the "blackout" is described as frightening experience

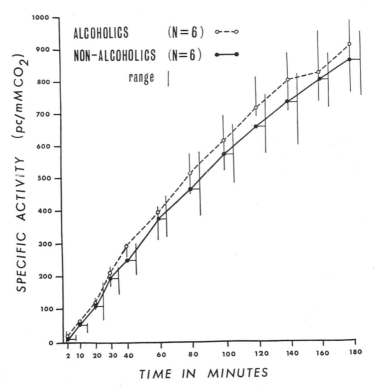

FIG. 6.—Output of $^{14}CO_2$ following 1-^{14}C-labeled ethanol intake by alcoholic and
nonalcoholic subjects. (From Mendelson, J. H.[62])

for the subject. Dissociative reactions to innocuous events have never been observed in our experimental studies of chronic inebriation in approximately 58 alcoholic subjects. In the case of more unacceptable and threatening situations, it is impossible to adequately differentiate between intentional denial and genuine dissociation in a clinical interview.

A second variant of dissociative reaction, often observed, is the alcoholic's tendency to present information about emotionally important experiences while inebriated, which he may not recall or may refuse to discuss during sobriety.[14,49,50] In those situations where a good working relationship has been established with the therapist, it would appear that this behavior is best described as dissociative rather than as deliberate evasiveness.

The role of alcohol in facilitating the occurrence of such dissociative reactions has not been examined experimentally. Simplistic (and unverified) notions about alcoholics "drinking to achieve oblivion" have almost certainly impeded formulation of testable hypotheses. If dissociative reactions are conceptualized in an information processing network (input–integration–output) as West[94] has proposed, the inaccessibility of affect-associated material during sobriety may reflect an inability to *integrate* stored information with current reactions. The "blackout" would reflect a dissociation of *output* insofar as the behavioral response is minimally controlled by and subsequently inaccessible to conscious awareness. Such a formulation has the advantage of emphasizing a difference between the two dissociative reactions without the implication of a gradient of relative severity. Whether persons prone to "forget" material revealed during inebriation are more likely to experience "blackouts" or the converse is unknown.

The mystical aura which has long overshadowed objective analysis of dissociative reactions may be dispersed in part by the recent experimental demonstrations of "drug dissociation" or "state-dependent learning" in animals. If the conditions that determine the occurrence of "drug dissociation" could be defined and manipulated, then clarification of the basic mechanisms involved in dissociative phenomena could proceed more rapidly. Experimental "drug dissociation" is based on the findings that 1) a drug can acquire discriminative properties and gain stimulus control over behavior; and 2) performance on a discrimination task may be impaired when there is a change from nondrug to drug state, from drug to nondrug state, and from one drug state to another drug state.[69] Overton[70] has recently reviewed the literature on "state-dependent learning" in man and animals. Although the phenomenon has been repeatedly demonstrated in animals, the few studies of man are equivocal, and more research is required to establish the experimental validity of this phenomenon in man and to determine the drugs, doses and conditions under which it occurs.

Sleep-Wakefulness Patterns

There has been little systematic study of the effects of alcohol on sleep patterns during a prolonged drinking spree. Perhaps because alcohol is categorized as a central nervous system depressant, it has often been assumed that large doses of alcohol facilitate sleep. However, the disruptive effect of alcohol on sleep patterns was observed even before 200 A.D. by Galen, who commented:

When people are comatose they stagger and are heavy in the head and even when force is applied they are unable to raise their eyelids; and owing to this heaviness they cannot sleep, being restless, turning from side to side and throwing themselves about and changing from one posture to another. We often see these things happen in drunken people when their head is full of drink; the heaviness leads to a coma and at the same time prevents sleep. (Leibowitz,[43] p. 84).

Studies of sleep patterns in *non*alcoholic individuals suggest that alcohol has a direct suppressive effect on Stage 1 REM activity. It has been consistently observed that alcohol tends to decrease the length of REM periods although the number of periods remains unaltered.[23,99,100] These effects were observed in normal subjects given doses of alcohol that yielded blood alcohol levels of between 100 mg./100 ml. and 50 to 60 mg./100 ml. Barbiturates and certain tranquilizers also produce suppression of Stage 1 REM activity.[68,40]

Our phenomenological observations of alcoholic subjects during periods of sustained inebriation suggest that chronic alcohol ingestion produces *fragmentation* of sleep patterns. Our data illustrate the importance of distinguishing between *insomnia* or lack of sleep and *fragmentation* or multiple episodes of sleep. Although some subjects tend to sleep less during a drinking episode, many subjects sleep more, and it is the sporadic quality of their sleeping, rather than sleeplessness, that appears to characterize an alcoholic's sleep pattern during inebriation and withdrawal.[63,64]

Twenty-four hour observations of sleep behavior have been obtained

A

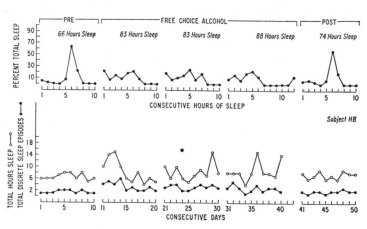

B

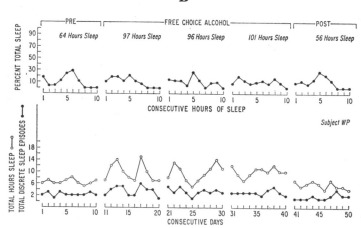

FIG. 7A & B.—Sleep patterns during a 10-day baseline period, a 30-day free choice drinking period and a 10-day withdrawal period are presented for individual subjects. Subjects were allowed to determine the volume and frequency of their alcohol intake by working at a simple operant task. **A:** Percentage of total sleep time accounted for by consecutive hours of sleep (blocks of 1 to 10 hours). The distributions of consecutive hours of sleep are shown for each successive ten-day period. **B:** Total hours of sleep per day and the total number of discrete sleep episodes (irrespective of length) per day. * indicate periods of at least 16 consecutive hours of abstinence.

on 12 alcoholic subjects over a twenty- to thirty-day period of free choice drinking. In each study, subjects were given an opportunity to obtain 43 per cent beverage alcohol (bourbon) without constraints as to the time of consumption or the amount consumed at any time. Data are presented for two subjects who worked for alcohol on a simple operant task over a 30-day period (period marked Free Choice Alcohol in Fig. 7A and 7B). Subjects earned one poker chip for every 1000 presses on a button attached to a small portable box that concealed a counter. Each chip was worth 30 ml. of alcohol. Alcohol was directly dispensed from an automatic apparatus. If subjects worked at a sustained high rate, they could earn one chip in about 10 minutes. The total number of chips earned during the preceding 24 hour period was dispensed once each day at 8:00 a.m. Observations were made of the subject's sleep status once every hour around the clock. The nursing staff judged whether or not a subject was sleeping most of an hour.

During the 30-day drinking period, subject HB drank between 20 and 40 ounces of bourbon daily and maintained blood alcohol levels ranging between 100 and 300 mg./100 ml. Subject WP's blood alcohol levels ranged between 150 and 250 mg./100 ml. and he drank an average of 20 ounces of bourbon per day.

Examples of the tendency towards fragmentation of sleep during chronic inebriation are shown in Figs. 7A and 7B. Sleep patterns are presented for individual subjects during a predrinking, drinking and withdrawal phase of 10, 30 and 10 days respectively. The top row of each figure shows the percentage of the total hours of sleep during each successive 10-day period that is accounted for by the number of consecutive hours of sleep in the range of 1 to 10 hours. During the predrinking phase, there is a peak at 6 consecutive hours of sleep for each subject and a secondary peak at one hour for subject WP. These data indicate that each subject usually slept about 6 consecutive hours each night with occasional brief naps.

During the first 10 days of the drinking period, the distribution of consecutive hours of sleep shifted from a predominant peak at 6 hours to a relatively constant distribution of percent total sleep over 1- to 6-hour blocks. These data indicate sleep fragmentation—i.e., subjects tended to sleep for short discrete periods of time. The percentage of total time spent sleeping in 1-, 2-, 3- and 4-hour blocks combined accounted for more of each subject's total sleep time than the 6 hour block, which had been predominant in the normal sleep pattern. Fragmentation of sleep relative to the baseline period persisted, with some variability, through the last 20 days of the drinking period. However, during the 10-day post-drinking period, each subject's sleep pattern returned to normal with a single predominant peak at 5 or 6 hours. Neither subject showed withdrawal signs and symptoms upon cessation of drinking. Sleep patterns during alcohol withdrawal will be discussed in a later section.

The lower portions of Figs. 7A and 7B show the total hours of sleep each day for the same subjects during the baseline, alcohol intoxication and withdrawal periods. Also shown are the number of discrete sleep episodes each day, irrespective of length. These data indicate that during the baseline period both subjects slept about the same number of hours each day and their total sleep occurred in two or three discrete episodes. During the 30-day drinking period there was considerably more variability in total hours of sleep; however, each subject tended to sleep somewhat more than during the baseline period. The overall increase in the total number of discrete sleep episodes per day is a second index of sleep fragmentation during chronic inebriation.

The implications of a disrupted sleep pattern for other behavioral and affective changes usually associated with sustained inebriation in alcoholics are a matter for speculation. It has been consistently observed that alcohol produces increases in anxiety and depression in the alcoholic as contrasted to the nonalcoholic individual.[55,50,51] The affective discomfort reported by these alcoholic subjects during chronic intoxication is strikingly similar to that reported by subjects deprived of Stage 1 REM activity.[13] It is not known whether alcohol-induced sleep *fragmentation* is associated with changes in overall Stage 1 REM activity.

BEHAVIORAL AND BIOLOGICAL CORRELATES OF ALCOHOL WITHDRAWAL

Concept of Dependence

The occurrence of withdrawal signs and symptoms upon cessation of drinking are evidence of physiological dependence. Dependence is the second major pharmacological criterion of alcohol addiction. At one time it was thought that the withdrawal syndrome reflected intercurrent illness or vitamin and nutritional deficiency rather than the effects of cessation of drinking. This interpretation of withdrawal phenomena was challenged by the clinical observations of Victor and Adams[89] and the studies of Isbell et al.[29] Subsequently, it was demonstrated experimentally that withdrawal signs and symptoms occur in alcoholics as a function of cessation of drinking and cannot be accounted for by associated nutritional deficiencies.[55] The critical determinants of the *onset* of withdrawal symptoms are unclear, since either a relative decrease in blood alcohol levels or abrupt alcohol abstinence may precipitate this syndrome. Abstinence signs have been observed in subjects with blood alcohol levels as high as 100 mg./100 ml.[29,63] Withdrawal onset does not appear to be related to the dosage or duration of a drinking period, since we have observed partial withdrawal signs in subjects who have been drinking small amounts of alcohol for as little as four days.[63]

Critical determinants of the *severity* and *duration* of withdrawal symptoms are also unknown and do not appear to be directly related to either the volume of alcohol consumed or the duration of a drinking spree. The deleterious effects of intercurrent illness and poor nutritional status are well known.[88] However, subtle environmental contingencies may also contribute to the overall clinical picture. There have been recurrent anecdotal reports that alcoholics admitted to hospitals where a humane and high standard of medical care prevails show considerably

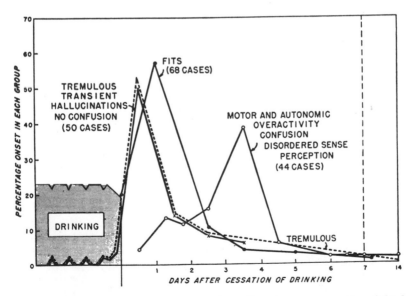

FIG. 8.—Relation of onset of acute neurologic disturbances to cessation of drinking. (From Victor, M., and Adams, R. D.[89])

less severe withdrawal symptoms than their counterparts in less desirable situations. The importance of environmental factors in facilitating the expression of withdrawal signs has been experimentally demonstrated in morphine-addicted rats by Wikler.[97]

The changes in levels of consciousness associated with cessation of drinking may vary widely from increased degrees of somnolence to profound insomnia and heightened responsiveness to environmental stimuli. The most commonly occurring constellation of withdrawal signs and symptoms consist of tremulousness, hyperhydrosis, hallucinosis, confusion and disorientation, seizures, autonomic dysfunction and a variety of disturbances of sleep, appetitive function, perception and thinking. The variability of the withdrawal syndrome has been emphasized by Victor.[88] A summary illustration of the variable time course and probable symptom constellations in alcohol withdrawal is presented in Fig. 8.

It should be emphasized that tremulousness and intermittent hallucinosis, which are relatively common withdrawal phenomena, are not equivalent to the severe and potentially lethal withdrawal state defin-

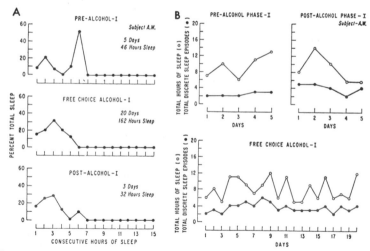

FIG. 9.—**A:** The percentage of total sleep time accounted for by consecutive hours of sleep (blocks of 1-15 hours) for an individual subject. The distribution of consecutive hours of sleep are shown for the predrinking period, the drinking period and the withdrawal period. **B:** The total hours of sleep per day and the total number of discrete sleep episodes (irrespective of length) per day are shown for a single subject for the last five days of the pre-drinking phase, the drinking phase (20 days) and the withdrawal period.

ed as delirium tremens. Delirium tremens are characterized by a triad of severe psychomotor agitation, confusion and disorientation and autonomic and metabolic dysfunction. Hallucinosis may or may not be associated with these signs and symptoms. A detailed description of the clinical manifestations of alcohol withdrawal will not be presented, since it would be difficult to improve upon or extend the comprehensive and detailed picture presented by Victor and Adams.[89] Rather this section will focus upon recent observations of withdrawal following experimentally induced chronic inebriation. Withdrawal-associated alterations in sleep patterns and concomitant metabolic changes will be described.

Sleep-Wakefulness Patterns

Most clinical descriptions of the effects of alcohol abstinence on sleep—wakefulness behavior have emphasized the occurrence of insomnia as a concomitant of the withdrawal state. Our data have shown that fragmentation of sleep rather than insomnia per se is the predominant sleep pattern during withdrawal.[63] We have rarely observed a decrease in total hours of sleep as compared with a subject's prealcohol baseline pattern. Moreover, many subjects sleep more during the early phases of withdrawal than during the immediately preceding period of experimentally induced intoxication.

These trends are illustrated in Figs. 9A and 9B, which present 24-hour observations of sleep patterns obtained on a single subject before, during and after a free-choice drinking period. This subject was given 32 chips each morning for 20 days and was allowed to spend these chips at any time. Each chip would buy 30 ml. of alcohol from an automatic dispensing machine. Subject AW drank between 24 and 38 ounces of bourbon each day and his blood alcohol levels ranged between 100 and 300 mg./100 ml.

The distribution of consecutive hours of sleep during the baseline, drinking and withdrawal period is shown in Fig. 9A. During the baseline period, this subject tended to sleep about 6 hours each night with an occasional two-hour nap. The total hours spent in sleep during the drinking period was somewhat variable. There was a sustained increase in the total number of discrete sleep episodes—i.e., the sleep pattern became fragmented, and this subject usually slept about three hours at a time. The pattern of fragmentation persisted during the withdrawal period. However, examination of the top row of Fig. 9B shows that this subject actually slept more during the first three days of the withdrawal period than during the first three days of the prealcohol baseline period. The number of discrete sleep episodes was also greater during the withdrawal period, indicating sleep fragmentation.

It appears that fragmentation of sleep is a reliable correlate of withdrawal signs and symptoms upon cessation of drinking. Subject AW had withdrawal symptoms characterized by impairment of orientation and memory, profuse sweating, tremor and some visual and auditory hallucinations. The sleep fragmentation shown in Fig. 9 during withdrawal is typical of that observed in other subjects who have shown definite withdrawal signs and symptoms. Subjects HB and WP (Figs. 7A and 7B) did not have withdrawal symptoms upon cessation of drinking, and their sleep patterns during this period were essentially normal.

Alterations in sleep patterns also appear to be related to the spontaneous initiation of periods of abstinence during a drinking spree. In a previous study in which subjects were allowed to determine the volume and frequency of their alcohol intake over a 30-day period, each subject initiated and terminated several episodes of drinking. The intervening periods of abstinence (2-4 days) were spent almost totally in sleep, and it appeared that the immediately preceding episode of drinking was associated with severe fragmentation of sleep behavior.[65] Periods of spontaneous abstinence of at least 16 consecutive hours are indicated in Fig. 7A and 7B by asterisks. These data are concordant with our previous observations of wakefulness prior to spontaneous cessation of drinking insofar as abstinent periods accompany or follow a relative decrease in total hours of sleep. However, the periods of abstinence indicated in Figs. 7A and 7B were not accompanied by an increase in total sleep time, as we found previously during abstinence periods of two or more days.[65]

A number of investigators have attempted to relate changes in sleep activity to hallucinosis and delusions during withdrawal. Alcohol hallucinosis is a frequent concomitant of withdrawal and is sometimes associated with difficulty in discriminating between sleeping and waking states. It has been speculated that hallucinosis and dreaming may be associated with increases in Stage 1 REM sleep; however, there have been relatively few studies of EEG correlates of sleep patterns during alcohol intoxication and withdrawal. Gross et al.[24] reported significantly higher Stage 1 REM activity in two alcoholic subjects during the first 24 hours of hospital admission for "acute alcoholic psychosis." Greenberg and Pearlman[21] have reported that 5 patients who developed delirium tremens following hospital admission for alcohol withdrawal symptoms showed a higher percentage of REM sleep than 8 other patients who did not develop delirium tremens. Interpretation of reports of EEG correlates of sleep activity during alcohol withdrawal must be made with caution, since it has usually been difficult to obtain adequate baseline sleep measures. The reported observations may be a function of acute hospitalization rather than the effect of alcohol withdrawal. Moreover, the intercurrent illness frequently associated with alcohol withdrawal—e.g., gastrointestinal disorders—may also be determinants of enhanced REM activity.

There is increasing evidence that changes in patterns of sleep are associated with alterations of steroid and endocrine activity. In particular, concomitants of endocrine activity during periods of REM activity suggest that the REM state may represent a unique level of central nervous system arousal. Mandell and his associates[45] have reported a biphasic change in urine volume output and osmolality during REM sleep. Mandell et al.[46] have also found that urinary excretion of 3-methoxy-4-hydroxymandelic acid (VMA) is increased during REM epochs of sleep. Similar increases in plasma 17 hydroxycorticosteroid levels during REM sleep have been reported by Weitzman et al.[95] These data converge to suggest that activation of endocrine output may correlate with frequency and duration of REM epochs during sleep.

We have consistently observed that serum cortisol levels increase significantly in alcoholic subjects during chronic ethanol ingestion.[59] Many of these subjects also showed fragmentation of sleep. It remains to be determined if sleep fragmentation is correlated with any significant change in frequency and duration of REM sleep. At the present time it would be most parsimonious to ascribe increases in cortisol levels to direct activation of the CNS-pituitary-adrenal axis by ethanol rather than to secondary effects related to fragmentation of sleep and possible changes in REM time and frequency.

Metabolic Aspects of Withdrawal Phenomenon

The complex interactions of the behavioral and biological correlates of alcohol withdrawal do not lend themselves to facile speculations about biochemical determinants of the abstinence syndromes. The fact that the decrease in or removal of alcohol, which itself induces behavioral change, may result in a more pronounced behavioral change presents something of a paradox at every level of analysis. The implications of the following sections on metabolic correlates of alcohol withdrawal are primarily heuristic and are in no way intended as explanations of mechanism.

a) Magnesium. The relationship of alcohol withdrawal symptoms and serum magnesium levels is poorly understood. It has been consistently observed that serum magnesium levels are lower during alcohol withdrawal.[19,80,54,55] It has also been reported that parenteral administration of magnesium sulfate produces an appreciable diminution of withdrawal symptoms.[80] There are data indicating that alcohol ingestion per se may increase renal excretion of magnesium in man.[39,48] However, it is unlikely that increased magnesium excretion persists during chronic alcohol ingestion, since serum magnesium levels measured in chronic alcoholic subjects prior to and at the end of a 24-day drinking period were not significantly different.[55]

Although magnesium deficit may be a concomitant of the alcohol withdrawal syndrome, two lines of evidence argue against a causal relationship between magnesium depletion and *initiation* of withdrawal

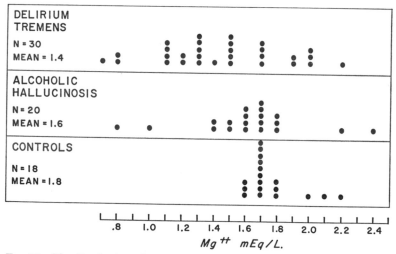

SERUM MAGNESIUM LEVELS

Fig. 10.—The distribution of serum magnesium levels observed in patients with delirium tremens, alcoholic hallucinosis and control subjects. (From Mendelson, J. H. et al.[54])

symptoms. First, although the distribution of serum magnesium levels in patients with alcoholic hallucinosis and delirium tremens is quite variable and mean values are significantly lower than controls (see Fig. 10), a spontaneous rise in serum magnesium was observed in 7 patients even though supplemental or parenteral magnesium therapy was not administered.[54] Second, in alcoholic subjects maintained on an adequate diet during sustained inebriation and withdrawal, magnesium levels remained relatively stable until twelve hours after withdrawal from ethanol (Fig. 11; from Mendelson[55]). Subsequently, magnesium values in serum rose spontaneously during the withdrawal period and were at normal levels when the subjects were asymptomatic.

Clinical studies strongly indicate that alcoholic patients showing withdrawal signs and symptoms may have a total body deficit of

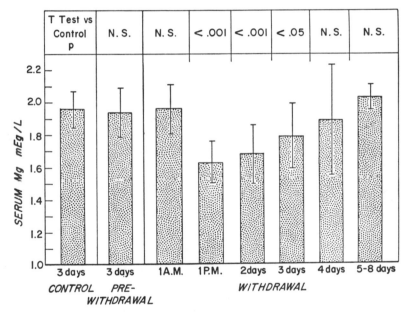

Fig. 11.—Group data for ten alcoholic subjects who consumed an average of one fifth of 86 proof bourbon for 30 consecutive days. Mean values and standard deviations of serum magnesium are shown for 3 control days prior to alcohol administration and the last 3 days of drinking immediately prior to withdrawal from alcohol. Withdrawal magnesium levels were obtained 12 and 24 hours following cessation of drinking and daily thereafter for 8 days. Statistical significance of differences between control and all subsequent values were assessed with a *t*-test.

magnesium.[47,57] Therefore, at least two sets of conditions appear to be relevant to magnesium balance and alcohol withdrawal states. First, alcoholic patients may have a total body deficit of magnesium which may be compounded by a decrease in magnesium levels in the intravascular compartment during alcohol withdrawal. Second, patients may have no significant total body magnesium deficit but show a transitory fall in serum magnesium levels during alcohol withdrawal. This fall in serum magnesium is not necessarily associated with increased excretion of magnesium by the kidney.[66]

The mechanism underlying the transient decrease in serum magnesium during withdrawal is unclear. One could postulate that increased intracellular pooling of magnesium occurs as a compensatory mechanism for increased muscular contraction during tremulousness. Since magnesium is both an activator and inhibitor for myosine adenosine triphosphatase, high intramuscular magnesium levels would suppress activity of this enzyme system with a concomitant decrease in frequency of muscle contraction.[96] On the other hand, some investigators have reported that a deficiency in intracellular magnesium levels (red blood cells) is a better correlate of severity of withdrawal signs than are extracellular magnesium levels.[78] The basic mechanisms will not be clarified until it is possible to accurately assess magnesium levels in both extracellular and intracellular compartments during successive phases of the alcohol withdrawal syndrome.

b) *Metabolic disorders and intercurrent illness.* Although it is possible to induce the alcohol abstinence syndrome in alcoholic subjects under experimental ward conditions without intercurrent infectious or metabolic disorders, this is not typical in most clinical situations. Usually, patients treated for alcohol withdrawal signs and symptoms have a number of intercurrent illnesses which may contribute to the severity of derangements in states of consciousness and occasionally obscure signs of the withdrawal state. Among those disorders which contribute to the severity of alcohol withdrawal states are the several central nervous system derangements induced by dietary and nutritional inadequacy.[89,90,28] The role of thiamine deficiency in Wernicke's syndrome has been well documented.[71,36] Peripheral neuropathy may also be induced by a thiamine deficiency, but is more commonly caused by deficiencies of other essential vitamins and co-factors.[79,17] These disorders usually accentuate alcohol withdrawal signs and symptoms. For example, a patient suffering with alcoholic hallucinosis and an external opthalmoplegia induced by thiamine deficiency presumably would be more prone to visual hallucinations than a patient with alcoholic hallucinosis and no significant history of vitamin deficiency.

A second frequent concomitant of prolonged problem drinking is progressive hepatic disease. The relationship between chronic ethanol ingestion, hepatic disorders and altered states of consciousness (i.e., hepatic decompensation and coma), will not be described, since this material has already been covered in a number of excellent reviews.[32,44] Severe derangements of liver function associated with coma or precomatose state could impede detection of alcohol withdrawal signs and mask the presence of psychomotor agitation associated with alcohol withdrawal. Similarly, trauma to the central nervous system (i.e., subdural hematoma) could produce a clinical state that could impair the objective detection of signs of alcohol withdrawal.

The medical complications associated with problem drinking have been reviewed in detail.[9] An examination of the effects of these complications reveals that many disorders may add or subtract algebraically from objective signs and subjective symptoms observed in the alcohol withdrawal state. For example, advocates of "sleep therapy" risk induction of a state of central nervous system depression that might prevent detection of toxic derangement and concomitants of trauma. Overzealous use of intravenous fluids and electrolyte replacement therapy may result in catastrophic complications for those alcoholic patients who have withdrawal symptoms and who also have increased total body water content[4,5] and hyperosmolality with decreased electrolyte excretion.[67]

As is the case with most toxic psychosis, the underlying mechanisms responsible for behavioral derangement associated with the numerous toxic, infectious and metabolic disorders remain to be determined. It is most important to emphasize that attempts to detect such disorders must be made on an individual basis. Subsequent therapeutic intervention should be guided by individual diagnostic assessments rather than by cookbook or formulary techniques.

CNS Models of Withdrawal

a) *Cellular adaptation.* Adaptation of cell systems to pharmacological agents has been demonstrated in systems ranging from autonomous single cell units to complex organ function. At the single cell level, it is well known that bacteria may become resistant to pharmacological agents that can directly destroy the cell or impede its growth and division. The enzymatic mechanisms of induction of penicillinase by penicillin are well known, and this mechanism has been used to explain the tolerance of certain bacterial strains for large concentrations of penicillin in their immediate milieu. Moreover, it has been shown that certain strains of bacteria not only develop adaptive enzymes which lyse the antibiotic but subsequently incorporate metabolic by-products of the antibiotic into crucial portions of their metabolic schema. Hence, some microorganisms can be killed by removing or deleting penicillin from their nutrient media.

Knowledge of the adaption of bacteria to noxious pharmacological agents has not been paralleled by our clarification of those adaptive processes that occur in the central nervous system following repeated administration of ethanol or other centrally acting drugs. Takemori[81] reported an instance of neurochemical adaptation to morphine as derived from studies of *in vitro* metabolism of rat neural tissue. This investigator claimed that morphine would not suppress potassium-stimulated respiration of isolated cerebral tissues of the rat in those animals which had been chronically injected with morphine. Attempts to replicate this finding in animals given large dosages of ethanol have not been successful.[91] No differences have been found in the sensitivity of potassium-stimulated neural tissues to added ethanol *in vitro* conditions from alcohol preferring and nonpreferring rats.[56]

Axelrod has reviewed data relevant to the several mechanisms that may underlie cellular adaptation in the development of tolerance to drugs.[1] Three possible factors are discussed: 1) reduced activity of the drug receptor; 2) depletion of endogenous substances that indirectly cause or mediate the drug action; and 3) enhanced metabolism and/or inactivation of the drug.

Axelrod has carried out studies that support the notion that the development of tolerance is based upon a drug interaction with N-demethylating enzymes.[2] He found that N-demethylating enzymes in liver microsomes continuously exposed to narcotic drugs showed a reduction in active metabolizing sites of these enzymes. He postulated that a similar phenomena might occur in the brain, since the molecular structure of drug receptors in the CNS closely resembles the N-demethylating enzymes in liver microsomes. However, Axelrod is careful to point out that this model for drug-induced reduction of receptor site activity has been challenged by a number of investigators.

Challenges to this theory have been based upon the findings of poor relationships between N-demethylation of narcotic drugs and their analgesic activity. In addition, development of tolerance to narcotics can occur in rats without reduction of N-demethylating activity.[26] In summary, Axelrod stresses that isolation and characterization of analgesic receptors in the CNS is a necessary precursor to testing hypotheses concerning reduction of receptor site activity by centrally acting analgesic drugs.

Tachyphylaxis, a form of tolerance, has long been known, but only recently has the mechanism of tolerance to repeated administration of sympathomimetic amines been clarified.[3] It has been shown that tolerance to sympathomimetic amines is associated with depletion of norepinephrine and that tachyphylaxis can be prevented by norepinephrine repletion.[12] It has been suggested that this model may have applicability to drug actions inducing depletion of endogenous transmitters, but there is no direct evidence that this phenomena obtains in the development of tolerance and dependence to alcohol. Indeed, there is some indirect evidence that tolerance to ethanol is associated with decreased release of acetylcholine. Kalant and Grose[38] have found that ethanol suppresses acetylcholine released by rat and guinea pig cerebral cortex slices *in vitro*. However, isolated cerebral tissues obtained from animals given large daily doses of ethanol do not show the degree of acetylcholine release found in tissues obtained from animals which have not been exposed to ethanol.[38]

Finally, more rapid metabolism or inactivation of narcotic drugs and ethanol has not been found to correlate with behavioral tolerance and dependence. Although there is good evidence that barbiturates may induce enhanced activity of those enzyme systems that are crucial in their metabolism,[72,73,11,10] similar findings have not been obtained with narcotic analgesics. There is little empirical support for the existence of a similar process in alcohol-induced tolerance and dependence. Experimental animal studies indicate a poor correlation between ethanol preference and rate of ethanol metabolism in the intact animal.[98] Although enhanced rates of ethanol metabolism have been demonstrated to occur in man following prolonged drinking, this enhanced metabolic rate cannot explain the significant degree of tolerance for alcohol shown by alcoholics who may have very high blood ethanol levels and continue to perform reasonably well.[52,58,82,83] Therefore, at the present time, there is no strong experimental evidence to support any of the proposed mechanisms of cellular adaptation discussed by Axelrod[1] for ethanol as contrasted with other centrally acting drugs.

One of the major difficulties in exploring cellular adaptation in experimental animals has been the surprising lack of effect of ethanol on a number of measurable parameters when ethanol is administered in relatively physiological concentrations. Suppression of several types of neurochemical and neurophysiological activities have been reported with extraordinarily large dosages of alcohol *in vitro* or semi *in vivo* systems. However, it has been difficult to ascertain a significant inhibition of any cellular function when concentrations of ethanol are employed that produce inebriation rather than death.[37] Recently, data have been obtained that suggest that active ion transport in the nervous system and in other tissues may be suppressed by relatively low ethanol concentrations.[31]

Israel and Salazar[30] have recently shown that ethanol inhibits Mg-activated and the $Na^+ + K^+ + Mg^{++}$-activated adenosine triphosphatases in brain microsomes. The inhibition was of a competitive type with respect to potassium ions. However, the concentration of ethanol employed in these experiments exceeded the lethal dosage for rat and man. The relevance of effects obtained with nonphysiological doses of alcohol to normal physiological function is open to some question.

Since alcohol freely diffuses into the central nervous system and the effective concentration of ethanol in any portion of the brain is a function of the water concentration of the cells involved, it appears unlikely that any region of brain will prove to be uniquely sensitive to ethanol as defined on a permeability basis. It is also unlikely that an overall suppression of metabolic activity of the central nervous system is at the basis of ethanol effects on behavior. Therefore, given a lack of regional susceptibility or undetectable metabolic decrement, the search for changes in cellular adaptation with currently available techniques is extremely difficult. A general consensus among many neurophysiologists and neurochemists is that ethanol acts upon membrane structure and function—a statement that at times reflects an evasive position for not being able to define a specific mechanism of action or effect. Nonetheless, the observables of behavioral tolerance and dependency indicate that some adaptational process is occurring in neural tissue. Clarification of the neural bases for this behavioral change presents a challenge to the ingenuity of the neurophysiologist and neurochemist.

b) Denervation/disuse supersensitivity. Although the mechanisms underlying the development of tolerance are not understood, it is somewhat easier to conceive of an adaptive change associated with prolonged exposure of the nervous system to alcohol than to speculate about the possible mechanisms of dependence. Dependence involves the anomalous situation in which the abstinence syndrome is evoked by the *removal* rather than the administration of the agent. Jaffe and Sharpless[34] point out that many withdrawal phenomena involve an exaggeration of behavior that is ordinarily suppressed by the agent which induces dependence. For example, morphine ingestion in man is associated with myosis, while mydriasis is frequently observed during the morphine abstinence syndrome. In addition to the concept of rebound hyperexcitability during withdrawal, it is postulated that a latent hyperexcitability exists during the time the agent is ingested.[34] In other words, the agent induces an increase in excitability of nervous pathways that is masked by the depressant action of the drug on the same pathways, or the drug induces depression through activation of suppressive pathways. The empirical relevance of these constructs to the alcohol abstinence syndrome remains to be demonstrated. However, the data bearing upon "denervation supersensitivity" are of considerable heuristic interest.[33,76,77]

The concept of "denervation supersensitivity" was originally introduced by Cannon and Rosenblueth[7] to account for the decreased threshold in prolonged response of autonomic effector organs following destruction of preganglionic cells and postganglionic axons. The mechanisms underlying the denervation supersensitivity are unknown. One possible mechanism may be a failure of inactivation of adrenergic transmitters via tissue uptake processes.[76] Following denervation, the transmitter uptake mechanisms of autonomic nerve terminals may be partially or completely impaired, with resultant supersensitivity of the effector organ to injected chemical stimuli. Moreover, it has been shown that supersensitivity can be induced by any process which blocks afferent impulses to effector sites.[85,86,87] Such would include preganglionic nerve destruction, pharmacological blocking agents and pharmacological block of adrenergic transmission. However, it has been suggested that presynaptic failure of inactivation may not account for denervation supersensitivity phenomena and that some postsynaptic sensitivity change must be postulated.[76] Collier[8] has postulated that altered synaptic sensitivity induced by changes in receptor sites may be related to development of tolerance and physical dependence. Jaffe and Sharpless[34] have argued that not only changes in receptor responsivity but alterations in those processes subserving transmitter receptor interaction are involved in physical dependence. As yet none of these constructs have been tested with regard to dependence induced by ethanol ingestion in the alcoholic, but a number of models, principally peripheral structures, have been utilized for studying concomitants of denervation supersensitivity.

One of the most interesting concomitants of "denervation supersensitivity" is that, in the salivary gland, pharmacological blockage of either adrenergic or cholinergic fibers results in supersensitivity when either cholinergic or adrenergic stimuli are applied to the effector organ.[16] Similarly, surgical denervation of sympathetic input to the salivary glands results in an increased sensitivity of the gland to both acetylcholine and norepinephrine. Parasympathetic denervation produces an equivalent effect. In the normal state, stimulation of both the parasympathetic and sympathetic inputs to the salivary gland results in a synergistic facilitation of salivary output.

The phenomenon of "denervation supersensitivity" has been used as a model to explain CNS seizure activity in severe abstinence syndromes. It has been suggested that chronic CNS depression by barbiturates, morphine, alcohol, etc., is tantamount to "disuse" (analogous to PNS denervation). Upon removal of the drug, there is a consequent rebound hyperexcitability of the functional systems depressed.[33] Therefore, drugs that elevate thresholds for chemically induced seizures would be expected to exhibit lowered seizure thresholds during withdrawal.

This formulation of "disuse supersensitivity" is supported by the finding that barbiturate withdrawal in the addicted cat is associated with a decreased threshold for pentylenetetrazol (PTZ)-induced seizures.[33] Jaffe and Sharpless[33] concluded that the lowered threshold for seizures was consistent with a "disuse supersensitivity" model of physical dependence. Their data also suggested that the time course for the development of physical dependence is similar to the time course for development of denervation supersensitivity observed in the peripheral nervous system.[16,18,25]

Surgical isolation of a cortical slab in cat results in the gradual development of increased susceptibility to epileptiform activity (reflected by increased duration of after-discharges induced by direct electrical stimulation). It was postulated that barbiturate intoxication functionally deprived the cortex of neuronal input in a manner analogous to chronic denervation produced surgically. Consequently, a comparable increase in duration of epileptiform activity might result from stimulation of cortical slabs in barbiturate-dependent cats surgically isolated immediately prior to drug withdrawal.[77] It was found that although the mean *duration* of stimulation-induced after-discharges in these acutely isolated, cortical slabs of cats in barbiturate withdrawal was greater than that in nonaddicted controls, *chronic* isolation of cortical slabs produced a far greater change (three-fold) in after-discharge duration. Thresholds were not appreciably different between experimental and control groups.[77]

The authors concluded that these data on changes in cortical excitability were not strongly supportive of a "denervation supersensitivity" hypothesis.[77] However, evidence previously adduced to support a "denervation supersensitivity" model of abstinence seizure activity was based on *threshold* changes.[33,75] Although it is entirely reasonable to assume a concordance between lowered threshold and duration of after-discharge, these data should be interpreted with consideration of the fact that this was not explicitly demonstrated in barbiturate-addicted cats. Also, no comparisons between PTZ and electrically induced seizure thresholds were reported.

Sharpless & Jaffe[77] have emphasized that barbiturates may act primarily on *subcortical* structures, and therefore changes in subcortical thresholds following barbiturate withdrawal could not be measured in isolated cortical tissues. Consequently, a denervation or disuse supersensitivity model may apply to subcortical structures with a concomitant increased cortical excitability during withdrawal. Unfortunately, data were not reported in which the after-discharge duration was compared between isolated cortical slabs and adjacent intact tissue in the barbiturate addicted cats. Consequently, the concordance between lowered thresholds to PTZ-induced seizures consistently found in barbiturate withdrawal[33] and the implicitly hypothesized prolonged after-discharge in intact cortex of a comparable preparation was not assessed. It was mentioned that PTZ-induced seizures often developed first in intact cortex and only later could be detected in isolated cortex.

There is some evidence to suggest that midbrain structures may be more important than cortical tissue with respect to the action of ethanol in the CNS. Kalant[37] has shown that the midbrain reticular activating system is relatively more sensitive to ethanol than are cortical tissues. Himwich[27] has found that primary somatosensory cortex is less sensitive than the reticular formation to the depressant effects of ethanol. However, Himwich[27] also reports that cortical association areas appear to be more sensitive to the depressant effects of ethanol than the reticular formation. Until the action of ethanol on specific sites in the central nervous system is further clarified, a denervation supersensitivity model will be difficult to test.

The possibility that denervation supersensitivity accounts for events in the peripheral nervous system is also difficult to substantiate. There is evidence that acute ethanol administration in animals is associated with an increased output of adrenal medullary hormones—i.e., epinephrine.[41] Although there is clinical evidence of increased autonomic activity during alcohol withdrawal in man, direct measures of catecholamine synthesis and turnover have not been carried out. Morphine addicts show an increased excretion of catecholamines and their metabolites during drug use. However, during morphine withdrawal, there is a decrease in catecholamine excretion relative to the predrug baseline.[93] One could postulate that the increased output of catecholamines during morphine administration was associated with an increased threshold at receptor sites as well as an increased rate of degradation or absorption of catecholamines at peripheral nerve endings. During withdrawal, the decreased output of catecholamines may reflect a compensatory response to relatively low thresholds at adrenergic receptor sites. This notion would be consistent with a denervation supersensitivity model. To test this hypothesis, it would be necessary to assess thresholds at receptor sites as well as turnover rates of catecholamines during chronic ethanol administration and following alcohol withdrawal.

In summary, although there are discernible alterations in many aspects of behavior and metabolic function differentially associated with alcohol inebriation and withdrawal, the basic biological mechanisms underlying these alcohol-induced effects are unknown. Yet the systematic study of psychopathological and biochemical aberrations related to alcoholism is facilitated by the fact that inebriation and abstinence syndromes can be *produced* by administration and removal of alcohol. Data obtained can be compared with baseline observations on the same subject.[64] Consequently, research on alcoholism has a distinct advantage as contrasted with most behavior disorders in which it is not possible to identify or manipulate a precipitating agent. Insofar as alcohol can initiate a sequence of altered behaviors, it is possible to study an encapsulated episode in which the disorder is manifest at many levels, and to make comparisons with the pre- and postintoxicated state. The data presented in this review attest to the fact that clarification of the biological bases of alcohol addiction will require the efforts and ingenuity of investigators from many disciplines.

REFERENCES

1. Axelrod, J.: Cellular adaptation in the development of tolerance to drugs. In: Wikler, A. (Ed.): The Addictive States. Baltimore, Williams & Wilkins, 1968. Vol. 46, Res. Publ. Ass. Nerv. Ment. Dis., pp. 247-264.

2. ——: Possible mechanisms of tolerance to narcotic drugs. Science 124: 263, 1956.

3. ——, Gordon, E., Hertting, G., Kopin, I. J., and Potter, L. T.: On the mechanism of tachyphylaxis to tyramine in the isolated rat heart. Brit. J. Pharmacol. 19:56-63, 1962.

4. Beard, J. D., and Barlow, G.: Influence of daily ethanol administration on fluid volumes and serum proteins. Fed. Proc. 21:77, 1962.

5. ——, Barlow, G., and Overman, R. R.: Body fluids and blood electrolytes in dogs subjected to chronic ethanol administration. J. Pharmacol. Exp. Ther. 148: 348-355, 1965.

6. Bloomquist, E. R.: Addiction, addicting drugs and the anesthesiologist. J.A.M.A. 171:518-523, 1959.

7. Cannon, W. B., and Rosenblueth, A.: The Supersensitivity of Denervated Structures, a Law of Denervation. New York, Macmillan, 1949.

8. Collier, H. O. J.: Tolerance, physical dependence and receptors. In: Harper, N. J., and Simmonds, A. B. (Eds.): Advances in Drug Research. New York, Academic Press, 1966, vol. 3, pp. 171-188.

9. Collins, J. R.: Major medical problems in alcoholic patients. In: Mendelson, J. H. (Ed.): Alcoholism. Boston, Little, Brown and Co., 1966, pp. 189-214.

10. Conney, A. H., and Burns, J. J.: Factors influencing drug metabolism. In: Garattini, S., and Shore, P. A. (Eds.): Advances in Pharmacology. New York, Academic Press, Inc., 1962, vol. 1, pp. 31-58.

11. Conney, A. H.: Enzyme induction and drug toxicity. In: Brodie, B. B., and Gillette, J. R. (Eds.): Drugs and Enzymes. New York, Pergamon Press, 1965, pp. 277-297.

12. Cowan, F. F., Cannon, C., Koppanyi, T., and Maengwyn-Davies, G. D.: Reversal of phenylalkylamine tachyphylaxis by norepinephrine. Science 134: 1069, 1961.

13. Dement, W. C.: The effect of dream deprivation. Science 131:1705-1707, 1960.

14. Diethelm, O., and Barr, R. M.: Psychotherapeutic interviews and alcohol intoxication. Quart. J. Stud. Alcohol 23:243-251, 1962.

15. Docter, R. F., Naitoh, P., and Smith, J. C.: Electroencephalographic changes and vigilance behavior during experimentally induced intoxication with alcoholic subjects. Psychosom. Med. 28, No. 4 (II):605-615, 1966.

16. Emmelin, N., and Muren, A.: The sensitivity of submaxillary glands to chemical agents studied in cats under various conditions over long periods. Acta Physiol. Scand. 26:221-231, 1952.

17. Fennelly, J., Frank, O., Baker, H., and Leevy, C. M.: Peripheral neuropathy of the alcoholic. I. Aetiological role of aneurin and other B-complex vitamins. Brit. Med. J. 2:1290-1292, 1964.

18. Fleming, W. W., and Trendelenburg, U.: The development of supersensitivity to norepinephrine after pretreatment with reserpine. J. Pharmacol. Exp. Ther. 133:41-51, 1961.

19. Flink, E. B., Stutzman, F. L., Anderson, A. R., Lontig, T., and Frasier, R.: Magnesium deficiency after prolonged parenteral fluid administration and after chronic alcoholism complicated by delirium tremens. J. Lab. Clin. Med. 43:169-183, 1954.

20. Goldberg, L.: Quantitative studies on alcohol tolerance in man. The influence of ethyl alcohol on sensory, motor and psychological functions referred to blood alcohol in normal and habituated individual. Acta Physiol. Scand. 5, Suppl. 16, 1943.

21. Greenberg, R., and Pearlman, C.: Delirium tremens and dreaming. Amer. J. Psychiat. 124:133-142, 1967.

22. Grenell, R. G.: Alcohols and activity of cerebral neurons. Quart. J. Stud. Alcohol 20:421-427, 1959.

23. Gresham, S. C., Webb, W. B., and Williams, R. L.: Alcohol and caffeine: Effect on inferred visual dreaming. Science 140:1226-1227, 1963.

24. Gross, M. M., Goodenough, D., Tobin, M., Halpert, E., Lepore, D., Perlstein, A., Serots, M., Debeanco, J., Fuller, R., and Kishner, I.: Sleep disturbance and hallucinations in the acute alcoholic psychoses. J. Nerv. Ment. Dis. 142:493-513, 1966.

25. Hampel, C. W.: The effect of denervation on the sensitivity to adrenine of the smooth muscle in the nictitating membrane of the cat. Amer. J. Physiol. 111:611-621, 1935.

26. Herken, H., Neubert, D., and Timmler, R.: Die enzymatische N-demethyllierung durch Lebermikrosomen bei der Morphin-Gewöhung. Arch. Exper. Path. Pharmakol. 237:319-333, 1959.

27. Himwich, H. E., Diperri, R., Dravid, A., and Schweigerdt, A.: Comparative susceptibility to alcohol of the cortical area and midbrain reticular formation of the cat. Psychosom. Med. 28, No. 4 (II):458-463, 1966.

28. Hornabrook, R. W.: Alcoholic neuropathy. Amer. J. Clin. Nutr. 9:398-403, 1961.

29. Isbell, H., Fraser, H., Wikler, A., Belleville, R., Eisenman, A.: An experimental study of the etiology of "rum fits" and delirium tremens. Quart. J. Stud. Alcohol 16:1-33, 1955.

30. Israel, Y., and Salazar, I.: Inhibition of brain microsomal adenosine triphosphatases by general depressants. Arch. Biochem. Biophys. 122:(2)310-317, 1967.

31. Israel-Jacard, Y., and Kalant, H.: Effect of ethanol on electrolyte transport and electrogenesis in animal tissues. J. Cell. Comp. Physiol. 65:127-132, 1965.

32. Isselbacher, K. J., and Greenberger, N. J.: Metabolic effects of alcohol on the liver. New Eng. J. Med. 270:351-356, 1964.

33. Jaffe, J. H., and Sharpless, S. K.: The rapid development of physical dependence on barbiturates. J. Pharmacol. Exp. Ther. 150:140-145, 1965.

34. ——, and ——: Pharmacological denervation supersensitivity in the central nervous system: A theory of physical dependence. In: Wikler, A. (Ed.): The Addictive States. Baltimore, Williams & Wilkins, 1968, vol. 46, Res. Publ. Ass. Nerv. Ment. Dis., pp. 226-243.

35. Jetter, W. W.: Studies in alcohol. II. Experimental feeding of alcohol to non-alcoholic individuals. Amer. J. Med. Sci. 196:487-493, 1938.

36. Joliffe, N., Watis, H., and Fein, H. D.: The Wernicke Syndrome. Arch. Neurol. Psychiat. 46:569-597, 1941.

37. Kalant, H.: The pharmacology of alcohol intoxication. Quart. J. Stud. Alcohol, Suppl. No. 1, pp. 1-23, 1961.

38. ——, and Grose, W.: Effects of ethanol and pentobarbital on release of acetylcholine from cerebral cortex slices. J. Pharmacol. Exp. Ther. 158:386-393, 1967.

39. Kalbfleisch, J. M., Lindeman, R. D., Ginn, H. E., and Smith, W. O.: Effects of ethanol administration on urinary excretion of magnesium and other electrolytes in alcoholic and normal subjects. J. Clin. Invest. 42:1471-1475, 1963.

40. Khazan, N., and Sawyer, C.: Mechanisms of paradoxical sleep as revealed by neurophysiologic and pharmacologic approaches in the rabbit. Psychopharmacologia 5:457-466, 1964.

41. Klingman, G. I., and Goodall, McC.: Urinary epinephrine and levartherenol excretion during acute sublethal alcohol intoxication in dogs. J. Pharmacol. Exp. Ther. 121:313-318, 1957.

42. Lee, T. K., Cho, M. H., and Dobkin, A. B.: Effects of alcoholism, morphinism and barbiturate resistance on induction and maintenance of general anesthesia. Canad. Anaesth. Soc. J. 11:354-381, 1964.

43. Leibowitz, J. O.: Studies in the history of alcoholism. II. Acute alcoholism in ancient Greek and Roman medicine. Brit. J. Addict. 62:83-86, 1967.

44. Lieber, C. S., and Davidson, C. S.: Some metabolic effects of ethyl alcohol. Amer. J. Med. 33:319-327, 1962.

45. Mandell, A. J., Chaffey, B., Brill, P., Mandell, M. P., Rodnick, J., Rubin, R. T., and Sheff, R.: Dreaming sleep in man: Changes in urine volume and osmolality. Science 151:1558-1560, 1966.

46. ——, Brill, P. L., Mandell, M. P., Rodnick, J., Rubin, R. T., Sheff, R., and Chaffey, B.: Urinary excretion of 3-methoxy-4-hydroxymandelic acid during dreaming sleep in man. Life Sci. 5:169-172, 1966.

47. Martin, H. E., and Bauer, F. K.: Magnesium 28 studies in the cirrhotic and alcoholic. Proc. Roy. Soc. Med. 55:912-914, 1962.

48. McCollister, R. J., Flink, E. B., and Lewis, M. D.: Urinary excretion of magnesium in man following the ingestion of ethanol. Amer. J. Clin. Nutr. 12: 415-420, 1963.

49. McGuire, M. T., Mendelson, J. H., and Stein, S.: Comparative psychosocial studies of alcoholic and nonalcoholic subjects undergoing experimentally induced ethanol intoxication. Psychosom. Med. 28:13-26, 1966.

50. McNamee, H. B., Mello, N. K., and Mendelson, J. H.: Experimental analysis of drinking patterns of alcoholics: Concurrent psychiatric observations. Amer. J. Psychiat. 124:1063-1069, 1968.

51. Mello, N. K.: Some aspects of the behavioral pharmacology of alcohol.

In: Efron, D. et al. (Eds.): Psychopharmacology. A Review of Progress. Proceedings of the Sixth Annual Meeting of the American College of Neuropsychopharmacology. PHS Publication No. 1836. Washington D.C., U.S. Government Printing Office, 1968.

52. ——, McNamee, H. B., and Mendelson, J. H.: Drinking patterns of chronic alcoholics: Gambling and motivation for alcohol. In: Cole, J. O. (Ed.): Clinical Research in Alcoholism. Washington, D. C., Psychiatric Research Report #24, Amer. Psychiat. Ass., 1968.

53. Mendelson, J., Wexler, D., Leiderman, P. H., and Solomon, P.: A study of addiction to nonethyl alcoholics and other poisonous compounds. Quart. J. Stud. Alcohol 18:561-580, 1957.

54. —— Wexler, D., Kubzansky, P., Leiderman, P. H., and Solomon, P.: Serum magnesium in delirium tremens and alcoholic hallucinosis. J. Nerv. Ment. Dis. 128:352-357, 1959.

55. —— (Ed.): Experimentally induced chronic intoxication and withdrawal in alcoholics. Quart. J. Stud. Alcohol, Suppl. No. 2, 1964.

56. ——, and Mello, N. K.: Potassium-stimulated respiration of rat cerebral cortex. Quart. J. Stud. Alcohol 25:235-239, 1964.

57. ——, Barnes, B., Mayman, C., and Victor, M.: The determination of exchangeable magnesium in alcoholic patients. Metabolism 14:88-98, 1965.

58. ——, Stein, S., and Mello, N. K.: Effects of experimentally induced intoxication on metabolism of ethanol-1-C^{14} in alcohol subjects. Metabolism 14:1255-1266, 1965.

59. ——, and Stein, S.: Serum cortisol levels in alcoholic and nonalcoholic subjects during experimentally induced ethanol intoxication. Psychosom. Med. 28: 616-626, 1966.

60. ——, and Mello, N. K.: Experimental analysis of drinking behavior of chronic alcoholics. Ann. N.Y. Acad. Sci. 133:828-845, 1966.

61. ——: Biochemical pharmacology of alcohol. In: Efron, D. et al. (Eds.): Psychopharmacology. A Review of Progress. Proceedings of the Sixth Annual Meeting of the American College of Neuropsychopharmacology. PHS Publication No. 1836. Washington D.C., U.S. Government Printing Office, 1968.

62. ——: Ethanol-1-C^{14} metabolism in alcoholics and nonalcoholics. Science 159:319-320, 1968.

63. ——, and Mello, N. K.: Experimentally induced intoxication in alcoholics: A comparison between programmed and spontaneous drinking. In preparation, 1968.

64. ——: A disease as an organizer for biochemical research: Alcoholism. In: Mandell, A. (Ed.): Some Current Issues in Psycho-Chemical Research Strategies in Man. New York, Academic Press, 1968 (in press).

65. ——, Mello, N. K., and Solomon, P.: Small group drinking behavior: an experimental study of chronic alcoholics. In Wikler, A. (Ed.): The Addictive States. Baltimore, Williams & Wilkins, 1968. Vol. 46, Res. Publ. Ass. Nerv. Ment. Dis., pp. 399-430.

66. ——, Ogata, M., and Mello, N. K.: Effects of alcohol ingestion and withdrawal on magnesium states of alcoholics: clinical and experimental findings. Ann. N.Y. Acad. Sci., 1969 (in press).

67. Ogata, M., Mendelson, J. H., and Mello, N. K.: Electrolytes and osmolality in alcoholics during experimentally induced intoxication. Psychosom. Med. 30:463-488, 1968.

68. Oswald, I., Berger, R., Jaramillo, R., Keddie, K., Olley, P., and Plunkett, G.: Melancholia and barbiturates: A controlled EEG, body and eye movement study of sleep. Brit. J. Psychiat. 109:66-78, 1963.

69. Overton, D. A.: State-dependent learning produced by depressant and atropine-like drugs. Psychopharmacologia 10:6-31, 1966.

70. ———: Dissociated learning in drug states (State-dependent learning). Proc. Amer. Coll. Neuropharm. 1968 (in press).

71. Phillips, G. B., Victor, M., Adams, R. D., and Davidson, C. S.: A study of the nutritional defect in Wernicke's syndrome. The effect of a purified diet, thiamine and other vitamins on the clinical manifestations. J. Clin. Invest. 31:859-871, 1952.

72. Remmer, H.: Drugs as activators of drug enzymes. In: Brodie, B. B., and Erdos, E. G., (Eds.): Proceedings of the First International Pharmacological Meeting, Stockholm, Vol. 6: Metabolic Factors Controlling Duration of Drug Action. New York, Pergamon Press, 1962.

73. ———: Drug tolerance. In: Mongar, J. L., and de Reuck, A. V. S. (Eds.): Ciba Symposium on Enzymes and Drug Action. London, J. & A. Churchill, Ltd., 1962.

74. Root, W. S., and Hofmann, F. G. (Eds.): Physiological Pharmacology. New York, Academic Press, 1963.

75. Sharpless, S. K.: Reorganization of function in the nervous system—use and disuse. Ann. Rev. Physiol. 26:357-388, 1964.

76. ———: The effects of use and disuse on the efficacy of neurohumoral excitatory processes. Paper presented at the Amer. Psychol. Ass. meetings (Sept. 4) 1967, Washington, D. C.

77. ———, and Jaffe, J. H.: The electrical excitability of isolated cortex during barbiturate withdrawal. J. Pharmacol. Exp. Ther. 151:321-329, 1966.

78. Smith, W. O., Warren, R. J., and Hammarsten, J. F.: Intracellular magnesium in delirium tremens and uremia. Clin. Res. 6:408, 1958.

79. Strauss, M. B.: Etiology of "alcoholic" polyneuritis. Amer. J. Med. Sci. 189:378-382, 1935.

80. Suter, C., and Klingman, W.: Neurologic manifestations of magnesium depletion states. Neurology 5:691-699, 1955.

81. Takemori, A. E.: Cellular adaptation to morphine in rats. Science 133:1018-1019, 1961.

82. Talland, G. A., Mendelson, J. H., and Ryack, P.: Experimentally induced chronic intoxication and withdrawal in alcoholics. Pt. 4. Tests of motor skills. Quart. J. Stud. Alcohol, Suppl. No. 2, pp. 53-73, 1964.

83. ———, ———, and ———: Experimentally induced chronic intoxication and withdrawal in alcoholics. Pt. 5. Tests of attention. Quart. J. Stud. Alcohol, Suppl. No. 2, pp. 74-86, 1964.

84. ———: Effects of alcohol on performance in continuous attention tasks. Psychosom. Med. 28, No. 4 (II):596-604, 1966.

85. Trendelenburg, U.: Modification of the effect of tyramine by various agents and procedures. J. Pharmacol. Exp. Ther. 134:8-17, 1961.

86. ———: The action of acetylcholine on the nictitating membrane of the spinal cat. J. Pharmacol. Exp. Ther. 135:39-44, 1962.

87. ———, and Weiner, N.: Sensitivity of the nictitating membrane after various procedures and agents. J. Pharmacol. Exp. Ther. 136:152-161, 1962.

88. Victor, M.: Treatment of alcoholic intoxication and the withdrawal syndrome. A critical analysis of the use of drugs and other forms of therapy. Psychosom. Med. 28, No. 3 (II): 636-650, 1966.

89. ———, and Adams, R. D.: The effect of alcohol on the nervous system. Res. Publ. Ass. Nerv. Ment. Dis. 32:526-573, 1953.

90. ——— and ———: On the etiology of the alcoholic neurologic diseases with special reference to the role of nutrition. Amer. J. Clin. Nutr. 9:379-397, 1961.

91. Wallgren, H., and Lindbohm, R.: Adaptation to ethanol in rats with special reference to brain tissue respiration. Biochem. Pharmacol. 8:423-424, 1961.

92. ———: Effects of alcohol on biochemical processes in the central nervous system. Psychosom. Med. 28:431-442, 1966.

93. Weil-Malherbe, H., Smith, E. R. B., Eisenman, A. J., and Fraser, H. F.: Plasma catecholamine levels and urinary excretion of catecholamines and metabolites in two human subjects during a cycle of morphine addiction and withdrawal. Biochem. Pharmacol. 14:1621-1633, 1965.

94. West, L. J.: Dissociative reaction. In: Freedman, A. M., Kaplan, H. I., and Kaplan, H. S. (Eds.): Comprehensive Textbook of Psychiatry. Baltimore, Williams & Wilkins, 1967, pp. 885-899.

95. Weitzman, E. D., Schaumburg, H., and Fishbein, W.: Plasma 17-hydroxy-corticosteroid levels during sleep in man. J. Clin. Endocr. 26:121-127, 1966.

96. White, A., Handler, P., Smith, E. L., and Stetten, DeW., Jr.: Principles of Biochemistry. New York, McGraw Hill, 1954.

97. Wikler, A.: Interaction of physical dependence and classical and operant conditioning in the genesis of relapse. In Wikler, A. (Ed.): The Addictive States. Baltimore, Williams & Wilkins, 1968. Vol. 46, Res. Publ. Ass. Nerv. Ment. Dis., pp. 280-287.

98. Wilson, E. C.: Ethanol metabolism in mice with different levels of hepatic alcohol dehydrogenase. In: Maickel, R. P. (Ed.): Biochemical Factors in Alcoholism. Oxford, Pergamon Press, 1967, pp. 115-124.

99. Yules, R. B., Freedman, D. X., and Chandler, K. A.: The effect of ethyl alcohol on man's electroencephalograph sleep cycle. Electroenceph. Clin. Neurophysiol. 20:109-111, 1966.

100. Yules, R. B., Lippman, M. E., and Freedman, C. X.: Alcohol administration prior to sleep, the effect on EEG sleep stages. Arch. Gen. Psychiat. 16:94-97, 1967.

Discussion of
Dr. Mello's and Dr. Mendelson's Paper

by HERBERT WEINER, M.D.

Albert Einstein College of Medicine, Bronx, New York

DR. MELLO's and Dr. Mendelson's work of the past few years has been truly a model of interdisciplinary work on the effect of alcohol as the independent variable on a number of wide-ranging dependent variables. Amongst the many findings that they and Talland have reported, one of the most significant is the differential effects of alcohol on moderate or even heavy drinkers and on alcoholic addicts when tested on various performance measures. These findings specify and make operational the clinical impressions recorded by Simmel and by Jellinek that drinkers do not constitute a homogeneous group. The phenomenon of "behavioral tolerance" for alcohol indicate that a dose-response gradient is not a sufficient explanation for the effects of alcohol, and that individual differences amongst drinkers do account for an important source of variance. Once having made such a statement it becomes necessary to specify just what the difference is between drinkers and alcoholic addicts, both in terms of the variables that account for their becoming so and of the mechanisms of tolerance.

I would agree that the most parsimonious theory (though not necessarily the correct one) that would account for all forms of addiction and for the phenomenon of cross-tolerance of which Drs. Mello and Mendelson have written is that proposed by Emmelin (1961), Grumbach (1961), and Sharpless and Halpern (1962). It would also and especially account for withdrawal symptoms such as rebound hyperexcitability. This hypothesis postulates that a form of "cellular adaptation" occurs to a depressant drug. This adaptation leads to a state of hyperexcitability that remains latent during the period of the drug's action. The drug, by reducing neural input and activity, renders the system more sensitive to all neurohumoral agents. This increased sensitivity and state of hyperexcitability remains latent during the period of the drug's action. The drug, by reducing neural input and activity, renders the system more sensitive to all neurohumoral agents. This increased sensitivity and state of hyperexcitability remains latent during the action of the depressant drug and is unmasked after its removal.

A similar hypothesis has been proposed for other forms of addiction—e.g., morphine addiction. Thus Maynert and Klingman (1962) and Gunne (1963) have suggested that the chronic administration of morphine leads to an increased rate of synthesis of catecholamines. The consequence of morphine withdrawal and the degree of its attendant excitation is directly related to the rate of release of catecholamines.

The testing of this hypothesis for alcohol addiction is rendered difficult, however, by the fact that so far experimental animals have resisted addiction to alcohol, but it might indirectly be tested in man.

Be that as it may, I would very much agree with Dr. Mendelson that a fruitful area is to study the effects of alcohol on the sleep-dream cycle in normal subjects. The work that he and others have done is tantalizing: e.g., the explosion of activated sleep during episodes of delirium tremens, or the findings of Yules et al. that alcohol suppresses activated sleep *at first*, but then the amount of activated sleep time begins to return to normal amounts and shows a trend to increase above normal levels (but Yules' observations ceased just at that point). It would also be intriguing to observe whether there are any positive or negative correlations between changes in sleep and dream time with content during drinking, or delirium tremens and/or withdrawal with behaviors such as hallucinosis or alterations in the formal properties of thought, reflective awareness, etc.

Equally important would be to study the phenomena of fragmentation of sleep in the addict, by more sophisticated criteria than sleep time. But such a suggestion must be obvious to workers as knowledgeable as Drs. Mello and Mendelson.

REFERENCES

1. Emmelin, N.: Supersensitivity following pharmacological denervation. Pharmac. Rev. 13:17-37, 1961.

2. Grumbach, L.: An hypothesis of opiate addiction. Committee on Drug Addiction. NAS-NRC. Appen. 16, 1961.

3. Gunne, L.-M.: Catecholamines and 5-hydroxytryptamine in morphine tolerance and withdrawal. Acta Physiol. Scand. 58. Suppl. 204:5-91, 1963.

4. Sharpless, S. K., and Halpern, L. M.: The electrical excitability of chronically isolated cortex studied by means of permanently implanted electrodes. Electroenceph. Clin. Neurophysiol. 14:244-255, 1962.

Discussion of
Dr. Mello's and Dr. Mendelson's Paper

by HARVEY LONDON, Ph.D.
Brandeis University

I SHALL NOT attempt a detailed critique of the research Dr. Mello and Dr. Mendelson have presented today. I believe I can serve my function as a discussant better, first, by telling you what I, as a social and personality psychologist, see as the value of Dr. Mendelson's work of the past several years, and second, by making certain broad suggestions based on my background in academic psychology.

As you may know from some of Dr. Mendelson's own writings, progress in alcoholism research has been hindered by too great a reliance on what people say about their drinking behavior and too small a commitment to the observation of ongoing drinking behavior. The great step forward in alcoholism research, exemplified in recent years by the work of a number of investigators, lies in the interest in examining actual drinking behavior and the correlates of that behavior. Not only has this new approach sought to *observe* drinking practices, but the observations have altered conclusions of the past. For example, an enormous amount of alcoholism research has been inspired by the anxiety-reduction hypothesis—i.e., the notion that people drink in order to reduce anxiety. Yet Dr. Mendelson and Dr. Mello have observed that drinking alcohol may actually increase the anxiety of alcoholics. New observations of this sort are leading us to rethink a number of our ideas about alcoholism.

Having indicated what, in general, I see as the value of the "new look" in alcoholism research, I should like to offer certain broad suggestions.

The first suggestion involves a turn-about of an old cliché. We have all heard the criticism that academic psychological research comes down to nothing but the psychology of the college sophomore. There is a real point to that cliché. Many psychologists need to leave the cloistered university laboratory more often than they do. They need to see whether their hypotheses hold up when confronted by mentalities other than that of the middle-class college student. By analogy, research in the field of drinking behavior must lead to something more than the psychology of the alcoholic. I do not say that we should lessen our efforts to understand the alcoholic. I do say that we need to come to a *general* understanding of drinking behavior. For such understanding we need research that deals in a comparative way with drinking in a variety of populations. It would be valuable indeed if Dr. Mendelson's and Dr. Mello's researches were replicated using a sample of normal social drinkers.

A second suggestion I would make concerns the research setting. Historically, this suggestion derives from the work of Kurt Lewin. Lewin stressed the notion that laboratory experiments on topics in social and personality psychology should attempt to create a relevant social environment. If you are studying groups, create a group. If you wish to study the difference between fascism and democracy, create a miniature model of each, and compare them.

While Dr. Mendelson's and Dr. Mello's work has been of value in that, among other things, they have managed to observe alcoholics drink and have made some important observations about their consequent behavior, the milieu chosen has been, by and large, the research ward of the hospital. The use of the research ward in this way itself constitutes a methodological advance. Nevertheless, it remains true that there may be knowledge to be gained by devising techniques for studying drinking in the atmosphere of the cocktail party, the cocktail lounge, and, for that matter, the home. In point of fact, there have been some promising beginnings along these lines.

Finally, I should like to say a word relating to Dr. Mello and Dr. Mendelson's focus today on states of consciousness. The very phrase "states of consciousness" is anathema to the strict behaviorist. Perhaps the major point of behaviorism has been that states of consciousness, whether or not they can be said to exist, are too subtle, too ephemeral, too "subjective" to be worthy of our attention. Yet today we find researchers as knowledgeable about behaviorist findings and techniques as today's authors not only willing to use the phrase "states of consciousness," but doing research of obvious relevance to the concept. Surely this is an indication that behaviorism's critique of social science has been absorbed and that there need be no conflict between a commitment to methodologically sound research and a curiosity about subject matter of great human and social relevance.

10

PRESIDENTIAL ADDRESS
A TRACT FOR THE TIMES:
SOME SOCIOBIOLOGIC ASPECTS OF SCIENCE,
RACE AND RACISM AND THEIR IMPLICATIONS

by BENJAMIN PASAMANICK, M.D.*

As THE lukewarm skirmish against poverty promises to turn into a hot war of rebellion for justice and equality, the fifth estate, science, rides precipitously into the fray, frequently to add confusion and to protect and give comfort to the establishment.

I would like to take as the thesis for my tract last spring's meeting of the National Academy of Sciences, where the smoldering mine of the implicit or explicit question of Negro inferiority exploded anew. This time the protagonists were William Shockley, the Nobel Prize winner for transistor work, Wallace Kennedy of Florida State, sponsored by Harlow, and finally the Academy itself.

The tired questions at issue again were: are Negroes genetically inferior; would an improved environment really improve their social functioning; were scientists inhibited from investigating these problems; etc., etc.? What was offered was a new, definitive test that on further scrutiny turned out to be neither new nor definitive.

Kennedy mentioned very briefly the massive 75 years of studies on Negro intelligence, stating that if there could be individual differences in some characteristics there could be race differences in intelligence.[1] He pointed to a 20 per cent difference in intelligence between Negroes and whites in the Southeast, narrowed to 10 per cent by so-called preschool "cultural enrichment" programs, although in the first two years of life Negro infants were indistinguishable. The latter, he said, "challenges the hypothesis of Pasamanick that one of the major effects of cultural deprivation and its poor prenatal nutritional and medical care is the

---

*New York State Department of Mental Hygiene.

production of sickly, underweight, and often premature infants who begin life at an inferior level of 'intelligence'." But he then went on to state that infant tests do not predict school-age test performance anyway.

The study he suggested would offer illegitimately pregnant Negro girls placement in maternity homes with good prenatal care and diet and then placement of the offspring in middle-class Negro homes. As controls he suggested lower-class Negro and white infants left in their biological environment.

He then asks the obvious question: Why should we do the study, "when intelligence tests themselves may not be the most sensitive instrument by which to study the effect of genetics on performance"? Part of his reply is a plea "simply to open the field of inquiry such that honest investigators may make careful study of racial differences in the hope that unique racial factors may be found which might well go undiscovered by default, and thus to keep the concept of racial differences in intelligence as an open question." He did stress that as far as he knew, "there is no convincing evidence that there are any racial differences in intellectual abilities that are based upon genetic factors."

Some months later a letter commenting on Kennedy's paper appeared in *Science,* pointing out that, "Some of the effects of a poor prenatal environment may not show themselves clearly until relatively complex intellectual tasks are presented later in the child's life."[2] The writer pointed to our own data indicating that "lower socioeconomic status is associated with dietary deficiencies during pregnancy, lack of adequate medical care during pregnancy and delivery, prematurity, greater maternal and infant mortality" and a higher incidence of maternal complications in non-white mothers attributable to their socioeconomic status. Further, that nutrition during pregnancy was associated with intellectual performance in offspring and that the mother's nutritional history and other aspects of her health history, even prior to the conception of the child, may influence the status of the child.

The final point made was that the "attributing to heredity any IQ differences (remaining) on the basis of such studies (as Kennedy's) could hardly be justified, 1) because not all of the known relevant environmental variables would have been controlled, and 2) because knowledge of the relevant environmental variables cannot be assumed to be complete."

To this Kennedy replied[3] "that when . . . mothers are given adequate prenatal care, even as late as the second trimester of pregnancy, the findings of Pasamanick do not hold. That is, if the mothers are given a vitamin and dietary supplement and adequate prenatal care, the Negro children, far from being born at a physical disadvantage, are born instead in what appears to be a superior position, as far as the general measures of intellectual and physical health are concerned. Although Pasamanick's study does indeed call attention to the necessity of controlling the prenatal environment, his findings are not consistent with those of almost any well-baby clinic with reports on Negro children born with hospital prenatal care. His findings evidently result from a combination of factors related to extreme poverty in a large city slum with very poor prenatal care."

Kennedy proposed that in his study "mothers could be eliminated if they showed any evidence that massive deprivation had occurred during the first trimester." He did not, however, reply to the issue of preconceptional malnutrition and disease related to socioeconomic variables, which has indeed been heavily implicated in reproductive casualty by Baird in Aberdeen.

Kennedy did acknowledge that "the study might not be definitive, particularly if significant differences between the experimental and control groups were obtained . . . given the use of the null hypothesis."

Before continuing with the next episode in the narrative, I would like to clarify, as briefly as possible, some of the confused and confusing issues raised in the foregoing and to discuss some biologic factors involved. (The latter is, after all, the theme of these meetings.)

Kennedy indicated that during the first two years Negro infants progress behaviorally at rates no different from those seen in whites. It is amusing to note that we were the first to demonstrate this more than two decades ago on what was probably a representative, if small, New Haven sample.[4] These findings were replicated twice on much larger and obviously representative samples in Baltimore and Columbus.[5]

These are not irrelevant measurements or measurements of variables unpredictive of school age functioning, as Kennedy states. On the contrary, we and others have demonstrated repeatedly that the prediction of performance on standard intelligence tests some seven years after infant examination is at least as good as the prediction of performance using the same tests seven years apart within the school age period. This is only further proof that the patterns of behavioral development during infancy contain all the precursor ingredients of behavior later, and any deficiencies in conduction time, perception, central nervous system integration, motor output, etc., etc., would show up in infancy. Indeed the prediction of such defects we have shown to be even better than that of intellectual performance.[6]

While we have found a greater incidence of severe damage in Negro infants, related to perinatal events, this was insufficient, during infancy, to influence the *mean* quotients of our Negro samples. As a consequence, again contrary to Kennedy, we never placed any great weight upon prenatal damage as a cause of Negro group intellectual dysfunction during the school years. We had some evidence on the basis of retrospective studies that prenatal damage disorganized all aspects of behavioral functioning, including cognition, but it wasn't until the recent analysis of longitudinal data that we were prepared to elucidate the seemingly paradoxical findings that prenatal damage results in no differences in mean quotients during infancy, and yet should be considered as one of the variables involved in school age differences.

First, I should point out that we are concerned with a not inconsiderable number of children. Approximately an eighth of the infants we examined were found to exhibit objective, reliable indices of brain damage. We now know these indices to be valid as well, since seven years later we found 90 per cent of these same children, no matter what their race or economic status, to differentiate clearly on a battery of tests of perceptual, integrational and motor items. But what we had not fully anticipated was how socioeconomic status, again irrespective of race, would differentially affect these injured children. As a total group, they fell from their early promise of intellectual potential, particularly if they had had any seizures (another frequent concomitant of injury). However, it was the middle and lower socioeconomic thirds who contributed to the decline and, as might have been anticipated, largely the latter group of children who fell most precipitously.

Let us examine a bit more closely the probable course of events leading to this decline and fall. The common explanation offered for the poor showing of lower-class children is lack of stimulation, for which the paradigm is the animal isolation experiments. While this might hold for the old orphan asylums, nothing could be less descriptive of the slum child's environment, living as he does in crowded quarters, being constantly bombarded by sensory stimuli of all modalities, blaring radios and television sets, extremes of heat and cold, surrounded by active adults and children—all of these frequently in disorganized and confusing array, and difficult for the intact child or adult to integrate or inhibit. The injured child with impaired inhibitory, attentional and integrative capacities responds with aphasias, autism and extremes of psychomotor excitation, making it difficult, if not impossible, to mature successfully. In addition we have demonstrated that he contributes to the further disorganization of his own environment and is subject to repeated illnesses and hospitalizations, so that it is not surprising that we end with a school child with a low IQ, demoralized by constant failure and a distinct handicap to his ghetto schoolmates.

At this time, I do not want to overemphasize the contribution brain damage makes to the decline of the group mean IQ, but rather indicate its cost to group functioning and what the needs are for individualized care. But I will return after discussing another biologic variable, which we can now begin to place in a more precise context. In our first longitudinal New Haven study we found that a number of commonly implicated social and demographic variables had played no role in influencing infant development. Physical growth was the only variable found to be significantly related to performance. Those infants below the median on height and weight curves, even by 40 weeks of age, were already significantly lower in intellectual potential than those above. Nevertheless, the group *as a whole* had growth curves similar to the best white rates and at school age had IQ's equal to whites. (It is true that those living in segregated areas and attending segregated schools were lower than the others.) We felt justified in assuming the probability of a causal relationship between nutritional intake before and after birth, in turn related to full employment and rationing during the war years, with consequent satisfactory behavioral progress.

Once again in Baltimore we confirmed precisely the same relationship of physical growth to performance in the Negro group. But two probably not unrelated differences from the New Haven findings struck us: first, that the weight curves, even for full term children, were significantly lower than white curves; second, that by three years of age the Negroes were also falling behind intellectually. A third, most telling, finding was the discovery that the white children did not have this relationship of low physical growth curves to low performance.

We can now, with support from other studies, begin to offer a simple explanation for these seemingly disparate findings. Amongst the whites, at least in Baltimore, the physical growth patterns are apparently largely reflections of differences in inherited physique rather than being related to nutritional intake; in large measure, and as a group, whites are above the threshold where dietary differences during childhood play a significant role. The Negroes, on the other hand, perched precariously on the low rungs of the economic ladder, as a group are significantly lower than whites in physical growth, and those sufficiently below the threshold exhibit the intellectual consequences of nutritional deprivation, primarily of protein and vitamins. (One can only imagine the devastation occurring in grossly undernourished populations abroad.)

We can also, at this time, begin to outline the probable biochemical and physiologic mechanisms involved. It seems clear that either RNA and/or protein synthesis in the neuron is involved in long-term memory and learning and consequently in behavioral and intellectual functioning.[7] Chronic or intermittent malnutrition could affect this synthesis and thereby have recurrent or permanent effects leading to disorganization or delay in the complex of reciprocal interweaving of developmental patterns which we term intellectual maturation. These effects would be greatest during fetal life, leading to measurable neurologic impairment, with lesser interference later during childhood impairing only intellectual growth in most cases.

We can now begin to fit these two biologic variables of brain damage and malnutrition into the highly interrelated complex of biologic factors (there are other variables such as infection, immunologic responses, toxic substances, etc.) and in turn into the matrix of biopsychosocial factors which cause racial differences in intelligence. And the biologic variables may not be the weightiest contributors to malfunction. All we need and can do is list some of the others: the powerlessness, the recurrent blasted hopes, the shame, the fear, the anger, the dirt, the noise, the poor health care, disease, strife, frustration, hunger, idleness, hard work, disorganization, lack of stimulation and dystimulation, and on, and on, and on.

And in how much dysfunction does this seemingly endless spiral result? In Baltimore, where one of the worst ghettos in the country exists, at six years of age the Negro children are 10 per cent behind the whites in IQ. (This is in stark contrast to the 20 per cent Kennedy reports in Southeast United States, indicating that, bad as conditions are in the cities, they are still worse in the South, particularly in the rural areas.) Even further, when the Negroes as a whole are compared to the lower socioeconomic half of the Baltimore whites, they are only 5 per cent behind and, were it possible to equate the socioeconomic conditions, there is no doubt there would be no significant differences at all.

In the face of what these children must contend with, day in and day out, and the significant but relatively small differences which become smaller or disappear with even minor improvement in their lot, how can one speak of innate racial inferiority? I can only stand in awe of man's stamina and his resilience in response to the continuous onslaught upon his functioning. I state hesitantly and, probably with some bias, that I believe whites could do as well under the same circumstances.

I would maintain that the successive approximations made to ultimate knowledge of group differences in intellecutal functioning make Negro innate inferiority exceedingly implausible, and that at this time we know enough of what must be done to erase this infamy. (It is of no little interest that in that long, sad document, President Johnson's State of the Union message [of 1968], proposing some crumbs of health care, the heaviest emphasis was on maternal and child health.)

What we can say quite clearly at this time is that, when a sample of Negroes approaches sociocultural comparability to a white sample (and I must add that, because of centuries of discrimination, even under the best of circumstances no precise comparability is currently possible), it becomes comparable in all important aspects—infant and maternal mortality, physical growth, morbidity, and intellectual performance. However, the common reply to this observation is that these samples are biased, containing those at the upper end of the curve of capacity. These circular polemics lead inevitably to the conclusion that, unless and until the Negro achieves full social and economic equality in our society, the definitive test of his capacity is not possible. The challenge to those eager and determined inquirers into scientific truth then becomes one of turning all the strength of their efforts and determination into achieving the type of society in which the definitive test is possible. It is at this point that the crucial decision arises and must be made. Until they do this we must doubt their intentions and, indeed, their scientific and social integrity.

I greatly fear that the most common rejoinder made to this challenge is that, because of their capacities, Negroes could not take advantage of opportunities or could not reach social and economic equality. This is, of course, to prejudge the outcome, and becomes the basis for the self-fulfilling prejudice with which we have been contending. The more ingenuous reply is that it would take too long, be too difficult, etc. All the more reason to hasten and devote all our energies to the task, instead of diverting them largely or wholly to trivial investigations of racial differences which lead us back into a meaningless circle of inconclusiveness.

In the light of this analysis, Shockley's call for public debate on Carleton Putnam's racist ideas becomes, indeed, shocking.[8] As for his hoary argument, as old as Galton, that the mean IQ of the population is declining because the genetically inferior families have more children, it can be dismissed along with a whole farrago of nonsense—as it was by the entire Genetics Department at his University—as "pseudoscientific" and falling "between mischief and malice."[9] Studies made in Britain over decades have indicated that rather than declining their IQs have risen, as have their physical growth curves. The British, with far less wealth and productive capacity than we, have achieved a lower infant mortality, lower rates of prematurity and of complications in pregnancy, and a rising intellectual potential merely by a more equitable distribution of their goods and an approach to a better system of social services.

Why do we keep harping on the subject? Why do we respond automatically to every prod? Certainly we have little hope of convincing the prejudiced or changing the racist.

Donald Campbell in his essay on stereotypy points out that, "In Southern legislatures in the last 100 years, the alleged intellectual inferiority of Negroes has played an important role. Removing the belief that Negroes are inferior would not, however, remove the hostility, although it would change the content of the stereotype. Had the World War I test results showing Northern Negroes to be more intelligent than Southern whites been effectively publicized in the South, opportunistic hostility could certainly have created an image of the Northern Negro carpetbagger whose opprobrious traits included shrewdness, trickiness and egg-headed intellectuality. Remedial education in race relations focused on denying or disproving stereotypes implicitly accepts the prejudiced ingroupers' causal conception rather than the social scientists', and is undermined where actual group differences are found."[10]

I do not wholly agree with this last, but why take this risk? Let me take my cue from the next scene in our tragic comedy.

In November of last year, *Science*, reporting on William Shockley's call for research on the effects of heredity and environment on intelligence, indicated that this has been uncomfortable to the National Academy of Sciences, adding up "to a loaded question that might be destructively exploited by racists if the Academy even ratified it as the right question."[11] And, in reaction, the Academy's president presented its Council's response in a long statement prepared with the assistance of several eminent geneticists.[12]

The statement began with the nature of certain questions that were being asked and then went on to the difficulties involved in such investigations and said on one hand this and, on the other hand, that, etc.; but amongst its conclusions, which were also hedged, it stated, "we question the *social urgency* of a greatly enhanced program to measure the heritability of complex intellectual and emotional factors.

"Likewise, we question the social urgency of a crash program to measure genetic differences in intellectual and emotional traits between racial groups. In the first place, if the traits are at all complex, the results of such research are almost certain to be inconclusive. In the second place, it is not clear that major social decisions depend on such information."

Wars, past and present, have stimulated research that has proved of benefit to mankind but that cannot, under any circumstances, justify the waging of war. Similarly the centuries-old war against injustices and inequality has taught us much about life processes and human functioning, certainly enough to end most of this strife. The social urgency is to do that which must be done to end the strife and not to work any longer on ascertaining what should be done. And we all know how great is the urgency.

At this time to call for more research on racial differences in intelligence is an exercise in futility and callousness. It is analogous to calling for research on the relationship of racial differences in pigmentation to resistance to burns, in the midst of a slum fire. We are on the verge of a holocaust and the research has been done.

The concern which drove the National Academy to issue its statement is a very real one. The *Iron Mountain* mentality of brutal repression of demands for a decent life has been endemic in American society since its inception, and is spreading as one of the reactions to our present crisis. We must not ignore it or its concomitant desperate search for scapegoats. The Indian, the Negro, the alien have served in the past, and racism has been its base.

It is sickening to recall that one of the items in the indictment of the

Jews drawn up in *Mein Kampf* was that of their defense of racial and ethnic groups and their opposition to the Nazi doctrine of the simian character of the Negro. This doctrine has served its purpose well in justifying slavery and second-class citizenship for the Negro.

Science in its comments upon Shockley hints at another rationalization: "Or will genetic inheritance produce such a low social capacity index that most will perform at frustratingly low social levels?" Mechanization and new methods have made the Negro superfluous in the rural South, condemning him to slow starvation or refugee status in the North. Is there now a suggestion that automation and urban life, which call for skilled labor and high social capacity indices, have made the Negro superfluous in our society, thus calling for "apartheid" or even "a final solution of the Negro problem"?

Might it be these implications that the Academy Council had in mind, recalling our genocidal efforts upon the American Indian and the recent Congressional cry to bomb a small country "into the Stone Age," which led to its statement?

We recoil in horror—and in this reaction lies our hope. We are in a crisis—urban, national, global—requiring no description here. We, as a society, have striven frantically for control over all animate and inanimate matter in this world, the moon, the planets and the stars with a system of values based upon self-interest dead-ending with power as an ultimate good. We have evaded the self-confrontation necessary to reorder our values to achieve a true community and a just society. We can evade it no longer and, uncomfortable as it may be, it is good that it is so.

John Gardner, voicing the concern of all humane people, has said that there are two overriding, immediate items on the agenda of American society—a decent, equal place for the Negro, and peace. The two are, of course, *totally interdependent*. The wherewithal for the jobs, housing, education, health care and other ingredients of a dignified existence can only come from those tremendous resources now allocated to destruction.

Half of the 160 billions of dollars the world pours into war and preparation for war is expended by our country. This is in violent contrast to the 7 billions from all nations going towards aid to the poverty-ridden countries, for which our contribution continues to fall, now ranking us fifth in proportion to our production. What a world this could be if we reversed these expenditures.

I am indeed sorry to have subjected you to this jeremiad—one of many now coming from all quarters and indicating the universal shock of recognition of our problem. They are the inevitable first reactions upon which we must build together that reordering of our values and reallocation of our resources. To remain quiet is to lapse into the cynicism or apathy which can follow upon the darkness confronting us. Gunnar Myrdal, who described the American dilemma of inconsistencies within the American dream, returned last year after two decades to offer his final warning against stupid optimism. We must operate from the most realistic view of things as they are and then go forward, because *blind* retreat is no longer possible.

REFERENCES

1. Kennedy, W.: Racial differences in intelligence: Still an open question? Presented at the National Academy of Science, April 26, 1967.

2. Erickson, T.: Letter. Science 157:1210, 1967.

3. Kennedy, W.: Letter. Science 157:1210, 1967.

4. Pasamanick, B.: A comparative study of the behavioral development of Negro infants. J. Genet. Psychol. 59:3, 1946.

5a. Knobloch, Hilda, and Pasamanick, B.: Prospective studies on the epidemiology of reproductive casualty: Methods, findings, and some implications. Merrill Palmer Quarterly 12:27, 1966.

5b. Pasamanick, B., and Knobloch, H.: Retrospective studies on the epidemiology of reproductive casualty: Old and new. Merrill Palmer Quarterly 12:7, 1966.

6. Knobloch, Hilda and Pasamanick, B.: Prediction from the assessment of neuromotor and intellectual status in infancy. In: Zubin, J. and Jervis, G. A. (Eds.): Psychopathology of Mental Development. New York, Grune and Stratton, 1967, 387-400.

7. Symposium on biochemical functions in memory and learning. 1967 annual meeting of the American Association for the Advancement of Science.

8. Shockley, W.: A "try simplest cases" approach to the heredity-poverty-crime problem. Proc. Nat. Acad. Sci. 57:1767, 1967.

8. ——: Interview. U. S. News and World Report, Nov. 22, 1965, p. 68.

9. Bodmer, W. F. et al.: Letter. Stanford M. D. 5:41, 1966.

10. Campbell, D. T.: Stereotypes and the perception of group differences. Amer. Psychol. 22:817, 1967.

11. Racial Studies: Academy states position on call for new research. Science 158:892, 1967.

12. National Academy of Science Council Statement on Racial Studies. Science 158:892, 1967.

11

SCHIZOPHRENIA: EVIDENCE OF A PATHOLOGIC IMMUNE MECHANISM*

by ROBERT G. HEATH, M.D., D.M.Sc.†

O BSERVATIONS during almost two decades of multidisciplinary research at Tulane suggest that schizophrenia is an immunologic disorder in which focal abnormalities of the brain produce clinical manifestations. Early studies that prompted and supported this hypothesis will be briefly reviewed as background for the present report of new findings.

PREVIOUS OBSERVATIONS

(1) In a series of 58 patients prepared with depth and cortical electrodes for long-term study and treatment, electroencephalograms (EEGs) recorded from the septal region during periods of psychotic behavior consistently showed focal abnormalities of spiking or slow waves, or both.[1,2,3,4,5] The aberration, which consistently occurs with psychotic behavior regardless of its underlying pathology, is present in patients whose psychotic behavior is associated with structural abnormalities of the brain and can be induced in normal persons by exogenous toxic agents, as well as being present in schizophrenics during psychotic episodes. The basis of the physiologic defect in schizophrenia, in the absence of cytopathologic change and exogenous toxin, has become the principal object of our studies of schizophrenia.

(2) Clinical observations of schizophrenic patients together with basic physiologic studies in animals first suggested correlations between overt signs of schizophrenic behavior and aberrant activity of the septal region.[6,7] We consider the basic behavioral aberrations of schizophrenia to be a) anhedonia, or impaired ability to integrate feelings of pleasure,

*Supported by grants-in-aid from The Ittleson Family Foundation, New York, N.Y., and the Evans Foundation, Chattanooga, Tenn.

†Tulane University School of Medicine.

with consequent pathologic emotional expression, and *b*) reduction in level of psychologic awareness and increased primary process thinking, characterized by distorted self-image (defined by Rado[8] as proprioceptive diathesis). Studies in monkeys and cats showed that ablation of the septal region reduced behavior to a catatonic-like state and grossly impaired emotional expression.[9,10] Contrariwise, electrical stimuli delivered to this site through electrodes implanted into the brain for long-term studies made the animals alert and seemed to induce pleasure.[11] Electrical stimuli delivered to the septal region of the 58 patients studied since 1950 induced general arousal, or alerting, and pleasant feelings ranging from mild well-being to intense pleasure.[1,2,4,12]

(3) Fluorescent antibody technics showed immunoglobulin on neural cells of the septal region and basal caudate nucleus of brains of schizophrenic patients who had psychotic symptoms immediately before death, but not on brains of control subjects.[13] This observation suggested an intimate relation between a human serum globulin and the site of physiologic abnormality in the brain of psychotic schizophrenic patients.

(4) Intravenous or intraventricular injection of a part of the gamma G immunoglobulin (IgG) (taraxein) from serum or plasma of acutely psychotic schizophrenic patients altered EEGs of the septal region and basal caudate nucleus of rhesus monkeys and induced catatonic-like behavior.[14] Intravenous injection of this fraction also induced symptoms of schizophrenia in prisoner-volunteers.[15,16] The corresponding fraction from serum or plasma of healthy control subjects, as well as from nonschizophrenic patients with various other diseases, was inert in both monkeys and volunteers.

We now exclusively use ion exchange chromatography to obtain the IgG fractions. Previous fractionation methods using ammonium sulfate precipitates have been abandoned because the fractions were unstable and because the ammonium ion can alter nervous system function.[17]

(5) Fluorescent antibody techniques showed globulin on cells of the septal region of monkeys who had received intravenous schizophrenic IgG, whereas none was seen on brains of monkeys who had received the control IgG.[14,18]

(6) That the psychosis-inducing portion of the schizophrenic IgG was possibly antibrain-antibody was further supported by experiments in which antisera was made against various tissues of monkeys and human

brains by inoculating sheep* with homogenates of tissues-with-adjuvant and then obtaining sera at the expected peak of antibody response.[19] The antisera against septal region had characteristics of psychosis-inducing serum fractions from acutely schizophrenic patients.[19] When given intravenously or intraventricularly to assay monkeys, fractions of antisera against monkey and human septal region and basal caudate nucleus induced spiking or slow waves, or both, in EEGs from the septal region, with associated behavioral changes, whereas the sheep antisera against other regions of monkey and human brains were inert.[19] In tissues of monkeys killed while responding to the IgG fractions of sheep antisera to septal-basal caudate tissue, indirect fluorescent antibody technics showed globulin to be attached to neural cells of the septal region, but only minimal globulin was randomly attached to brain sites of monkeys that received sheep antibody against other brain parts.[19] Thus a highly specific antibody produced against precise antigenic sites of the septal region acted like taraxein in its effects on brain function and behavior, and therefore reinforced the concept that taraxein is antibody.

(7) In 1959 Porter[20] showed that papain splits the IgG molecule into three approximately equal fragments. Two of these were identical fraction antibody (Fab-) fragments, each with a binding site for antigen. The third, a crystalline (Fc-) fragment, chemically and biologically different, included the part of the molecule involved in complement fixation. By the method of Hsiaso and Putnam,[21] papain digestion was done on psychosis-inducing schizophrenic IgG (taraxein) fractions. The resulting fragments were separated from undigested IgG by chromatography on a Sephadex G100 column and equilibrated with a 0.05M sodium acetate buffer, pH 5.5, after which the Fab-fragments were separated from the Fc-fragment by starch gel or pevicon electrophoresis. The uncontaminated Fab-fragments (as determined by electrophoresis) had psychosis-inducing activity (like taraxein) when tested intraventricularly in the assay monkey. Papain digests of the IgG molecule containing both Fab-and Fc-fragments, but free of undigested IgG molecule, induced focal EEG and behavioral changes in the monkey when administered either intravenously or intraventricularly. During definite response to the injections, recipient monkeys were killed and their brain tissues were obtained, as previously described, for study by fluorescent antibody technics.[13] Globulin was present on neural cells of

---

* When goats and rabbits have been used instead of sheep, the antiseptal antibody has had essentially the same characteristics.

the septal region, indicating that the antibody-binding Fab-fragment of the molecule was responsible for the psychosis-inducing activity, and supporting the concept that psychosis-inducing schizophrenic IgG (taraxein) is (probably) antibody.

(8) Suggestive evidence that impaired neurohumoral conduction might be responsible for physiologic changes in the septal region and accompanying disordered behavior came from studies in which a series of compounds, assumed neurohumoral agents, was introduced, through a specially designed cannula,[22] into the septal region and other parenchymal sites of monkey brains. Introduction of the anticholinergic, atropine, into the septal region consistently induced spiking or slow wave activity alone, or combined, along with catatonic behavior. Introduction of this compound and other anticholinergic agents into other brain sites effected no change. Moreover, when acetylcholine was introduced into the septal region of the brains of two human subjects, it induced high amplitude spindling and pleasurable behavior, such as followed electrical stimulation of the septal region.[12] Acetylcholine at other deep sites of the brain caused no changes. Thus the septal region, a brain site associated with activation of awareness and pleasant feelings, appeared to be uniquely cholinergic, being activated by acetylcholine and grossly impaired by anticholinergic agents.

Before arriving at our immune hypothesis of schizophrenia, we considered taraxein to be an abnormal enzyme, a concept that we failed to substantiate. When findings were reported indicating that antibody might be involved in the impairment of acetylcholine activity in myasthenia gravis,[23] we began using technics which provided initial substantiation of our immune hypothesis of schizophrenia.

Our current formulation is that schizophrenic patients produce abnormal immunoglobulin, probably as a result of genetically abnormal clones of cells, and that this antibody, capable of binding to specific sites in the septal region, impairs activity at the synapse by altering neurochemical transmission, thereby inducing aberrant physiologic activity in the septal region, which is basic to the psychotic state. We do not know the source of this unusual globulin (antibody) in schizophrenic serum or why it seems to fluctuate.

Present Observations

The data presented heretofore are somewhat incomplete in supporting our present concept of the pathogenesis of schizophrenia. Electroencephalograms are not precise, and their meaning is dependent on individual interpretation. Moreover, it is difficult to categorize behavior of monkeys and, especially, of human subjects. We have not always been able to produce a taraxein response with passive transfer, the method used in inducing schizophrenic-like symptoms in monkeys and human volunteers. Variations in antibody (taraxein) sensitivity from person to person may be analogous to the varying responses obtained with use of drugs. Because of such problems in previous studies, we recently developed more direct technics that show objectively that the unique globulin in schizophrenic serum, taraxein, apparently enters the brain at focal sites, localizing in the septal region, principally in the cytoplasm of satellite glial cells. It is conceivable that the presence of schizophrenic IgG at this site could induce the septal EEG aberration which has consistently correlated with psychotic behavior.

Localization of Globulins

In preliminary studies reported here, schizophrenic and control IgG fractions were tagged with ferritin and sometimes with fluorescein isothiocyanate as well, and then injected into the femoral vein of rhesus monkeys. Recipient monkeys were killed at specific intervals after injections, their brains removed as rapidly as possible, and specific regions rapidly dissected for study by ultraviolet or electron microscopy. These methods permit identification and localization of serum globulins in the brain.

In one study, IgG seral fractions from two acutely ill schizophrenic patients and one healthy control subject were obtained by ion exchange chromatography. When tested in monkeys, the two schizophrenic fractions were psychoactive, whereas the control fraction was inert. Fractions from 80 ml. of sera of each of these subjects were then tagged with ferritin and fluorescein isothiocyanate. Each tagged fraction was injected intravenously into a monkey: one schizophrenic fraction into a monkey prepared with the standard array of cortical and subcortical electrodes,[14] the other schizophrenic fraction into a monkey without electrodes, and the control fraction into a monkey without electrodes. The electrodes permitted monitoring of EEGs, but since the inevitable lesion from implantation could conceivably alter the blood-brain barrier, monkeys without electrodes were included for comparative purposes. Immunoelectrophoretic analysis (IEA) of the tagged fractions showed essentially the same protein bands as the untagged fractions.

The two monkeys that received the tagged schizophrenic fractions showed characteristic behavioral effects of taraxein, and the one with electrodes showed the characteristic focal abnormality in septal EEGs. Tagging did not, therefore, eliminate psychosis-inducing activity. No response was observed in the monkey that received the tagged control fraction. Twenty minutes after injection, at the usual peak of the clinical and EEG response to taraxein, the monkeys were killed, their brains removed as rapidly as possible, and the septal region, caudate nucleus, hippocampus, brain stem, cerebellum, and cortex rapidly dissected. Half the tissue of each region was frozen for sectioning and examination by ultraviolet microscopy for the presence of fluorescein. The other half was immediately sectioned into standard small 1-mm. cubes, and alternate cubes were dipped into the same conjugated ferritin-tagged schizophrenic IgG that had been injected intravenously into the monkey. Both dipped and undipped cubes were fixed in 4 per cent gluteraldehyde and sectioned for examination by electron microscopy for the presence of ferritin.*

Ultraviolet microscopic examination of the frozen tissues showed brightly fluorescing cells in the septal region of both monkeys that received the tagged schizophrenic IgG, but no distinct fluorescence on any brain tissues of the monkey that received the control IgG fraction.

Electron microscopy showed ferritin granules on extranuclear, intracellular structures of undipped septal tissues of the two monkeys that received ferritin-tagged IgG of schizophrenic sera, and much more, but diffuse, ferritin throughout septal tissues that had been dipped in the tagged schizophrenic serum. Ferritin was not observed on either dipped or undipped septal tissues of the monkey that received the ferritin-tagged IgG of normal serum.

To improve tissue fixation and introduce additional controls, we did another study with ferritin, in which the monkeys were not killed until 40 minutes after injection of the test material into their femoral veins. Moreover, instead of rapid decapitation and dissection of the brain tissues, the brains of these monkeys were perfused with 4 liters of 1 per cent gluteraldehyde plus 1 per cent paraformaldehyde cacodylate buffer for more effective tissue fixation.

Four monkeys were used in this study: one received ferritin-tagged IgG of schizophrenic serum (taraxein), one the corresponding ferritin-

---

*Electron microscopy procedures were done by Austin Fitzjarrell in the laboratory of, and under the direction of, Dr. Eugene Copeland.

tagged IgG from serum of a patient with myasthenia gravis, one un-tagged IgG of schizophrenic serum (taraxein) followed immediately by injection of ferritin-tagged IgG from the serum of a healthy control subject, and one only ferritin. Ferritin was not seen on the brain of the monkey that received ferritin alone. In contrast, the brains of the monkeys that received the ferritin-tagged taraxein and the untagged taraxein followed immediately by ferritin-tagged IgG from serum of a healthy control subject showed significant ferritin in tissues from a focal site in the center of the septal region (Fig. 1). Minimal ferritin was also present at this site of the brain of the monkey that received ferritin-tagged IgG of a patient with myasthenia gravis. In each in-stance, the ferritin was largely confined within the membrane of specific cells, diffuse in the cytoplasm. It was not detected in the nucleus. And clumps of ferritin were seen in capillary walls. Small amounts were also seen within the myelin, probably on processes of glial cells.

The ability of a molecule the size of the schizophrenic IgG (taraxein) to penetrate the blood-brain barrier has previously been questioned.[17] In these studies with tagged globulins, not only the intravenously injected IgG molecule (150,000 molecular weight), but also the ferritin used for tagging (430,000 molecular weight) were demonstrated in the brain. These data suggest that IgG of patients with some neurologic diseases not associated with structural lesions of the brain (in par-ticular, myasthenia gravis and schizophrenia) can penetrate the blood-brain barrier of intact rhesus monkeys.

Changes in EEGs which occur with administration of taraxein indi-cate altered neural cell activity. The presence of tagged material in satellite glial cells suggests that taraxein may assert its effect on re-cordings, and consequently on behavior, by altering the relationship between satellite glial cells and neural cells. But these studies must be considered preliminary. More experiments are required, and all brain tissues of recipients must be studied in much greater detail before the findings can be considered conclusive.

Relation of Taraxein to the Clinical Signs of Schizophrenia

Although many variables prevent precise evaluation of the relation between taraxein and clinical schizophrenia, we speculate, on the basis of extensive studies over many years, that taraxein is probably present in all schizophrenic patients. But we have failed to substantiate this postulate with our present assay methods. The passive-transfer monkey

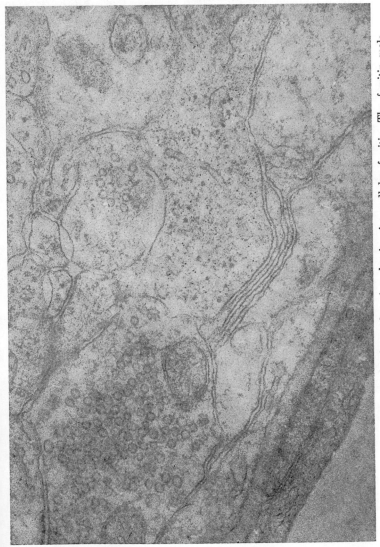

Fig. 1.—Electronmicrograph of septal region showing intracellular ferritin. The ferritin molecules are the small, diffuse black dots almost completely confined within one structure. Tissue was stained with uranyl acetate and lead citrate. Magnification about 75,000.

test requires high titers of taraxein, which appear to be obtainable only from serum of fully symptomatic patients. Our speculation, therefore, will be proved or disproved only when methods that we are trying to develop for detection of minute amounts of the psychosis-inducing globulin are perfected. Nevertheless, recent evidence, along with earlier findings from clinical studies of taraxein, suggest that schizophrenia is a single disease process. The evolution of this concept, and the difficulties involved in proving it, are illustrated by a review of 25 subjects from whom plasma was recently obtained.

Plasma donors. Of the most recent 25 subjects studied in the taraxein investigation, 19 were schizophrenic patients who represented all major symptomatic subcategories of schizophrenia (paranoid, hebephrenic, catatonic, undifferentiated). The other 6 donors were control subjects: two were healthy medical students, one a patient with systemic lupus erythematosus, one a patient with myasthenia gravis, one a healthy laboratory technician, and one a patient with toxic psychosis.

Methods and results. Plasmapheresis ion exchange double blood-pack was used to obtain a large volume of plasma (about 500 ml.) from a single drawing from a single subject. Plasma was withdrawn from the donors at intervals of two to three days, in some subjects as few as two times and in others as many as 20 times.

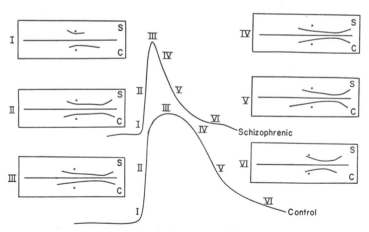

DEAE Sephadex A-50 Chromatograph TRIS pH 7.0

Fig. 2.—Uvicord graph (254 millimicrons) of eluates from ion exchange column showing essentially no differences between fractions of schizophrenic and normal serum. IEA of various sub-fractions from each column shows IgG only.

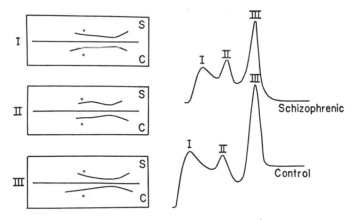

DEAE Sephadex A-50 Rechromatograph TRIS pH 8.0
of IgG Fractions

Fig. 3.—Uvicard graph (254 millimicrons) of fractions obtained by rechromato-
graphing globulins obtained from the pH 7.0 eluate shown in Fig. 2. Psychosis-
inducing activity was found only in the schizophrenic fraction I.

Plasma or serum was fractionated by modifications of the previously
described ion exchange chromatography (DEAE-Sephadex A-50) procedure,[14] and serum fractions were tested by our standard assay procedure, with use of Macaca rhesus monkeys prepared with depth and
cortical electrodes and intraventricular cannulas.

Although the standard pH of the buffer used in the fractionation was
7.5, it was sometimes adjusted to pH 7.0 or 8.0 in efforts to study properties of the psychosis-inducing fraction. Sometimes an initial 40 per
cent ammonium sulfate precipitate of the globulin was obtained to
remove albumin and globulin other than IgG. On other occasions, whole
serum was dialyzed overnight, with 60 ml. being placed on a 100 cm.
column.* Parts of the initial column were rechromatographed to obtain
a taraxein fraction that was more refined and contained less total protein (Figs. 2 and 3).

Psychosis-inducing activity (taraxein activity) was demonstrated in
serum fractions of each of the 19 schizophrenic patients at least once,
and usually repeatedly. But we failed, at least once, to demonstrate
taraxein activity in serum fractions of all but 2 of these patients; both
these exceptions were in patients who had been overtly psychotic

*A procedure we are presently using routinely.

throughout the study. Serum fractions from the 6 control subjects were consistently inert.

The most consistent observation in the study was the demonstration of taraxein activity in serum fractions of schizophrenic patients from whom plasma had been obtained when they were showing full-blown, well-developed secondary signs of schizophrenia with undeniable, gross delusions and hallucinations. In contrast, we have failed to observe taraxein activity in the monkey assay, essentially a passive transfer phenomenon, after patients had significant remission of signs.

Other variables further complicate efforts to correlate clinical signs with taraxein activity. On ten occasions when the schizophrenic patient-donors were fully symptomatic, we failed to observe taraxein activity in their serum fractions; these failures we attribute to inconsistencies in the fractionation procedure. Although DEAE Sephadex A-50 ion exchange chromatography has by far proved the most efficient method for obtaining taraxein, the columns are by no means identical from one run to the next. When we have fractionated samples of the same serum more than once, we have observed differences in activity, as well as in physical qualities of the fractions. We have noted variations, for example, in rate of flow, in concentration of protein eluting from the column at equivalent time intervals, and in the place on the Uvicord graph where the taraxein activity appears.

Continual minor modifications in our column fractionation methods are gradually increasing our effectiveness in obtaining taraxein, but considerable improvement is still required. We are now consistently successful in obtaining pure IgG in all preparations. But since taraxein is but a minute part of the total schizophrenic IgG fraction, methodologic problems are concerned with consistently locating taraxein within the IgG fraction. Testing of the entire IgG fraction in the monkey usually fails to show activity—apparently because the taraxein is too diluted by inactive IgG molecules. Because of the many variables, other researchers engaged in taraxein studies should start with a large pool of serum from acutely psychotic schizophrenic patients and should fractionate many samples from this pool in examining the relation of taraxein to psychotic schizophrenic behavior.

Obviously, we are not sufficiently advanced technologically, in either fractionation or assay methods, to obtain specific statistics in order to conclusively prove the contention suggested by our data—that taraxein is present in all schizophrenics and that schizophrenia is a single disease.

REFERENCES

1. Heath, R. G., with Tulane University Department of Psychiatry and Neurology: Studies in Schizophrenia. Cambridge, Harvard University Press, 1954.

2. Heath, R. G., and Mickle, W. A.: Evaluation of seven years' experience with depth electrode studies in human patients. In: Ramey, E. R., and O'Doherty, D. S. (Eds.): Electrical Studies on the Unanesthetized Brain. New York, Paul B. Hoeber, Inc., 1960, pp. 214-247.

3. Heath, R. G., and Gallant, D. M.: Activity of the human brain during emotional thought. In: Heath, R. G. (Ed.): The Role of Pleasure in Behavior. New York, Hoeber Medical Division, Harper & Row, Publishers, Inc., 1964, pp. 83-106.

4. Heath, R. G.: Developments toward new physiologic treatments in psychiatry. J. Neuropsychiat. 5:318-331, 1964.

5. Heath, R. G.: Schizophrenia: Biochemical and physiologic aberrations. Int. J. Neuropsychiat. 2:597, 1966.

6. Heath, R. G.: Schizophrenia: studies of pathogenesis. In: Biological and Clinical Aspects of the Central Nervous System. Presented at the 50th Anniversary Symposium of the Pharmaceutical Department of Sandoz, Inc., Basle, 1967.

7. Mettler, F. A. (Ed.): Selective Partial Ablation of the Frontal Cortex. New York, Paul B. Hoeber, Inc., Harper & Brothers, 1949.

8. Rado, S., Buchenholz, B., Dunton, H., Karlen, S. H., and Senescu, R.: Schizotypal organization: preliminary reports on a clinical study of schizophrenia. In: Rado, S., and Daniels, G. (Eds.): Changing Concepts of Psychoanalytic Medicine. New York, Grune & Stratton, 1956, pp. 225-235.

9. Heath, R. G.: Behavioral changes following destructive lesions in the subcortical structures of the forebrain in cats. In: Studies in Schizophrenia. Cambridge, Harvard University Press, 1954, pp. 83-84.

10. Heath, R. G.: Physiological and biochemical studies in schizophrenia with particular emphasis on mind-brain relationships. Int. Rev. Neurobiol. 1:299, 1959.

11. Heath, R. G., Leach, B. E., Monroe, R. R., Mickle, W. A., and Strohmeyer, F. B.: Immediate chemical and behavioral effects with stimulation of chronically implanted electrodes in rhesus monkeys and in patients. In: Studies in Schizophrenia. Cambridge, Harvard University Press, 1954, pp. 555-564.

12. Heath, R. G.: Pleasure response of human subjects to direct stimulation of the brain: physiologic and psychodynamic considerations. In: Heath, R. G. (Ed.): The Role of Pleasure in Behavior. New York, Hoeber Medical Division, Harper & Row, Publishers, Inc., 1964, pp. 219-243.

13. Heath, R. G., and Krupp, I. M.: Schizophrenia as an immunologic disorder. I. Demonstration of antibrain globulins by fluorescent antibody technics. Arch. Gen. Psychiat. 16:1, 1967.

14. Heath, R. G., Krupp, I. M., Byers, L. W., and Liljekvist, J. I.: Schizophrenia as an immunologic disorder. II. Effects of serum protein fractions on brain function. Arch. Gen. Psychiat. 16:10, 1967.

15. Heath, R. G., Martens, S., Leach, B. E., Cohen, M., and Angel, C. A.: Effect on behavior in humans with the administration of taraxein. Amer. J. Psychiat. 114:14, 1957.

16. Heath, R. G.: An antibrain globulin in schizophrenia. In: Himwich, H. E. (Ed.) : Biochemistry, Schizophrenia, and Affective Illnesses. Baltimore, Williams & Wilkins Company, in press.

17. Lehmann, H.: Discussion of Heath, R. G., and Krupp, I. M.: Schizophrenia as a specific biologic disease. Amer. J. Psychiat. 124:1024, 1968.

18. Heath, R. G., and Krupp, I. M.: Catatonia induced in monkeys by antibrain antibody. Amer. J. Psychiat. 123-12, 1967.

19. Heath, R. G., Krupp, I. M., Byers, L. W., and Liljekvist, J. I.: Schizophrenia as an immunologic disorder. III. Effects of antimonkey and antihuman brain antibody on brain function. Arch. Gen. Psychiat. 16:24, 1967.

20. Porter, R. R.: The hydrolysis of rabbit gamma globulin and antibodies with crystalline papain. Biochem J. 73:119, 1959.

21. Hsiaso, S., and Putnam, F. W.: The cleavage of human gamma-globulin by papain. J. Biol. Chem. 236:122, 1961.

22. Heath, R. G., and Founds, W. L.: A perfusion cannula for intracerebral microinjections. Electroenceph. Clin. Neurophysiol. 12:930, 1960.

23. Strauss, A. J. L., Seegal, B. C., Hsu, K. C., Burkholder, P. M., Nastuk, W. L., and Osserman, K. E.: Immunofluorescence demonstration of a muscle-binding, complement-fixing serum globulin fraction in myasthenia gravis. Proc. Soc. Exp. Biol. Med. 105:184, 1960.

Discussion of Dr. Heath's Paper

by CURTIS A. WILLIAMS, Ph.D.

The Rockefeller University

IT IS WELL that you understand that I come to this podium wearing two hats, that of a collaborator as well as that of a critical discussant. Also, since I am a biochemist, specifically an immunologist, my remarks will be limited to these aspects of the problem.

The proposal that schizophrenia finds its origins in part in auto-immune phenomena is most intriguing. The model fits at least one of the major categories of auto-immune phenomena, that involving a normally *sequestered antigen*. It also fulfills, at least in spirit, the "postulates" of auto-immune disease. These are: 1) there is a known antigen, 2) the antigen can be used experimentally to induce disease symptoms, and 3) a specific antibody can be detected and/or localized in affected structures or compartments.

Starting with the last of Witebsky's postulates,[*] we cannot help but be impressed by the results of experiments with fluorescein-labelled anti-human globulin and ferritin-labelled γG immunoglobulin (IgG) from schizophrenic donors. All pathologists will agree that these are definitive diagnostic methods when properly performed and controlled. Those experienced with immunofluorescence techniques, however, all agree that they are difficult to apply in a routine manner that affords uniformly confident interpretation. Due to a variety of non-specific effects often of the most frustrating nature, rigorous controls are essential. No investigator should be sensitive about being questioned in this regard, and I know that Drs. Heath and Krupp have welcomed careful scrutiny of their methods. The remarkable finding, in this case, according to those who are interested in antibrain antibodies, is the specificity of the "schizophrenic" immunoglobulin for a limited region of the brain. Apparently, this is the first instance of such specificity.

The intracellular localization of ferritin-IgG by electron microscopy is triply impressive. First, it confirms the fluorescence study; second, it shows up the "blood-brain barrier" as a rather leaky dike; and third, it suggests that brain cells probably use a mechanism akin to pinocytosis for intake (one does not readily imagine a complex of molecular weight greater than 600,000 passing through the cell membrane).

---

[*] See Dameshek, W.: Autoimmunity: theoretical aspects. Ann. N.Y. Acad. Sci. 124:1, 1965.

The first and second postulates, that there is a known antigen, and that it will induce experimental symptoms of the disease, will have to be accepted in spirit pending further exacting investigation. Some antigenic substance in the septum induces an antibody in sheep, which in turn induces the same symptoms that are induced by schizophrenic human IgG in monkeys. Thus, while the antigen is not known, it is known to exist, which in itself is very significant. The imaginative use of the sheep antibody may help in identifying the target site which binds the psychoactive human IgG.

Determining the nature of this site seems to me critical to the understanding of the auto-immune hypothesis. Cautious interpretation of the phenomena Drs. Heath and Krupp have already described, however, tell us something about the target site. Fluorescent antibody detects bound IgG on brain sections from acute schizophrenics only if the tissue is obtained within a few hours *post mortem*. Also, the physiological and behavioral effects of psychotogenic IgG injected into monkeys and human volunteers are of relatively short duration (2 to 3 hours). It is not likely that rapid destruction of bound IgG can account for the transitory nature of these phenomena, since this does not occur elsewhere in the body nor has it been observed in other auto-immune states. I therefore suggest that the target site is part of a macromolecular structure that is labile, and that in the living cell it is rapidly replaced. In autopsy material it is also broken down, releasing the now blocked (or neutralized) IgG. Blocked IgG released *in vivo* cannot bind anew to the replenished target sites; in tissue sections, of course, it is washed away with other unbound IgG. This interpretation is consistent with the fact that there are no consistently observable histological abnormalties in brain sections of schizophrenics.

In some other auto-immune diseases there are characteristic signs of tissue damage, but the target site in such cases is usually on the cell surface, and the production of the lesion often involves complement and/or auxiliary cellular responses. In the case of schizophrenia, the evidence suggests a model in which none of these events occur. Instead, we have a cytophysiological embarrassment in the brain cell due to the binding of a specific antibody globulin to a vital intracellular structure, whose function is impaired so long the antibody is present.

There are, however, several biologically active "spots" on immunoglobulin molecules, and it is proper to question whether any of these activities (e.g., placenta and membrane passage, complement fixation, etc.), rather than simple antigen binding capacity, are responsible for the effects observed. Until the antigen is identified, this question cannot be conclusively answered, but since the DEAE method of preparation has been introduced, there is no question but that IgG is the humoral component implicated in the studies reported by Heath and his co-workers.

The experiment concerning the papain fragmentation of immunoglobulin to which Dr. Heath alluded was performed to provide further evidence for the association of the characteristic physiological activity (focal spiking and slow wave activity in septum of monkeys) with the immunoglobulin in its capacity to bind antigen. The fragments—Fc, which has the sites required for membrane and complement-fixing activity, and Fab, which has the antigen-binding sites—are readily separable from undigested IgG and smaller digestion products by column chromatography on Sephadex G-100, and then from each other by electrophoresis on powder blocks such as starch or Pevikon. We have found Fab fragment to be active and the Fc fragment to be inactive when introduced intraventricularly to the monkey. We tentatively conclude, therefore, that schizophrenic human IgG expresses its activity through its ability to bind via the specific antibody sites to a substance in the neural cells of the septum. We can definitely conclude from these results that, whatever the reason for the psychotogenic activity, the activity does not depend on complement fixation or on Fc–dependant membrane activity.

In conclusion, I would like to mention some of the crucial questions that must be answered by further research: 1) Is the active IgG an antibody induced by the brain antigen, or an exogenous antigen? 2) Is the specificity not induced but inherited, encoded in the genetic repertory for immunoglobulin production? 3) What affects the plasma level of the active IgG?

There are more questions, of course; the one most frequently posed concerns the causal relationship of schizophrenic human IgG to the disease. At the present state of knowledge, the charitable view toward this question is that it is premature. The auto-immunity hypothesis is neither bold nor farfetched; it is merely the only working hypothesis into which the observations described this morning will fit. If they are real phenomena, then the question of their being epiphenomena translates thus: is the production of a psychotogenic immunoglobulin due to a set of conditions induced in part by the immunoglobulin itself? But here, as a biochemist, I must abandon the discussion, since it has gone beyond my depth.

Discussion of Dr. Heath's Paper

By THEODORE MILLON, Ph.D.

Lehigh University

EXCEPT for a few aspects, the Tulane group is to be commended for its scrupulous approach to matters of control, and for its efforts to recast earlier theoretical speculations in line with new data. The impressive and intriguing experiments reported by Professor Heath illustrate the fruits of his ongoing 18-year project. That these studies have an aesthetic unity and internal merit of their own cannot be denied, but questions still remain as to whether they validate schizophrenic biogenesis, and whether the immunologic thesis presented is the most parsimonious of explanations in this regard.

I shall limit my comments to a brief critical discussion of two assumptions underlying not only the Tulane studies, but many of the papers presented in this symposium. The *first*, the assumption of schizophrenic homogeneity, cannot be ignored because it continues to impede progress in psychopathologic research; the *second*, the assumption of biochemical causality, must be spelled out experimentally if we are to achieve some clarity concerning the nature of psychopathologic biogenesis.

1. The view that schizophrenia represents a homogeneous entity has been a persistent and unproductive assumption both in clinical and laboratory research. On every criterion, save that of pathologic severity and disturbed regulatory controls, patients labeled schizophrenic are more different than alike. In fact, one of the more consistent findings of research is that there is greater within-group variability among so-called schizophrenics than is true of a comparable normal population. Those who maintain the single disease assumption handle this troublesome finding by reference to Bleuler's distinction between primary and secondary clinical symptoms. Primary signs such as anhedonia, deriving directly from alleged biogenic sources, are seen as common to all schizophrenics; heterogeneity arises in the form of secondary symptoms, such as the specific content of delusions, and are attributed to the inevitable diversity of psychogenic experience.

The distinction suggested by Bleuler *can* account for schizophrenic heterogeneity, via secondary symptomatology, but it does not negate the possibility that the primary symptoms themselves may reflect a host of *different* biogenic aberrations. For example, those who opt for a genetic explanation of schizophrenia need not assume that the same defective gene underlies the entire realm of "schizophrenic behavior"; rather, different genes may be involved, each resulting in a matrix of different physiochemical and anatomic abnormalities, yet producing similar regulative dysfunctions. An illustration from another, appreciably less complicated, medical syndrome may clarify this point. It has been shown that there are upwards of 40 different genetically-based auditory defects conducive to deafness. Should we not expect in so much more complex an organ system as the brain that at least as many different genetic factors may give rise to schizophrenic vulnerability? And if we are to take our genetic colleagues seriously, should we not recognize their concept of phenocopies, and expect that regulative dysfunctions produced by genetic defects may be simulated, in indistinguishable form, by environmental conditions? It seems to me that research and explanatory models must take cognizance of a primary schizophrenic heterogeneity; otherwise, we are destined to continue the treadmill of past confusion and contradictory findings.

2. That biochemical dysfunctions can give rise to psychopathology is not debatable. However, the fact that a chemical substance may be associated with a mental disorder is no reason to assume that its role was causal, or even that it be implicated as a significant factor in the mediation of the pathologic outcome. There is an unfortunate tendency in the recent literature to assume that if unanticipated chemical findings are located within the brain, then they must be central to psychopathology. What this line of thinking fails to recognize is the possibility that these neurochemical factors may reflect epiphenomena, superficial signs that happen to correlate with the behavior disturbance, but are not their cause. Neurohormonal indices may be as peripheral to pathology as are changes in heart rate, muscle potential, adrenal activity, etc. Suggestive though findings of neurochemical "anomalies" may be, and important though they may prove to be in elucidating the mechanisms of neurophysiology, we may assign them unwarranted etiologic significance simply because we do not understand their role in the brain. Combined with the fragmentary nature of knowledge concerning neural transmission, brain locus becomes a powerful stimulant for ingenious, but often unverifiable, speculation.

The fact that endogenous substances may induce psychotic-like behavior in normals in no way strengthens the causal argument. To use an analogy—facile though they are, adrenaline extracts from hyper-anxious patients injected into normals will induce anxiety-like symptoms; by no stretch of the imagination, however, do we conclude that the *original* cause of the patients' anxiety was adrenaline excess. Extrapolating from this analogy, it may be that taraxein and IgG are but secondary or tertiary phases of a complicated causal chain. The fact that taraxein rapidly induces psychotic-like behavior in normals supports this thesis, as does the fact that its presence decreases rapidly with the abatement of clinical signs.

If the Tulane hypothesis surmounts this complication by postulating that schizophrenics are constitutionally disposed to produce taraxein under conditions of stress, then we should be able to identify its presence before it attains clinical proportions. Unless it takes an all-or-none form, which would be inconsistent with the insidious development of schizophrenia, these substances should be manifest in reduced magnitude in a variety of premorbid states. If this cannot be demonstrated, it should be shown to "act up," so to speak, in disposed individuals, such as normal monozygotic twin controls, under specially arranged stressful laboratory conditions. Studies of this type are necessary if we are to make more explicit the character and timing of the ostensive chemical action, and the environmental precipitants that are likely to potentiate its presumed effects.

12

PSYCHOPHARMACOLOGY AND PSYCHOPATHOLOGY

by JONATHAN O. COLE, M.D.*

IN TRYING to develop a meaningful presentation appropriate to the title of this paper, I have spent time trying to decide what I or anybody else means by "psychopathology." It appears to be a word almost as protean in its meanings as "stress" or "improvement" or "systems analysis." Webster and I agree that it covers the study and understanding of abnormalities in thought and behavior associated with mental illness. Oscar Diethelm,[1] my original teacher in psychiatry, felt that the term included both the abnormal phenomena presented by the patient and the understanding of their origin and cause. He assigned Kraepelin, Freud, and Adolph Meyer the key roles in the development of the science of psychopathology as he understood it. Nowadays one would have to include abnormalities in family structure and patterns of communication, and someone may even have written on the psychopathology of cities and the psychopathology of poverty. In short, I think it is a very broad term covering almost anything that is wrong with anybody anywhere at any time, what its nature is, and how it came to be that way. I am not prepared to cover so wide a terrain, having neither the time, the skill, nor the knowledge. Since this symposium as a whole covers the biological understanding of mental illness, I will focus on the abnormal signs and symptoms associated with major mental illness—e.g., schizophrenia and depression, with some side excursions into anxiety, an equally global concept.

It seems to me that after 15 years of experience with chlorpromazine and more than 25 years of experience with LSD, not to mention even longer experience with related biological treatments such as insulin coma, electroconvulsive therapy, and lobotomy, the science of

---

*Boston State Hospital.

psychopathology should have been greatly enriched. It does not appear to me that that is the case.

My earliest major contact with psychopharmacology and psychopathology is still in many ways the most dramatic. The administration of sodium amobarbital intravenously to a mute, rigid, and withdrawn catatonic schizophrenic in near stupor, can temporarily create an individual who speaks coherently, communicates appropriately both cognitively and affectively, and appears singularly free from major psychopathology, except for perhaps a little flatness of affect and a lack of understanding as to the cause of the catatonic stupor from which he or she has just emerged. It would seem to me that this ought to tell us something about the nature of catatonic schizophrenia and the abnormalities in brain function underlying it. To date nothing very creative or definitive has come out of this fascinating and replicable phenomenon. The best I can do as a psychobiological interpretation of it is to utilize Irwin's[2] thesis, supported by data of several investigators, that drugs like amobarbital and the other barbiturates and the minor tranquilizers have a specific effect on approach–avoidance conflicts, permitting rats to risk getting a shock to get something they want. This would fit with some psychoanalytic theories that catatonic stupor is the result of a severe conflict between fear of action and desire for action. If this were the case it would explain amytal's remarkable effect to some extent. This effect of amytal in catatonic stupor has been little studied in recent years.

There has, however, been a good deal of attention given to the concept of sedation threshold and the use of barbiturates as a tool in the study of mental illness. There appears to be reasonable evidence that intravenous sodium amytal administered at a standard rate with the use of reasonably reliable and standardized criteria for determining a sedation threshold, whether by EEG or GSR, will discriminate in an intriguing manner between patients showing different kinds of gross psychopathology. Crudely, non-psychotic patients show a higher sedation threshold, the more intense their anxiety and tension. Psychotic patients, whether schizophrenic or depressed, tend to show a much lower sedation threshold even in the presence of relatively severe anxiety or tension. The sedation threshold technique may therefore have real diagnostic value, and may also indicate major differences in central nervous system functioning between psychotic patients and non-psychotic patients.[3,4] If we can then take as a fact that schizophrenics are more sensitive to barbiturates and neurotics are less sensitive to barbiturates, we must add to this the equally interesting fact that, by and large, clinical experience suggests that schizophrenics are much less sensitive to the adverse affects of phenothiazines than are neurotics, and that schizophrenics can tolerate a dose of 1500 milligrams of chlorpromazine without batting an eye, while a normal or neurotic patient may be almost totally incapacitated by 100 milligrams of Thorazine. This phenomenon has not been studied with any care experimentally, and no one has tried to develop a phenothiazine threshold, though Shagass has suggested the possibility of such a thing. Gilberti and Rossi[5] have utilized an autonomic blood pressure and pulse threshold in developing a stimulation threshold measure with intraveneous methamphetamine. They found quite clearly that psychotic depressives had a higher threshold than neurotic depressives. Again, this suggests the drugs may tell us something about differences between gross psychopathological conditions. It would be interesting to see whether this method would or would not discriminate between non-depressed neurotics and schizophrenics, acute or chronic.

The effect of barbiturates, phenothiazines, and amphetamines on chronic schizophrenics have been examined by Kornetsky and his co-workers.[6,7] Their underlying hypothesis is that the barbiturates will primarily impair higher cognitive functions and will result more in errors of commission, while a phenothiazine will impair tasks requiring sustained attention and alertness (watching for an irregularly appearing stimulus). Paradoxically, schizophrenics are substantially worse than normals on the sustained attention task, and their performance is improved by the phenothiazines, while performance on this task is selectively impaired in normals by the phenothiazines. Kornetsky explains this by utilizing an apparent U-shaped relationship between level of alertness or activation, functioning being optimal at the middle of the U and impaired at either end. He hypothesizes that chronic schizophrenics are over-alert, and the phenothiazines reduce their alertness in the direc- of the center of the U, thereby improving performance. Fragmentary data[6] on the effects of 20 milligrams of amphetamine on the sleep of 7 chronic schizophrenics suggests that amphetamine may increase sleep in such individuals. It becomes difficult to fit Dr. Kornetsky's findings in with those of Dr. Shagass and the other workers who have tended to confirm his results. Dr. Kornetsky has not found schizophrenics to be more sensitive to barbiturates than are normals. However, he has used sleeping time in response to hypnotic doses as an end point, not sedation threshold. Also, many of his schizophrenic subjects have been chronic, and Shagass does not find lowered sedation threshold to barbiturates in chronic schizophrenics, only in acute ones.

An equally intriguing set of data, which I am unable to place appropriately into this examination of the effects of sedatives, stimulants, and phenothiazines on behavior, is the ability of amphetamine and related stimulants to improve the performance and functioning of hyperkinetic school children.[8] Here amphetamine appears to enable the children to focus their attention more appropriately and to resist distraction. They appear more cheerful and better organized. Children who are benefited by amphetamine tend to be made more distractable and more hyperactive by the barbiturates. If many of these children have some kind of minimal brain damage possibly affecting the cortex, one could fit the exacerbation of their symptoms with barbiturates into Dr. Kornetsky's model. A further impairment of cognitive function by a barbiturate would certainly not benefit such a child. It also would fit with Irwin's model holding that barbiturates increase response to the environment and reduce sensitivity to aversive controls over behavior. It is conceivable that amphetamines would push children who are already over-aroused into still further arousal and therefore make them less alert, but it is hard to see why that should actually improve their school performance. It is also hard to make this jibe with the ability of the amphetamines to produce paranoid schizophrenic-like states[9] characterized by paranoid misinterpretation of stimuli coming in from the environment.

In terms of our understanding of the psychopathology of schizophrenia, it is difficult to identify any studies utilizing phenothiazines that have made major or revolutionary contributions in this field. Our interpretation of data from collaborative studies carried out under the National Institute of Mental Health's Psychopharmacology Program have led us to three gross conclusions. One is that the phenothiazine drugs have a rather broad effect on a wide variety of schizophrenic symptom areas.[10] They produce more improvement than placebo in almost every symptom area found in schizophrenics. The absolute amount of change attributable to the drug is greatest in a cluster of symptoms we call "core" symptoms, such as indifference to the environment, hebephrenic behavior, and poor self-care. These symptom areas tend to improve little on placebo and improve substantially more on drugs. The secondary symptoms of schizophrenia, such as paranoid ideas, hallucinations, and hostility, tend to improve somewhat on placebo and even more on drug, the difference between drug and placebo being somewhat less than that observed in the core symptoms.

Generally then, our position is that these drugs make schizophrenics somewhat better across a wide variety of symptom areas. This observation does not contribute greatly to our knowledge of either schizophrenia or the drugs. It appears to make things more amorphous rather than better understood. It could be considered an argument in favor of the general concept of schizophrenia. If phenothiazines make better many symptoms which Bleuler included within the schizophrenias and Kraepelin put in his broad category of dementia praecox, then perhaps schizophrenia is really a single disease entity. Perhaps the drugs are having a more basic effect on some underlying phenomenon like arousal level. In this case in Kornetsky's terms the phenothiazines are making schizophrenics less pathologically aroused and therefore better able to cope with their environment and able to function better and, therefore, they show less intense symptoms in all areas. In Killam's terms,[11] the phenothiazines may be improving the schizophrenic's ability to filter information coming in from the environment and to attend to important stimuli and to screen out irrelevant stimuli. This in turn would presumably lead the schizophrenic to become less hyper-aroused. The effects of these drugs seem so much broader than their effect on manifest anxiety that it seems difficult to use anxiety as the central construct upon which the drugs are presumed to act. On the other hand, perhaps I have just traded one rather vague construct, anxiety, for another, arousal. If both could be measured in pure form, they would probably correlate positively to some extent.

If, as Fink and others suggest, chlorpromazine[12] and thioridazine[13] are both effective treatments of depression and effective treatments of schizophrenia, maybe these drugs are good for psychosis of all kinds. This idea is somewhat weakened by Hollister's finding[13] that thioridazine is better in anxious depressions (presumably neurotic) and is less good than imipramine in retarded depressions (presumably psychotic).

Moving one step deeper into our data, the discrimination between core symptoms and secondary symptoms of schizophrenia[14] may well fit with some ideas of Venables. The core symptoms seem to share a common property of no further significant change after five weeks of treatment, while secondary symptoms continue to show significant further improvement between five weeks and thirteen weeks. This would suggest that there are two major types of schizophrenic symptomatology and possibly two major types of schizophrenia.

A major finding growing out of our third collaborative study[15] dealing with chronic schizophrenia and two dosage levels of chlorpromazine is that schizophrenics under 40 years of age, hospitalized less than 10 years, benefit from a high dose of chlorpromazine more than they do from a low dose, while schizophrenics over 40, hospitalized more than 10 years, show no further benefit from the higher dose, and, in fact, suffer a higher proportion of unpleasant side effects.

To state our findings in the most negative manner, it could be claimed that the large series of relatively expensive studies of phenothiazines in schizophrenia have led to the conclusions that 1) schizophrenics have something in common with each other; 2) paranoid schizophrenics are different from non-paranoid schizophrenics; and 3) more acute schizophrenics respond better to drugs than do more chronic schizophrenics.

I do not think any of these three statements would have been seriously challenged before the drug studies were done. My interpretation of another large and much more intensive study of a group of schizophrenic patients carried out by Gerard and his co-workers[16] at Ypsilanti State Hospital was that they found the paranoid schizophrenics performed better on a number of tests than did nonparanoid schizophrenics—another predictable finding.

The one finding growing out of our studies which seems to me to be truly relevant to psychopathology, in its most scientific sense, is the work[17] Goldberg and his co-workers did on a Shakow-type reaction time measure in our second acute schizophrenia collaborative study. This finding grew out of the baseline data and did not concern drugs at all. Here, utilizing the large sample available in this study, they correlated both paranoid symptomatology and core symptomatology with reaction time abnormality. They found that the degree of schizophrenic withdrawal did correlate very nicely with the defect in reaction time, while the amount of paranoid symptomatology present was uncorrelated with the abnormality in reaction time. Here the availability of a larger sample made possible the clarification of an issue arising out of earlier smaller studies. In the earlier studies the paranoid schizophrenics had generally done better on the reaction time measure and the non-paranoid schizophrenics had done worse, and it was not possible to partial out the effects of these two dimensions of schizophrenia on reaction time.

In conclusion, then, I am left with my mildly pessimistic original appraisal of this area, namely, that the newer drugs have made fewer discrete contributions to our knowledge of psychopathology than one might expect. Accumulated knowledge about psychopathology has certainly been useful in the evaluation of drugs, in that many rating scales of various sorts have been developed for the purpose of measuring drug effects in psychiatric conditions, and these have drawn heavily on an accumulated wisdom about psychopathology.

The use of such rating scales in large samples of patients, and the concomitant accumulation of knowledge about the factor structure of such complex instruments and of the inter-rater reliability of items and factors, has accumulated and is accumulating a large volume of data. This may some day be helpful in expanding our knowledge of the way in which various psychopathological symptoms are observed by observers, and the ways in which they relate to one another within patients, at a single point in time, and also the ways in which they change in individual patients, or in groups of patients over time, in response to drug or placebo therapy. However, this potential gold mine of varying degrees of reliability and validity has yet to be utilized in any remarkably insightful manner, and hence has not contributed any striking advances to our knowledge of psychopathology.

I think, in part that I and others actively interested in the field of psychopharmacology over the past ten years may have expected too much, both of the drugs and of psychopathology. There is a primitive simplistic hope in many of us that a drug, or for that matter a biochemical measure, will appear which relates so closely to a concept of anxiety that it can be used as a tool to either measure anxiety or to specifically alter it. If such a discovery were ever made, it is the fantasy of many investigators and clinicians that much about psychiatric patients that is now complicated and confusing would become simple and obvious, and that the role of anxiety in causing other psychiatric sequelae would then become clear. The universe would become more rational and great wisdom would be achieved by all. Similarly, one has the fantasy that there should be drugs which have specific unique and discrete effects upon such things as depression, hostility, apathy, obsessive thoughts, or even auditory hallucinations. Unfortunately, neither drugs nor the human mind, healthy or sick, seems to be as simple as we would like it. Drugs appear to be cursed with a variety of effects at a variety of levels in the central nervous system, and the signs and symptoms of mental illness appear to change or abate in widespread and complex ways in response to drugs. In general, it seems more likely that signs and symptoms of any mental disorder, whether schizophrenia or depression, will generally improve together, or will generally stay unchanged, rather than there being an abrupt change in one parameter, like anxiety or depression, followed by clearly secondary changes in other manifestations of a mental disorder.

Perhaps because drugs have not done clear, single, dramatic things to clear, single, dramatic psychiatric symptoms, they have, indeed, served a purpose in psychopathology—namely, to remind us that individual symptoms or signs of mental illness should generally not be studied or treated in isolation from other aspects of the patient or his illness, and that the complexity of phenomena, both pharmacologic and psychopathologic, must be faced and coped with.

REFERENCES

1. Diethelm, O.: Treatment in Psychiatry, 3rd ed. Springfield, Ill., Charles C. Thomas, 1966.

2. Irwin, S.: A rational framework for the development, evaluation, and use of psychoactive drugs. Amer. J. Psychiat. 124:8, 1968 (Feb. supplement).

3. Shagass, C.: Sedation Threshold: Technique and Concept in Neuropsychopharmacology, H. Brill et al., Eds., Excerpta Medica Foundation, Netherlands, 1967, pp. 921-925.

4. Perez-Reyes, M., Shands, H. D., and Johnson, G.: Galvanic skin response inhibition threshold: a new psychophysiologic technique. Psychosom. Med. 24:274-8, 1962.

5. Gilberti, F., and Rossi, R.: Stimulation Threshold. Technique, Concept and Results in Depression, in Neuropsychopharmacology, H. Brill et al., Eds., Excerpta Medica Foundation, Netherlands, 1967, pp. 926-930.

6. Kornetsky, C., and Mirsky, A. F.: On certain psychopharmacological and physiological differences between schizophrenics and normal persons. Psychopharmacologia, 8:309-318, 1966.

7. Orzack, M. H., Kornetsky, C., and Freeman, H.: The effects of daily administration of carphenazine on attention in the schizophrenic patient. Psychopharmacologia 11:31-38, 1967.

8. Conners, C. K., Eisenberg, L., and Barcai, A.: Effect of dextroamphetamine in children. Arch. Gen. Psychiat. 17:478-485, 1967.

9. Connell, P. H.: Amphetamine Psychosis. Maudsley Monograph No. 5. London, Institute of Psychiatry, 1958.

10. Klerman, G. L., Goldberg, S., and Cole, J. O.: Changes in schizophrenic pathology and ward behavior as a function of phenothiazine treatment. Brit. J. Psychiat. 3:120-133, 1965.

11. Killam, E. K.: Drug action on the brainstem reticular formation. Pharmacol. Rev. 14:175-197, 1962.

12. Fink, M., Klein, D. F., and Kramer, J. C.: Clinical efficacy of chlorpromazine-procyclidine combinations, imipramine, and placebo in depressive disorders. Psychopharmacologia 5:27-36, 1964.

13. Overall, J., Hollister, L., Meyer, F., Kimbell, I., and Shelton, J.: Imipramine and thioridazine in depressed and schizophrenic patients. J.A.M.A. 189:605-608, 1964.

14. Goldberg, S. C., Schooler, N. R., and Mattson, N.: Paranoid and withdrawal symptoms in schizophrenia. Prepublication Report 7, November, 1966.

15. Prien, R. F., and Cole, J. O.: High dose chlorpromazine therapy in chronic schizophrenia. Arch. Gen. Psychiat. 18:482-495, 1968.

16. Mattson, N. B., and Gerard, R. W.: Typology of schizophrenia based on multidisciplinary observational vectors. In: Katz, M. M., Cole, J. O., and Barton, W. E. (Eds.): The Role and Methodology of Classification in Psychiatry and Psychopathology. Publ. No. 1584, U.S. Government Printing Office, 1965, pp. 507-534.

17. Goldberg, S. C., Schooler, N. R., and Mattson, N.: Paranoid and withdrawal symptoms in schizophrenia: differential symptom reduction over time. J. Nerv. Ment. Dis. 145:158-62, 1967.

Discussion of Dr. Cole's Paper

by DANIEL X. FREEDMAN, M.D.

University of Chicago Medical School

THROUGH his sustained, searching, and successful work in the broad area of psychopharmacology, Jonathan Cole is clearly entitled to even a pessimistic overview of the extent to which our knowledge of psychopathology has been advanced by the use of pharmaceuticals. His is not a nihilistic commentary, but rather a challenge of naive assumptions and—implicitly—a program indicating the complexity of the tasks which yet confront us. Yet in assessing the extent of progress in a field, one's initial viewpoint is crucial. I was recently reminded of the fact that real experts are often impatient. I was watching an encounter between a sensation-seeking roving TV reporter and some of our colorful lay pharmacologists. Avid with expectation, he combed a hippie colony confidently asking about the known flood of drugs and marijuana in the area. After several cautiously equivocating replies, he found one honest beaded and bearded flower child who gave him a doleful gaze. "Do we have lots of pot here? Man, there's a shortage!"

Perhaps it is only out of a sense of perversity (or—as I conceive it—an initial pessimism) that I would stress the immense progress the introduction of these drugs has meant to the entire effort our professions give to the study of psychopathology, psychotherapeutics, and the organization of various behavioral states. Given the prevailing theories and attitudes of the early 1950's, one can see that the questions raised by the appearance of a number of psychoactive drugs gave a thrust to widely different neurobehavioral and clinical investigations, a momentum in problem-posing and in the development of methodologies and research attitudes which should carry us much further in the decades to come.

There was indeed progress. Appropriately, priority had to be given (as in Dr. Cole's collaborative NIMH studies) to the question of whether the drugs were efficacious in different disorders. Few studies in clinical pharmacology have been as well designed or as convincing.

Secondly, the very basic question of whether or not the neurochemistry of the brain was consequentially related to normal and

262

abnormal behavior was directly confronted by the presence of psychoactive drugs. The data compelled a consequential attitude: namely, that such parameters could not be ignored as determining factors and that their investigation was to be valued and pursued. At the least, students of behavior could not leave such factors out of account in their attempts to construct adequate theories, approaches, and responses to the problem of behavior disorders. Such fundamental orientations toward the nature of a problem are critical if a field is to develop and if people are to be willing to engage in a research effort. These advances, then, have turned attention to a new array of investigations and have given the kind of hope that launches work, the results of which we cannot yet foresee.

Of course there were naive assumptions prevalent at the onset of many of these studies. It was clear that we had not outlined what we *could* expect of drugs as a tool to analyze the organization of behavior. With respect to psychopathology, it would be naive to expect that drugs would be a direct route to those descriptions of the manifest outcome of different biobehavioral states with which our descriptive language is concerned. Processes and mechanisms have to be described in the language appropriate to the operations by which they are analyzed; we have to guard against reifying constructs. I suppose there was at one time a notion that an SKF center of the brain was not making sufficient chlorpromazine and that a Sandoz center was overproducing LSD!

And even if we were not this explicit, there were frequently notions that a therapeutic agent produced a "reversal" of a psychopathological process and hence that study of the drugs' effects could be a direct route to the psychopathological processes. The fact that an agent can facilitate organized behavior in the presence of disorganization does not mean that the mechanisms of therapeutic action allow us to recapitulate the factors leading to disorganization. In biology we are dealing with equilibria, with various steady states, and it is with the ongoing state that our therapeutics intervene; in a certain sense, we cannot run the film backwards.

Thus it has been clear that drugs change the milieu in which the contingencies controlling behavior operate, that we deal with different periods of drug action over time, and that we can expect different sets of variables to be more or less important as sequences of behavior unfold. Experimental work with drugs tells us something about how behavior *might* be organized with a different chemical milieu of the brain. The importance of prior state to drug action has, as Dr. Cole notes, long been observed. Joel and Charmian Elkes many years ago pointed out that amytal aroused and amphetamine sedated the catatonic. Numerous studies, such as those of Kornetsky's, have indicated that the prior biobehavioral state of a schizophrenic or the depressive is different than that of the normal. The clinical response to phenothiazines of the so-called functional psychoses and delirium tremens sharply differs; for the latter, drugs with sedative effects (paraldehyde, barbiturates, chlordiazepoxide) are far more effective, and thus we may search for different mechanisms. The challenge of course is to develop methodologies which could delineate the basis for such differences at a variety of levels—from the neurochemical to the behavioral.

Thus we have staked out a number of questions which can be pursued, and I am not surprised that we have a long way to go in delineating and differentiating a variety of psychopathological sequences. Currently one can see a far more sophisticated interest in differentiating the schizophreniform psychoses from the schizophrenic psychoses, stimulated in part by an attempt to refine the data on placebo and drug responders in the multi-hospital studies. Similarly, progress is discernible in the attempt to establish predictors in terms of personality or psychopathological features for specific and selective drug response. Scrutiny of the sequence of effects under a variety of behavioral contingencies observed with LSD indicates a number of hitherto unobserved mechanisms by which psychopathological end results might occur; for example, the failure to suppress a prior input leads to a coexistence of the past and present perception leading to illusions and—with loss of ego distance—hallucinations. Are such suppressive mechanisms and "boundary-establishing" functions basic psychopathological dimensions and, if so, how do we study them?

The problem always has been to refine our psychophysiological, psychophysical, and behavioral measures and aim them relevantly toward the way things might actually be. Thus the phenothiazines and the antidepressants have focused our attention on the varieties of ways by which behavior can be dissociated. We have begun to note the factor, rates of change of subsystems in therapy; for example, the frequent initial motor response to antidepressives—or lithium—is followed by changes in cognitive appreciation of this and in mood. Drugs such as lithium have raised the question of the control of the cycling of behavioral states. The phenothiazines indicate that the relationships between motor stimulation and sedation, between both of these and perceptual filtering, require fine investigation. The electrophysiological and perceptual studies of Callaway indicate that the array of processes we call habituation are relevant in the study of psychopathological states and that the response to slightly dissimilar inputs (the schizophrenic being unable to ignore the differences) distinguishes patients from normals. As I see it, then, there is growing expertise, a growing skill at devising situations and questions which promise to advance our knowledge of psychopathology. In the search for relevant mechanisms we have to discover the relevant dimensions and sequences, and I cannot believe that—whether it is on the level of clinical discriminations, individual differences, or neuropsychological and neurochemical investigations—the problems posed and studied because of the psychoactive drugs will not advance our knowledge. After all we have only begun widespread and seriously sustained effort in these ventures. I think the era over which Dr. Cole presided was a good beginning.

13

CYTOGENETIC ASPECTS OF PSYCHOPATHOLOGY

by LISSY F. JARVIK, Ph.D., M.D.*

IT WAS IN 1959 that the presence of an extra chromosome was recognized by Lejeune and colleagues[22] as the cause of the most common form of mental deficiency. Ever since this startling description of a chromosome abnormality in mongolism, or Down's syndrome, human cytogenetics has rivaled biochemical genetics in the rapidity of its advance. Barely a decade ago, the presence or absence of an entire chromosome was considered to preclude human viability. Today there are numerous examples of both.

Presence of an extra autosome, as distinguished from an extra sex chromosome, is often lethal *in utero* or early in infancy.

Complete absence of an autosome (presumed monosomy 21) has been reported only once in a living human being—a four and a half year old retarded girl with low-set ears and antimongoloid slanting eyes, among other characteristics—and remains to be confirmed.[2] By contrast, presence of one or more extra female sex chromosomes (XXX, XXXX, XXY, XXXY, etc.) is relatively common (frequency exceeds two per 1,000 newborns) and is compatible with survival to adulthood. Extra X chromosomes are found more often among samples of institutionalized mentally retarded than among samples of infants in nurseries, yet there are cases of Klinefelter's syndrome (XXY) with superior intelligence.

By and large, nearly all types of chromosomal aberration appear to be associated with impaired mental functioning. The lack of a sex chromosome in cases of Turner's syndrome (gonadal dysgenesis—XO) may be responsible for a specific deficit in space-form perception and numerical ability despite the manifestation of superior verbal ability.[23] Whatever the chromosomal aberrations, the behavioral correlates generally can be said to lie in the realm of intellectual rather than af-

---

* New York State Psychiatric Institute and Columbia University.

fective or social functioning. Surveys of institutions for mentally disturbed patients, unlike those for mentally retarded ones, usually fail to reveal significant cytogenetic abnormalities.

Like the proverbial rule, the above generalization has its exceptions, and it is to an exception that the next portion of this paper will be directed. First described just over two years ago,[17] it was succinctly summarized by the medical press as "XYY error makes men grow tall and go wrong."[4] The headline referred to the finding of 8 individuals with an extra Y chromosome in a group of 197 mentally retarded men with dangerous, violent, or criminal propensities in an institution where they were treated under conditions of special security. Indeed, the authors suggested that "in this particular group a man more than 72 inches in height has an approximately one in two chance of having an XYY constitution."

The full impact of this report can be understood in the light of the fact that, until its publication, the entire world literature contained perhaps a dozen scattered cases with an extra Y chromosome—compared to hundreds of cases with one or more extra X chromosomes. Further, Jacobs and her collaborators suggested for the first time that a behavioral anomaly other than mental retardation could result from a gross chromosomal anomaly. During the subsequent two years there have been over 20 publications describing persons with an extra Y chromosome, so that there have been over 100 recorded to date. Some of them have extra X chromosomes as well as one or more extra Y chromosomes, and there are several mosaics. While many of the previously described patients with an extra Y chromosome had physical stigmata, Jacobs and colleagues could discover no physical characteristics, other than the tall stature, that would differentiate their patients from other males, patients or not.

The XYY males described in the literature so far are about equally divided between those derived from isolated case reports and those discovered in more or less systematic surveys. In general, surveys of tall mentally defective or psychotic males have not yielded an unusual number with an extra Y chromosome unless the selection was based on antisocial behavior as well. Jacobs and collaborators pointed out in their initial report that it was unclear whether the increased frequency of the extra Y chromosome was related to the tall stature, the mental deficiency, the aggressive behavior, or a combination of all or some of these factors. Two years later, the situation is still equally unclear.

Some authors emphasize the presence of normal intelligence in persons with an extra Y chromosome,[6,26] while others stress the mental deficiency[8] and yet others emphasize that so far "no XYY male has been described with a superior intelligence."[32]

The tall stature, while usually associated with the syndrome, may not be a necessary concomitant either, a patient no taller than 66½ inches having been described (Barnard, personal communication). Again, the possibility exists that without the second Y chromosome this particular patient might have been of considerably shorter stature.

Even the unusually aggressive, antisocial or criminal behavior does not appear to be a *sine qua non* of the "YY" syndrome. The early literature often lacked behavioral information. Recently, however, a psychiatric patient with a compulsion to steal (which he had successfully resisted) was found to have an XYY karyotype.[24]

Our own search for persons with the XYY karyotype was begun early in 1966, at which time no information was available concerning the incidence of this abnormality among psychiatric patients. Male patients over six feet tall who were unusually difficult to manage because of aggressive behavior were designated by four mental hospitals, one penal institution and one hospital for the criminally insane.* Mental deficiency was not a criterion of selection.

As recently reported,[18] karyotype analyses of peripheral leukocytes were performed for 50 of these men. The normal male XY genotype with 46 chromosomes was found in all but two cases. One of these was a Klinefelter's with 47 chromosomes (XXY) and one a "supermale" with 47 chromosomes (XYY).

The XYY patient exhibited many of the characteristics described in the literature. At the time of our examination, he was 26 years old, 79 inches tall and weighed 205 pounds. He had been transferred to the hospital for the criminally insane after assaulting and threatening to kill an attendant and a patient at the mental hospital where he had been confined for many years. He had been a disciplinary problem from early childhood and at the age of 10 years was institutionalized at a special

---

*We hereby gratefully acknowledge the generous cooperation of Dr. W. C. Johnston, Matteawan State Hospital; C. L. McKendrick, Eastern Correctional Institution; Dr. H. Pleasure, Middletown State Hospital, now Deputy Commissioner, New York State Department of Mental Hygiene; Dr. H. B. Snow, Hudson River State Hospital; Dr. A. M. Stanley, Rockland State Hospital; and Dr. Z. Wisinger, Antigua Mental Hospital.

school for disturbed children. At the age of 20 he was sent to a mental hospital because of violent assaultive acts and after discharge committed various offenses including robbing, stealing and pocket picking. In addition to his anti-social behavior, he showed inappropriate affect as well as a thought disorder, was diagnosed as schizophrenic, and received electroconvulsive therapy, apparently without benefit. His history of hospitalization includes many assaultive acts and many escapes. Even in the hospital for the criminally insane, he was one of the most difficult management problems because of impulsive assaultive behavior. On psychological testing* he was rated of dull-normal intelligence (IQ 83) with performance exceeding verbal score. (It is of interest that the absence of a Y chromosome (XO) is associated with superior verbal ability and the presence of an extra Y (XYY) with inferior verbal ability.) His responses on a variety of projective tests were characteristic of chronic schizophrenia with aggressive preoccupation. The question of possible organic involvement was raised, but so far the patient has refused to submit to an EEG.

A single XYY located in a group of 50 males over six feet tall specifically selected on the basis of aggressive behavior (35 psychiatric patients and 15 prisoners) represents a low yield in comparison with some reports—e.g., two out of 24 prisoners[8] or four out of 34 prisoners.[32] Yet, other investigators have recorded frequencies as low as ours. Welch et al. examined the chromosomes of 24 defective delinquents over six feet tall, at least half of whom were unusually aggressive, and failed to find any with an extra Y chromosome.[31] They located only a single one among 22 similar cases when the minimum height in a second sample was raised from six feet to six feet two inches. Daly examined approximaetly 200 males over six feet tall, partly from hospitals for the retarded and partly from "maximum security hospitals," and found six with an extra Y chromosome.[11]

Further investigations will be needed in order to clarify the different frequencies as well as many other aspects of this intriguing new syndrome. Thus, several of the cases have had epileptic seizures,[12,13,31] (Barnard, personal communication) some of which have been controlled with dilantin. Even though most XYY males show no gross physical abnormality, abnormalities of the external genitalia have been observed in some. Similarly, some patients have had normal hormonal assays, while

---

*We are grateful to C. J. Bryson who administered the psychological test battery and generously made the results available to us.

in at least one an unusually high level of plasma testosterone has been observed.[31]

A convulsive diathesis would serve to explain the impulsive and unpredictable nature of the aggressive behavior, while the hormonal abnormality is consonant with the observation in several animal species of aggressive behavior resulting from the administration of androgens. If the extra Y chromosome leads to the production of excess androgens early in development, then even normal hormone levels in later life would be compatible with unusually aggressive behavior patterns. As suggested by Hamburg and Lunde with regard to normal sex differences in behavior, it is possible that ". . . the influence of androgen during a critical period in brain development on the circuits destined later to mediate aggressive behavior would have CNS-differentiating effects that would facilitate ease of learning aggressive patterns and increase readiness to learn such patterns." (p. 14).[15]

Incidentally, children with cerebral gigantism, normal karyotypes and normal endocrine functions have not been reported to show unusually aggressive behavior.[28] Exaggeration of the normal biological determinants of aggressive behavior through the actions of a second Y chromosome may engender aggression beyond the limits sanctioned by modern western culture for its masculine members and lead to conflict with society.

Aggressive behavior is not the only anti-social action with which the interests of geneticists have become identified. Diametrically opposed in behavior are today's "flower children," who in their quest for peaceful existence have collided with the law and have unwittingly performed cytogenetic experiments. Widely publicized reports, first appearing in 1967, emphasized the chromosomal damage in persons using LSD and the possibly deleterious effects upon their descendants. Simultaneously, a number of studies ascribed increasing fetal mortality and morbidity to LSD administered early in pregnancy to rats;[3] hamsters;[14] and mice.[5] The association between chromosome breakage and malignant neoplastic disease demonstrated for carcinogenic agents (e.g. radiation, nitrogen mustard) and for certain genetically determined syndromes—e.g., Fanconi's anemia[27] and Bloom's syndrome[7]—raised the spectre of neoplastic disease, malformation and genetic illness for untold future generations—the progeny of LSD users.

Not all investigators, however, reached similar conclusions. Loughman and collaborators cultured the leukocytes of 8 persons with a history of LSD ingestion and failed to find a single chromosome break in the 697 cells they examined.[21] By contrast, Cohen and collaborators had found 15.2 per cent breaks in 18 LSD users compared with 3.8 per cent breaks in 12 drug-free controls.[9] There was practically no overlap between the two groups (controls and drug users). Irwin and Egozcue, despite much higher absolute frequencies, reported similar relative differences between LSD users and drug-free controls.[16] In our own laboratory only a single case could be studied with high enough LSD ingestion (up to 1000 μg.) to warrant the expectation of an increase in chromosome breaks, but none was found.[19]

Differences in frequency of breaks recorded by various investigators may be due to a variety of factors, notably presence of unsuspected viral infection among drug-users, and exposure to other drugs or noxious chemicals. Individual differences in susceptibility to chromosome breakage induced by the ingestion of LSD may also account for the divergent results.

Among other drugs which may or may not produce chromosome breaks is chlorpromazine. Cohen and collaborators, for example, reported in the first publication[10] that "screening of chromosomes from 35 schizophrenic patients, some of whom were treated with these tranquilizers (chlorpromazine and chlordiazepoxide) in a double blind study, revealed no increase in the frequency of chromosome breakage over that in untreated individuals." In a later study, however,[9] two patients who had taken chlorpromazine showed 13.7 per cent and 17.4 per cent breaks, respectively, while the control value of these authors was 3.8 per cent. In our own laboratory, two patients who had received chlorpromazine (one of them at the rate of 3000 mg. per day) as well as other major tranquilizers but had discontinued medication at least two years prior to the leukocyte culture did not differ significantly from normal (2 per cent and 7 per cent breaks, respectively). Nonetheless, chlorpromazine has been shown capable of producing chromosome breaks in cultures of human fibroblasts with concentrations corresponding to those commonly used in clinical psychiatry.[1]

When added to cultures of human leukocytes, LSD too produces chromosome breaks. In doses ranging from 10.0 μg./ml. down to 0.01 μg./ml. for periods ranging between four and 48 hours, Cohen et al. observed chromosomal breaks ranging from 7.7 to 15.2 per cent compared with a control mean—i.e., similar cultures without addition of drug—of 3.9 per cent.[9] In a similar experiment, using a dose of 0.01

μg./ml. with a four-hour exposure of cultured leukocytes, Jarvik et al. report 10.2 per cent breaks with a corresponding control frequency of 5.2 per cent.[19] However, similar frequency of breaks was observed by Jarvik et al. upon the addition of ergonovine maleate (9.6 per cent) and aspirin (10.0 per cent).[19] The concentrations of aspirin (0.1 and 1.0 μg./ml.) were considerably below the therapeutic levels of 100 to 120 micrograms per milliliter two hours after the ingestion of four aspirin tablets (2.0 grams). The concentration of LSD (0.01 μg./ml.) approximates the blood level of one to four hours after the ingestion of one mg. LSD.[21] Caffeine too has been reported to induce chromosome breaks in human leukocytes.[25]

What are the implications of the above findings? Can substances like aspirin and caffeine, generally considered innocuous, be implicated in the production of neoplastic disease and congenital malformation? Caffeine has long been known as a mutagen, while back in 1959 there appeared an article entitled "Experimental production of congenital malformations in rats by salicylate poisoning."[30] The malformations produced were craniorachischisis, exencephaly, hydrocephaly, facial clefts, eye defects and various other abnormalities. Let me hasten to add that the salicylates used were methyl salicylate and sodium salicylate rather than acetylsalicylic acid, and that the dosages were toxic and not therapeutic. Incidentally, Warkany reports[29] that LSD given in huge doses to pregnant rats did not produce congenital malformations, while use of methyl salicylate in tissue cultures did not produce chromosomal damage (personal communication).

Thus, once more we have many intriguing and contradictory leads which serve to emphasize the urgent need for further carefully controlled experiments by a number of independent laboratories. Individual differences in susceptibility of various organisms may well prove to be important factors in the etiology of conflicting results. The biochemical uniqueness of the individual, long emphasized by Williams[33] has begun to be explored in pharmacogenetic research.

Cytogenetics may yet prove to be a valuable tool in determining optimal use of an ever-expanding pharmacopeia, while continuing to provide gradually increasing knowledge of man's molecular composition.

REFERENCES

1. Abdullah, S., and Miller, O. J.: Effect of drugs on nucleic acid synthesis and cell division in vitro. Dis. Nerv. Syst. (in press).

2. Al-Aish, M. S., de la Cruz, F., Goldsmith, L. A., Volpe, J., Mella, G., and Robinson, J. C.: Autosomal monosomy in man. New Eng. J. Med. 277:777-784, 1967.

3. Alexander, C. J., Miles, B. E., Gold, C. M., and Alexander, R. B.: LSD: Injection early in pregnancy produces abnormalities in offspring of rats. Science 157:459, 1967.

4. Anonymous: XYY error makes men grow tall and go wrong. Med. World News 72, April 8, 1966.

5. Auerbach, R., and Rugowski, J. A.: Lysergic acid diethylamide: effect on embryos. Science 157:1325-1326, 1967.

6. Balodimos, M. C., Lisco, H., Irwin, I., Merrill, W., and Dingman, J. F.: XYY karyotype in a case of familial hypogonadism. J. Clin. Endocr. 26:443-452, 1966.

7. Bloom, G. E., Warner, S., Gerald, P. S., and Diamond, L. K.: Chromosome abnormalities in constitutional aplastic anemia. New Eng. J. Med. 274:8-14, 1966.

8. Casey, M. D., Blank, C. E., Street, D. R. K., Segall, L. J., McDougall, J. H., McGrath, P. J., and Skinner, J. L.: YY chromosomes and antisocial behavior. Lancet 2:859, 1966a.

9. Cohen, M. M., Hirschhorn, K., and Frosh, W. A.: In vivo and in vitro chromosomal damage induced by LSD-25. New Eng. J. Med. 277:1043-1049, 1967.

10. Cohen, M. M., Marinello, M. J., and Beck, N.: Chromosomal damage in human leukocytes induced by lysergic acid diethylamide. Science 155:1417-1419, 1967.

11. Daly, R.: The frequency and characteristics of XYY males in selected populations. Abstr., Meeting Amer. Soc. Hum. Genet., Toronto, December 1967.

12. Forssman, H.: Epilepsy in an XYY man. Lancet 1:1389, 1967.

13. Fraccaro, M., Davies, P., Bott, M. G., and Schult, W.: Mental deficiency and undescended testis in two males with XYY sex chromosomes. Folia Hered. Path. 11:211-220, 1962.

14. Geber, W. F.: Congenital malformations induced by mescaline, lysergic acid diethylamide and bromlysergic acid in the hamster. Science 158:265-266, 1967.

15. Hamburg, D. A., and Lunde, D. T.: Sex hormones in the development of sex differences in human behavior. In: Maccoby, E. E. (Ed.): The Development of Sex Differences. Stanford, Calif., Stanford U. Press, 1966.

16. Irwin, S., and Egozcue, J.: Chromosomal abnormalities in leukocytes from LSD-25 users. Science 157:313-314, 1967.

17. Jacobs, P. A., Brunton, M., Melville, M. M., Brittain, R. P., and McClemont, W. F.: Aggressive behavior, mental subnormality and the XYY male. Nature 208: 1351-1352, 1965.

18. Jarvik, L. F., Abdullah, S., Kato, T., Chang, P., and Straus, D.: XYY karyotype among selected psychiatric patients. Abstr. Meeting Amer. Soc. Hum. Genet., Toronto, December 1967.

19. Jarvik, L. F., Kato, T., Saunders, B., and Moralishvili, E.: LSD and human chromosomes. In press.

20. Kelly, S., Rydia, A., and Barnard, M.: Another XYY phenotype. Nature 215:405, 1967.

21. Loughman, W. D., Sargent, T. W., and Israelstam, D. M.: Leukocytes of human exposed to lysergic acid diethylamide: lack of chromosomal damage. Science 158:508-510, 1967.

22. Lejeune, J., Gautier, M., and Turpin, R.: Etude des chromosomes somatiques de neuf enfants mongoliens. C.R. Acad. Sci. [D] (Paris) 248:1721-1722, 1959.

23. Money, J.: Cytogenetic and psychosexual incongruities with a note on space-form blindness. Amer. J. Psych. 119:820-827, 1963.

24. Nielsen, J., Christensen, A., Johnsen, S. G., and Froland, A.: Psychopathology and testis histology in a patient with the XYY syndrome. Acta Med. Scand. 180:747-757, 1966.

25. Ostertag, W.: Koffein- und Theophyllinmutagenese bei zellund leukozyten-kulturen des Menschen. Mutat. Res. 3:249-267, 1966.

26. Price, W. H., and Whatmore, P. B.: Behaviour disorders and patterns of crime among XYY males identified at a maximum security hospital. Brit. Med. J. 1:533-536, 1967.

27. Schmid, W., Scharer, K., Baumann, T., and Fanconi, G.: Chromosomen-bruchigkeit bei der familiaren Panmyelopathie (Typus Fanconi). Schweiz. Med. Wschr. 95:1461-1464, 1965.

28. Stephenson, J. N., Mellinger, R. C., and Manson, G.: Cerebral gigantism. Pediatrics 41:130-138, 1968.

29. Warkany, J.: Lysergic acid diethylamide (LSD): no teratogenicity in rats. Science 159:731-732, 1968.

30. Warkany, J., and Takacs, E.: Experimental production of congenital malformations in rats by salicylate poisoning. Amer. J. Path. 35:315-331, 1959.

31. Welch, J. P., Borgaonkar, D. S., and Herr, H. M.: Psychopathy, mental deficiency, aggressiveness and the XYY syndrome. Nature 214:500-501, 1967.

32. Wiener, S., Sutherland, G., Bartholomew, A. A., and Hudson, B.: XYY males in a Melbourne prison. Lancet 1:150, 1968.

33. Williams, R. J.: Biochemical Individuality. New York, John Wiley and Sons, 1956.

Discussion of Dr. Jarvik's Paper

by CARLO VALENTI, M.D.

Downstate Medical Center, State University of New York

As POINTED OUT by Dr. Jarvik early in her presentation, trisomy is often lethal *in utero.* In fact, of a total of 972 spontaneous abortuses studied by 22 laboratories throughout the world, including our own,[1] almost half of the 201 chromosomal aberrations were trisomies (Fig. 1). The vast majority of them involved the autosomes. On the other hand, monosomy for the sex chromosomes is the single most frequent error found: 19 per cent of all cytogenetically abnormal spontaneous abortuses. It is possible that in some of the 45,XO specimens the missing chromosome was the Y.

The abnormal behavioral pattern illustrated by Dr. Jarvik in connection with XYY human subjects has been studied in the fish *Oryzias latipes* by Dr. Hamilton in our Medical School. The YY fertile male fish is obtained by mating XY males with XY females, the latter produced by estrogenic treatment of XY fry. In comparison with XYY humans, the YY fish represent a relatively uncomplicated situation in that their cells have two sex chromosomes, the normal number for this species. When competing to mate with the female, the YY males showed definite dominance over the XY males, being responsible for 88 per cent of 155 spawnings studied.[2] Competition for food also was investigated in Dr.

CHROMOSOMAL ABNORMALITIES IN 972 SPONTANEOUS ABORTUSES

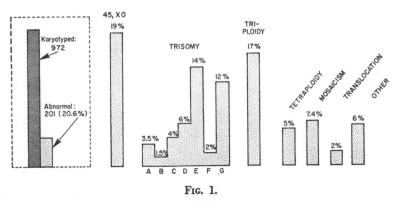

FIG. 1.

275

Hamilton's laboratory, and it was found that the YY males were always significantly more aggressive than the XY males. This behavioral pattern seems to be androgen-, not Y-chromosome-dependent, since treatment of the YY fish with anti-androgens made them less aggressive than the XY males.[3]

The last part of Dr. Jarvik's presentation dealt with the possible teratogenicity of LSD, which, admittedly, is far from proven and urgently needs further experimentation and controls. The urgency of the situation is perhaps well illustrated by two examples of a relatively new situation, which has come to my attention in the past few months. The first case is a 20-year-old girl who presented herself to a hospital in Brooklyn for therapeutic interruption of her 14 week pregnancy. During the previous 6 months she had allegedly used a total dose of 7 mgm. of LSD, including 1,000 μg. at the time of conception and 500 μg. 12 weeks later. The patient denied consumption of other hallucinogenic drugs, opiates or barbiturates. The fear of bearing a defective child had been a contributing factor leading to her severe psychotic state, characterized by suicidal tendencies. Therapeutic abortion was carried out. The

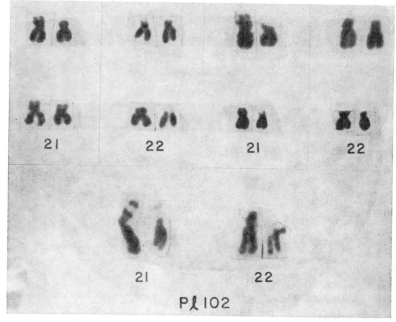

Fig. 2.—Chromosomal analysis of placental tissue from a therapeutic abortion in an LSD user. This figure shows asymmetry of pair 21 in five representative cells.

material obtained by curettage of the uterine cavity and consisting entirely of placental tissue was cultured *in vitro* and subjected to cytogenetic analysis. Asymmetry of the chromosomes of pair 21 (Fig. 2), probably due to a double break and translocation, was noted in all the 100 cells analyzed. Also chromatid breaks were observed in 6 per cent of the cells (Fig. 3). Peripheral blood cultures of the patient herself failed to reveal an incidence of chromosome breaks higher than the 2 per cent ordinarily seen on our laboratory.

The second case is a 19-year-old girl, ten weeks pregnant, who presented to us a letter from her psychiatrist recommending a therapeutic abortion. A written police report substantiated the fact that five weeks previously the patient had taken one dose of LSD. The fear of bearing a malformed child was her main reason for wanting to have her pregnancy interrupted. Further psychiatric evaluation revealed that the patient had moderate to severe depression. While she had never made overt suicidal gestures, she did admit to suicidal thoughts. The abortion committee of our hospital decided against interrupting the pregnancy.

Was the fear in these two patients justified? Was therapeutic abortion indicated in the second case? We do not have a definite answer to these questions as yet, and under the circumstances a conservative attitude seems to be advisable for the time being.

There are two provinces to be considered insofar as the genetic effects of LSD are concerned: one, chromosomal damage, and two, birth defects. The *in vitro* and *in vivo* studies reported on the chromosomal effects of the drug are contradictory, as Dr. Jarvik pointed out. Only one case of human congenital defect ascribed to LSD ingestion has been published in the medical literature.[4] The *in vitro* experiments carried out by Cohen et al. and Jarvik et al. were repeated in our laboratory. Following the same protocol, LSD was added to cultures of human leukocytes as well as human fetal fibroblasts. Several thousand cells were analyzed and the structural anomalies noted did not exceed 2 per cent, which is the rate found in the controls. We also carried out the cytogenetic analysis of leukocytes from 10 LSD users (Table 1). Only two of the 10 individuals studied had taken LSD and no other drugs. In patient No. 10, no chromosomal changes were noted after a total dose of 7 mgm., whereas case No. 5 showed an increased number of breaks. No reliable figures could be obtained from this latter patient as to duration of use and dosage of drug. All other cases had used other hallucinogenic drugs, most frequently marijuana. Patient No. 9, who showed the highest percentage of chromosomal breaks, had admitted use of marijuana, methedrine and barbiturates. Subsequently, during psychotherapy, it became known that she had not used any of these drugs. The highest number of dicentric chromosomes was found in patient No. 6, who had taken a single dose of 500 μg. of LSD and repeated doses of methedrine and heroin. An accurate ascertainment of the effects of LSD on human chromosomes is extremely difficult to obtain because users of this drug give very poor histories, and often have experimented with numerous

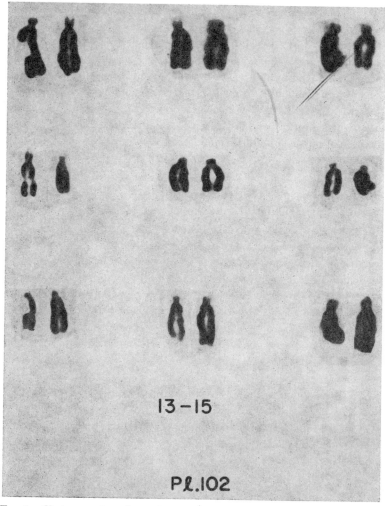

13-15

Pℓ.102

FIG. 3.—Chromosomal analysis of placental tissue from a therapeutic abortion in an LSD user. This figure shows chromosomal breaks in the D group of three cells.

TABLE 1.—*LSD Effects on Human Chromosomes (Peripheral Blood Cultures)*

No.	Case	Sex	Age	LSD			Other drugs				No. of cells anal.	Breaks		Dicentrics	
				Durat. (mos.)	Lapse (days*)	Total dose (mgm.)	Mar.	Meth.	Her.	Others		No.	%	No.	%
1	H.S.	F	20	6	130	0.750	+	+	—	—	100	1	1	5	5
2	D.S.	M	22	24	14	24?	+	—	—	—	110	3	2.7	2	1.8
3	R.S.	M	25	12	7	25?	+	—	—	—	80	1	0.8	1	0.8
4	D.M.	M	18	7	210	0.250	—	—	—	+	110	1	1	5	5.5
5	M.L.	M	21	?	?	?	—	—	—	—	100	5	5	7	7
6	G.P.	M	23	3	90	0.5	+	+	+	—	96	—	—	10	9.6
7	G.M.	M	19	5	150	0.250	+	—	—	—	50	—	—	—	—
8	G.I.	M	15	5	150	0.250	+	+	—	—	50	—	—	—	—
9†	T.N.	F	23	?	10	?	+	+	—	+	98	6	5.8	6	5.8
10	N.M.	F	20	7	30	7	—	—	—	—	100	—	—	—	—
	Totals:										894	17	2.0	36	4.0

*Time lapse from last dose of LSD.
†At the time of this writing, the psychotherapist treating this patient became convinced that she had never used any psychotropic drugs.

other psychotropic or narcotic agents, and also because prospective studies are not feasible.

It is reasonable to suspect that drugs other than LSD, or their synergism with LSD, may be responsible for the chromosome changes. It is also possible that more sensitive tissues and cells, such as spermatogonia, might be damaged. Since the results of *in vitro* and *in vivo* experiments are not consistently reproducible, I agree with Dr. Jarvik in postulating the existence of an important variable factor of individual susceptibility to the drug. The significance of the changes, when observed, should be related to similar changes observed in individuals exposed to atomic radiation and in persons considered highly vulnerable to leukemia. If one considers the possibility that LSD may cause leukemia, studies of identified individuals become imperative. Short-term chromosomal changes may not have any pathological significance.

Contradictory reports have appeared about the effects of LSD on the offspring of experimental animals. In humans, one report in the New York Times on the 11th of February, 1967, reports one child with mental retardation described by W. Frosch, who pointed out that there was no direct evidence that LSD was the etiologic agent. Another report is the fibular aplastic syndrome described by Zellweger et al. in a girl born to a woman who had taken LSD in the first trimester of pregnancy.[4] At best, so far, there is only presumptive evidence that hallucinogenic drugs can cause birth defects in exposed humans, and no action should be taken in the cases who may present themselves in the near future for therapeutic abortion on a genetic basis. The findings so far made available must be considered preliminary and should simply add to the usual warnings about LSD use, in particular to women in the childbearing age.

REFERENCES

1. Valenti, C., and Levy, C.: Chromosomal analysis of human abortions. Trans. Fifth World Congress of Gynaecology and Obstetrics, Sydney, Australia, September, 1967.

2. Hamilton, J. B., Walker, R. O., Daniel, R. M. and Mestler, G. E.: Supermales (YY sex chromosomes) and ordinary males (XY): competition for mating with females and evidence that the double Y chromosomal complex results in effects during adulthood. Anim. Behav. (in press).

3. Hamilton, J. B.: Personal communication.

4. Zellweger, H., McDonald, J. S., and Abbo, G.: Is lysergic-acid diethylamide a teratogen? Lancet 2:1066-1068, 1967.

DEDICATION

THIS paper is dedicated to the memory of Paul H. Hoch, to whose leadership this association owes its continued existence and whose impress is still felt in our activities and programs. Elsewhere[22] I have indicated his contributions to our association; here I wish to indicate the debt owned him by the Biometrics Research staff, a unit which he fathered and whose program this paper reviews. Above all, however, we all valued his deep and abiding friendship and collaboration and his deep compassion for the mentally stricken, in whose behalf he labored to the very last moment of his all too short life.

14

THE BIOMETRIC APPROACH TO PSYCHOPATHOLOGY – REVISITED

by JOSEPH ZUBIN, Ph.D.

Biometrics Research, New York State Department of Mental Hygiene, and Columbia University

SEVENTEEN years ago, in a presidential address before this association, I suggested a program for research in psychopathology based on biometric methods, in contrast to the clinical method generally in use. Only the mere outline of the method was presented, but stress was placed on its underlying theme—objectivity and quantification. Though some data were already available, the proposal was more in the nature of a blueprint than of a practical program.

Since then, however, the biometric approach has spread to several other centers and under various guises has become a permanent part of psychopathology. If my presidential address assisted in its birth, this talk tonight may signal its adolescence. While the ultimate usefulness of the approach must be left to history, it would not be amiss to report the developments that have taken place.

The implementation of our program began in 1953, about two years

The Paul H. Hoch Lecture, delivered before the American Psychopathological Association, February 17, 1968, at the Park Sheraton Hotel, New York, N.Y.

after my description of it to this association, with a project on prognosis in schizophrenia that applied a battery of objective techniques to the prediction of outcome. In 1956, when the man whose memory we are honoring today became Commissioner of Mental Hygiene of the State of New York, I was given the opportunity further to implement the biometric program. It had become quite clear that our small permanent staff and the somewhat larger grant-supported staff of students who had in the meantime obtained their Ph.D's were insufficient to deal with the entire biometric problem. There was need for more personnel and more funds. Thus we were fortunate in attracting more students from Columbia University, in the departments of psychology, psychiatry, sociology, anthropology, and mathematical statistics, and in being granted research funds from the NIMH.

In addition, several skilled and imaginative researchers, trained elsewhere, had joined our staff. There is hardly an idea, concept or paper written under the aegis of Biometrics Research that does not owe much of its value to one of the staff that has joined our ranks in the past 15 years. The dictum of one of the ancient sages characterizes well my estimate of their share in this common effort: "Much have I learned from my teachers, and from my colleagues more than from my teachers, but from my pupils more than from all of them." (From the Talmud)

My purpose today is to compare the blueprint offered in the early 1950's with the accomplishments of the biometric approach, both in our group and elsewhere, during the succeeding fifteen years.

From our 1950's review of the available literature on the biometric approach—i.e., the objective measurement of b e h a v i o r — i n psychopathology, it became quite clear that the available instruments for assessing patient behavior for diagnosis and for prognosis were far from ideal, leaving much to be desired from the point of view of reliability and validity. Clinically used tools like the Rorschach, TAT or other projective techniques turned out under inspection to be less like tests and more like interviews. Reliable and valid instruments such as intelligence tests, though useful for measuring intellectual functioning, were of little value in assessing psychopathology other than in the field of mental retardation. Personality tests of the self-reporting type, attitude tests, interest tests, and value tests were of limited use with mental patients.

As a consequence, we turned to the classical categories of human behavior and the methods for their elicitation and constructed a

Mendelejeff-like table consisting of physiological, sensory, perceptual, psychomotor, and conceptual responses which can be elicited under idling state, energy, and signal stimuli (Table 1).

This taxonomy of responses and of stimuli or methods for their elicitation proved heuristic in our prognostic study of schizophrenia, but the heterogeneity of the patients classified as schizophrenic soon led us to realize that before success can be attained in assessing deviant behavior we must have a more reliable method of classifying patients.

At the present time, overt behavior and self-reported symptoms are the only bases we have for suspecting, identifying and diagnosing most of the mentally disordered. The primary tool for observing and identifying is the clinical interview. By mental disorder we mean any progressive condition which unless therapeutic intervention takes place leads to premature death, severe reduction of efficiency, severe limitation of happiness, or to all three of these ends. Some of the mental disorders are stationary, and we designate them as defects.

Our review of the literature of reliability of diagnosis led to a conclusion similar to Mark Twain's response when asked how he liked Wagner's music: "It is better than it sounds." But despite agreement of 70-80 per cent in the gross diagnosis of schizophrenia, for example, sufficient heterogeneity was left to cause concern. Other conditions such as neuroses are much less reliably diagnosed. Consequently, we turned our attention to the study of clinical diagnosis itself and to the tool most often used in arriving at it—the interview.

But the behavior exhibited by a given patient could be due to a variety of aetiological factors. It was not sufficient to know the behavior alone; its antecedents were of the utmost importance. Since aetiological knowledge is still poorly developed in psychopathology, we resorted to the description of potential or "ideal" aetiologies in the form of scientific models. These have arisen on the basis of the phenomenological observations made by countless observers throughout the 33-century history of psychopathology. Among these were demonology, witchcraft, sin, familial degeneracy, brain disease (Griesinger), metabolic disorder (Kraepelin), genetics (Rüdin), development (Freud), learning (Meyer), focal infection (Cotton), social-cultural stresses (Durkheim), and many others. Out of the welter of possibilities, we chose six to work with: ecology, learning, development, genetic (heredity), internal environment, and neurophysiological (brain function).

While these models are conceived of as independent for heuristic

TABLE 1.—Examples of Measurable Activities

Level of observed behavior	Stimulus variables					
	Idling state		Energy variables			
			Appropriate energy		Inappropriate energy	
	Variable	Function	Variable	Function	Variable	Function
Conceptual:	—	Reverie and fantasy	Uniformly diffused light	Fantasy	Inversion of gravitational attraction	Subjective account of experience
Psycho-motor:	—	Spontaneous movement	Painful stimulus	Arm withdrawn	Electroshock	Movements of limbs
Perceptual:	—	Spatial and temporal orientation	White noise	Orientation to direction of sound	Pressure stimulation above retina	Phosphene
Sensory:	—	Background noises; cortical gray	Light of graded intensity	Threshold response	Electrical stimulation of thermal receptors	Warmth or cold sensation
Physio-logical:	—	BMR; basal EEG; basal PGR	Increase in carbon dioxide concentration	Change in rate of respiration	Pressure on carotid sinus	Change in heart rate

*From ref. 2.

purposes, they are in reality interdependent to a greater or lesser degree. This interrelationship is indicated by a Venn Diagram in Fig. 1.

Until recently, the first of these models—the ecological—has been referred to in our papers as the social-cultural, the social-cultural-physical, or even the social-cultural-physical-environmental model. We have wanted to refer to a very wide range of variables or factors, ranging from social class, family income, urbanization, etc., to geography, diet, climate, and so on, but the term has clearly become unworkable. Without attempting to move into the realm of general systems theory, which has recently become modish in social science, we here use the term "ecological model" to express the idea of the individual's ocas Functions of Stimulus Variables*

Stimulus variables					
Signal variables					
Configurations		Signs		Symbols	
Variable	Function	Variable	Function	Variable	Function
Aircraft forms or silhouettes	Recognition of identity of forms	Practical trouble-shooting test	Diagnosis of trouble	Stimulus word in association test	Association to stimulus word
Star-shaped maze	Mirror tracing	Classical delayed response stimuli in animal experimentation	Successful response by animal subject	Reinforcement of affect in focused interview	Electromyographic response
Rotating Benham Disc	Subjective color experience	Usual visual alternatives in animal discrimination experiment	Selective response of animal subject	Musical chords	Pitch discrimination
Patterned light stimuli	Visual threshold	Infant's faint cry	Mother's auditory threshold	Words or sentences presented tachistoscopically	Visual threshold
Photic driving	Change in EEG pattern	Bell ringing in Pavlovian conditioning	Salivation	Verbal instructions to prevaricate	Effect on PGR

cupying a "niche," relative to the cultural and physical environment—that is, being in a particular place at a particular time.

The ecological model and the learning model refer primarily to exogenous factors impinging on the individual. The developmental model is partly exogenous, influenced by ecological and learning factors, and partly endogenous, reflecting maturation. The genetic, internal environment and neurophysiological models operate entirely within the skin but they are mutually interrelated as well as influenced by the ecological forces via learning and development.

We have thus far devoted a great deal of effort to measuring the deviant responses arising from the variety of factors tentatively subsumed by each of the scientific models that were proposed for explaining the aetiology of psychopathology. The classification of these responses has been going on for a long time, and much more is known about responses than about the stimuli that give rise to them. In fact, the search for the stimulus is one of the perennial problems in behavior analysis. It is also quite likely that the number of different stimuli that can elicit these responses is greater than the number of responses observed. (This, however, may simply reflect the greater ease in observing and classifying responses than in observing and classifying stimuli, which are by definition what is being sought. It is probably true that the number of ways of classifying responses is large indeed, thus increasing the number of responses that might be considered.) But in order to provide good scientific models in which the links between stimuli and responses can be ascertained, we need a taxonomy of the stimuli that control deviant responses. This is one of the burdens of our current effort.

We shall now take up each of the models in turn, describing its assumptions, the causal agents presumably salient to it, the deviant behaviors associated with these agents, and the techniques provided for measuring them. For heuristic purposes, we deal one at a time with the causal factors of the model under discussion, assuming that the factors assigned to the other models are not also involved in the disorders under examination. Thus, when we deal with the ecological model, we will assume that it alone is responsible for the particular deviation, and that the basic capacities involved in development, learning, genetic expression, internal environment, and neurophysiology were intact to begin with. When these models become sufficiently specified we can turn to them for experimentally investigating the aetiology of the mental disorders. Considering these six models and the hypotheses each engenders for exploring a given question, we can continue experiments to test the tenability of each of them.

1. The Ecological Model

The human ecology model is built on the assumptions that *all* mankind is vulnerable to mental disorders and that, given sufficient deprivation, stress-producing loads, or other alterations in our environment, our behavior will be altered to the point where our ability to continue living normally as independent individuals in society is endangered. The evidence for social-cultural-environmental pressures as aetiological agents comes largely from studies of socio-economic status, isolation, educational and social deprivation, and social-cultural change due to migration or rapid acculturation. Even the most sanguine environmentalist will not be satisfied with merely pointing to the above-mentioned factors as "causal" agents, but will try to determine just how the malignant factors bring about their deleterious effect.

To cope with the stimuli assumed to operate under this model, we need techniques and methods that will delineate the various environmental forces that underlie the production of psychopathology. Our handicap here is tremendous, because even preliminary descriptive work is yet to be done. We do not have a taxonomy of ecological factors that is suitable for psychopathology, nor do we know the links between these global forces and the proximate forms by which they may bring about psychopathology. Except for such relations as radiation affecting behavior through the mediation of genetic factors, or nutrition affecting behavior through metabolic deficiencies, we have thus far failed to specify the parameters of the environmental factors eliciting deviant responses.*

Recent work by Richard Wolf[20] has illustrated how the correlation between social status and intelligence, which is usually found to be between .20 and .40, can be boosted to as high as .69 if the parameters of the socio-economic environment that have a bearing on intellectual potential are measured and included in the multiple correlation. Similarly, the correlation between social status and achievement, which is usually found to be .50, can rise to .80 if the parameters of social status pertinent to achievement are identified and measured. How the factors presumably underlying low socio-economic status will relate to the occurrence of psychopathology when their parameters are explicated and measured, no one can tell, but arguments such as those provided by the

---

*It is, of course, the case that social science has developed a number of sophisticated taxonomies in what I am calling the "human ecology" realm. We have classification systems for economic modes, social organization, kinship, cultural complexity, and so on. But in relating psychopathology to these, we generate a rather frightening plethora of "intervening variables"; conspicuously, we lack parametric control. For example, in face of the often-demonstrated fact that the prevalence rates of major psychiatric disorders are quite constant across cultures, we find ourselves invoking such constructs as "individual stress" or "personality" to explain differences between the subgroups within a culture. These may be just the right middle-level constructs—they may pay off. But we will not know until they can be achored objectively and measured either in the causal or consequential realm. If, indeed, such constructs can be objectified, we may find that the more molar taxonomies no longer serve our purpose.

Dohrenwends[6] lead one to suppose that at least transient, if not permanent, psychopathology is highly related to the stresses and strains of the environment. Perhaps persistent noxious stress can even lead to permanent psychopathology.

Until the day arrives when we have these variables under control, we may have to continue to resort to the blunderbuss of interviewing and observation as our basic approach to uncovering the aetiology of the disorder. The difficulties of the interview technique in aetiological investigations stem from the fact that with it we cannot separate causal agents from their effects, because often the two interact in the response of the patient. We cannot distinguish antecedent from consequent nor can we distinguish distorted from non-distorted reporting. This tendency to lean on the interview for determining both the causal factors underlying the disorder as well as the response of the patient to the disorder leads to a circularity which at the present time seems unavoidable. However, we can at least objectify the interview and make it more comparable from patient to patient and interviewer to interviewer; furthermore, we can provide specific interviews with informants (e.g., "significant others") for specifying the particular environment and its potential assets and liabilities for adjustment by the patient.

In summarizing the ecological model, we might point out that the current revolution in management in psychopathology with regard to hopefulness of treatment, reduction of patient population, rehabilitation, etc., is to a considerable extent a social, cultural and physical change in-

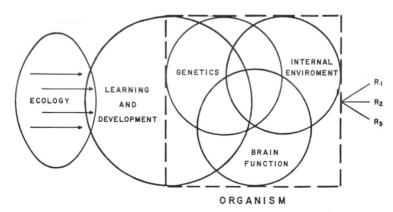

Fig. 1.

volving changes of attitude on the part of patient, family, therapist, social planners, and even taxpayers. Hence, though the role of environmental forces in *aetiology* of some disorders is not entirely clear, they are of great importance in detection, treatment and rehabilitation.

2. The Developmental Model

The developmental model of aetiology is built on the assumption that mental disease develops as a result of some specific deprivation or interference during a critical period in development, when the resulting deficit is crucial. Identification of the critical periods of development is still moot, with research covering the entire ontogenetic range: foetal and neonatal periods, childhood, adolescence, adulthood, middle age, and old age. Moreover, the values of the variables that may affect behavior at the critical junctures are still to be specified. At present, such obvious factors as toxemia during the gestation period, restricted early experience, limited peer interaction during early childhood, deviant friendship patterns during adolescence, poor psychosexual adjustment patterns, poor vocational adjustment patterns, unsatisfactory role development in family, vocation, and society, and social isolation in old age can be tabulated as important *potential* causal agents. How to measure degree of toxemia, extent of peer relationship, pattern of friendship, etc., is still beyond us. Even the categorization of family interactions in terms of degree of relationship between its members shows no universal agreement, as shown by the diversity that exists between Bateson's, Lidz's, and Wynne's nomenclature.

Since the developmental model represents the unfolding of the individual, it seems that in this model the nexus between personality and psychopathology might be found. In tracing back toward this nexus, we are really entering into the anamnesis or history of the individual, and this aspect of the investigation of psychopathology is one of those most urgently in need of further research and instrumentation, as is prospective research in this area.

If we define personality as the systematic aspect of a person's behavior, and psychopathology as those aspects of his systematic behavior attributable to illness, an important question arises regarding the possible connections between premorbid personality and psychopathology. Elsewhere[23] I have discussed these three possibilities: that personality and psychopathology are one and the same and no distinction can be made between them, even in the premorbid stage; that psychopathology represents an interaction between the premorbid personality and the noxious aspects of the illness; or that they are independent of each other—i.e., anyone can become mentally ill regardless of his premorbid personality. Until recently, the literature gave no definitive preference for any one of these three alternatives, but a recent series of studies using Sjöbring's method of personality evaluation has thrown its weight definitely on the side of the independence hypothesis.

Sjöbring's system[19] postulates that individuals are either normal or suffer from some underlying neurophysiological "lesion." The lesion cases are the result of damage due to noxious influences—single-gene substitutions of a noxious for a wholesome allele, genic mutation, birth injury, accidents, etc. Virtually all serious mental disorders are regarded as lesional, though of course even lesion cases have personality characteristics other than those imposed by their lesion. But normal personality can be subdivided into four dimensions (considered genotypic by Sjöbring): capacity, validity, solidity, and stability.

Essen-Möller[7] applied the Sjöbring method in a study of 2550 individuals in "Lundy" outside of Lund, Sweden in 1947, and was able to assess 98.8 per cent of all individuals in the district over 15 years of age. The same population was re-examined by Olle Hagnell ten years later, in 1957.[9]

The principal finding of interest in the Hagnell study, on the relation between personality and psychopathology, is that 1947 Sjöbring ratings did not predict mental illness incidence in the following ten years. That is, 1947 Sjöbring "deviants" in the (sub- and super-) categories of his four dimensions did not become mentally ill in greater proportions than did members of the population as a whole. This does not mean, of course, that those who have become mentally ill will demonstrate "normal" personality in the Sjöbring system. It appears that psychopathology and premorbid personality are distinct and independent things. Whether the premorbid personality has prognostic significance *once the disorder strikes* remains to be determined. What also needs to be investigated is whether psychopathology, once it has appeared, takes on a coloration that can be related to the personality that pre-existed, or whether the personality can be said, in some sense, to be suspended for the duration of illness.

Though Sjöbring personality deviation does not "predict" mental illness, there is an aspect of the Hagnell 1957 study that suggests that

Sjöbring deviation may predict other illness.[10] Of 22 women who developed cancer between 1947 and 1957, 20 women had been classified in 1947 as "substable." There was no such relation demonstrated for men with cancer. Moreover, the relation seemed "linear," in that the observed/expected ratio (when corrected for age by the Weinberg method) for each scale point on the stability dimension was progressively greater as the stability scale descended. However, the n's were too small at the lower scale values for statistical significance to be demonstrated.

The deviant behavioral responses elicited by developmental factors are difficult to separate from the deviations in the factors themselves. For example, how much of the child's withdrawing behavior is a natural consequence of the type of friendship patterns he is exposed to, and how much of it is endogenous? Here again, we must have independent measures of parameters of the environment that are still unidentified. Meantime, we can point to some of the behaviors that seem to be direct reflections of good or poor development: linguistic or verbal behavior, comprehensibility of speech, greeting, eating, sleeping, and other types of daily behavior accompanying socialization.

Finally, it should be pointed out that certain kinds of developmental models may be considered as special cases of the ecological model. In a model, for example, that postulates weak family structure—e.g., broken homes—as crucial for the development of psychopathology, what is really being suggested is that childhood is an optimal period for *transmitting* certain effects from the social-cultural environment to the individual. Such a conceptualization may lead one to consider the role of learning in relation to psychopathology.

3. The Learning Model

The learning or conditioning model postulates that the source of the deviant behavior of the patient is to be sought in his reinforcement history and the current behavior-reinforcement contingencies. Because learning is dependent on innate mechanisms like sensory analyzers and unconditioned responses, it is difficult to separate the learning process from them, but for heuristic purposes we shall assume these underlying mechanisms not to be deviant to begin with and discuss only the maldevelopment due to the learning process itself. (This *caveat* also holds for the ecological model, but it is of special significance to both the developmental and learning models.)

It seems reasonable to assume that many behavior deviations, especially in the neuroses and other non-organic conditions, must be acquired in accordance with known learning principles or with those which are still to be discovered. The learning procedures, intentional or unintentional, that our culture utilizes in shaping behavior are gradually becoming known. Some of the basic principles (such as schedules of reinforcement) have been studied extensively in animals and are beginning to be applied to human beings, especially in the area of verbal and other social behavior. The acquisition of adaptive emotional responses is still largely to be investigated in humans. In general, the parameters of the learning process itself are slowly revealing themselves, since the products of such learning, whatever the process may consist of, are easily observable and often measurable.

Some of the aspects of the learning situation likely to result in maladaptive behavior are those due to intrafamilial learning, as postulated, for example, by Bateson's double-bind model,[1] in which the mother's ambivalence in her relationship to her offspring produces ambivalent behavior and other types of deviation in him that we recognize as schizophrenic. While Bateson's double-bind model has aroused considerable interest in psychodynamic circles, it has thus far defied experimental testing of any of its hypotheses. Other more experimentally based models have been provided by psychologists. Thus, Sarnoff Mednick bases his approach on the evidence that the early or acute schizophrenic conditions more quickly and shows greater stimulus generalization (less steep gradients).[16] These are related to the higher level of arousal or drive that is attributed to an "innate" factor in early schizophrenia. Alternately, in studying schizophrenic behavior, one can postulate, as Kurt Salzinger has recently done,[17] the interaction of learning processes with an "innate" tendency to respond to immediate, rather than remote, stimuli.

The physical basis of learning also may cast light on deviational possibilities. The identification of biochemical processes involved in consolidation of learning and the finding that certain stimulants injected after a learning episode can exert a retrograde facilitation effect that shows up after the drug has worn off have potentialities for perhaps reducing the difference between learning by retardates and by normals. Similarly, the role of attention (perhaps conceived of as involving nervous-system "efficiency") in learning of both retardates and schizophrenics has been investigated; according to Zeaman and House one reason why retardates of certain levels fail to learn quickly is the long trial-and-error period before they select the proper stimulus to attend to.[21]

Further illustrating the possibility of interaction between models, a study by Salzinger and colleagues demonstrated that the administration of chlorpromazine affected only that class of behavior that was being reinforced.[18] When verbal behavior in general was being reinforced, it was emitted at a lower rate than when no drug was administered. On the other hand, when self-referred affect statements were being reinforced, only these showed a lower rate of emission, speech remaining unchanged. Finally, when movement in the subject's chair was measured (another class not under the reinforcement contingency), it showed, if anything, a higher rate owing to the administration of the tranquilizer. It was therefore concluded (based on a n of only 4 subjects) that the effect of the drug was not directly upon the behavior, but was indirect, perhaps through some aspect of the reinforcement process.

Another consideration in the aetiology of deviant behavior is the role played by the original stimulus in producing the deviant behavior—the role of traumatic events, for example, as distinct from the factors maintaining the behavior long after the effect of the initial stimulus has disappeared. The contingencies of reinforcement for specific deviant behavior may serve to maintain it, whether the reinforcement is intended or not.

With regard to measuring the deviation in behavior referrable to learning, the entire gamut of patient behavior is involved; much of it can be observed in the clinic and hospital, and some of it measured under laboratory situations. Here, observational techniques and interviewing under individual or group conditions are available, but standard procedures for the assessment of degree of psychopathology in relation to learning principles are only beginning to be provided on a practical basis.[12]

It might be pointed out here, that learned behavior, as a basis for detection, diagnosis and elimination of psychopathology, has received a new impetus from some of the successes reported for behavior therapy. No one can deny that, at least at the present time, there is no other way to detect the presence of functional psychopathology except through overt behavior, verbal or non-verbal. But it must also be realized that the same behavior may receive a positive reinforcement in one culture, a negative valence in another, and be completely ignored in a third. This fact may lead us to adopt either a purely relavistic view on mental disorders or to search for other indicators which may accompany or underlie the pathology. The learning theorists for the most part object to this, saying that the behavior and its functional relationship to the environment is the psychopathology and nothing else is needed. Yet, if we discover that a neonate is incapable of some metabolic process (say metabolism of phenylalanine) and neglect it because the neonate is not demonstrating any pathological behavior, we may lose the opportunity of saving him from mental retardation later. It is in this sense that we should be critical of the statement that we need to pay attention only to current behavior—unless we wish to include all activity of the organism, even the cellular or the segmental, as behavior. In this way, a thorough survey of the various response systems of patients, other than their overt behavior, may permit the detection and diagnosis of even latent conditions that have not yet come to fruition, in addition to providing a more objective indicator of the presence of the illness.

4. The Genetic Model

The genetic model postulates that the basic origin of mental deviation is an inherited propensity. The genetic origins of some types of mental disorders can be demonstrated in the form of certain inborn errors of metabolism, as in PKU or galactosemia, or can be associated with specific chromosomal anomalies, as in mongolism, or can be inferred from studies of consanguinity ranging from absence of any blood relatedness to monozygocity. Comparing hereditary factors with social-cultural factors, it is clear that we have a better measure in consanguinity than we have in environmental similarity. The relationship between degree of consanguinity and resemblance in IQ is quite linear and positive. The relationship between resemblance in environmental factors and resemblance in IQ is practically zero.[11] But this may be a reflection of the fact that we have good measures of hereditary resemblance but few good measures of environmental resemblance. Indeed, the genetic stimuli that give rise to deviant behavior have been detected and described in much better fashion than the environmental factors or those underlying any of the other models that may account for deviation. Among the genetic factors leading to mental deviation are some identifiable genetic anomalies, such as translocation and non-disjunction as evidenced in Down's Syndrome, mosaics, and specific alleles or combinations of alleles that because of their enzymatic activity interfere with normal cell development and functioning. Some of the other genetic principles that have been employed in aetiological considerations are polymorphism (or the balance maintained between alternative genic structures in given internal or external environments), penetrance, and expressivity of genes.

Genetics may be viewed in terms of biochemical mechanisms by which the genes serve as precursors for the production of certain enzymes, whose absence (or excess) prevents the organism from prospering. There is, therefore, considerable hope that an investigation of the internal environment of the body may reveal the particular metabolic deficiency or excess that characterizes the patient. A particular error of metabolism may, of course, be inherited or acquired. A considerable amount of effort has been spent in the attempt to relate schizophrenia to metabolic error. Certain fractions of schizophrenic blood have produced metabolic changes and changes in such behaviors as rope-climbing in rats, as well as transitory changes in the psychomotor behavior of normal human subjects. Presumably similar fractions from the blood of normals do not produce such changes.

5. The Internal Environment Model

The specific aspects of the internal environment, such as homeostasis, endocrine balance, acid-base balance, electrolyte metabolism, and other internal mechanisms and circulating fluids are too many to mention, but there is again a need for classifying them into stimulus classes that may be useful in relating them to behavior. Here again, their mediation of factors operating in other models, such as the genetic or the neurophysiological, is important.

6. The Neurophysiological Model

The final model, the neurophysiological or brain-function model, postulates that the psychopathological deviation is dependent upon the malfunctioning of the organ that most directly controls behavior—the brain. The nature of this malfunctioning can only be guessed at, but certain behavioral characteristics have been found in some types of mental disorder that differentiate patients from normals in a way that seems to be independent of ecological factors and that presumably reflects brain function (either innately, by endowment, or in the course of ontogeny). For example, slower recovery of evoked potentials to rapidly succeeding stimuli, and slower reaction time when a stimulus modality shift occurs, have been found. The actual brain substrates or processes underlying these deviations are still to be discovered. Except for certain "textbook" neurological syndromes, we probably know less about neurophysiological factors for the production of deviant behavior than we know about factors or stimuli in any of the other models (except, perhaps, for the internal-environment model).

In order to test the hypothesis emanating from the six models described previously, we must provide techniques and methods for measuring the hypothesized deviant behavior accounted for by each of the models. We have tentatively divided the models themselves into three groups: (1) the ecological model; (2) the developmental and learning models; and (3) the genetic, internal environment, and brain-function models. For the first, the social-cultural model, culture-dependent interviewing techniques seem currently to be the most satisfactory way of assessing deviant behavior. For the second group, culture-fair techniques are being provided. For the third group, culture-free techniques are being developed.

Time will permit a sampling of the methods and results for only a few of the techniques that have proved useful.

Culture-Dependent and Culture-Fair Techniques

For the social-cultural model we had available the interview technique in its structured form to catch culture-bound deviations in behavior attributable to the influence of social-cultural forces.* For the heredity, internal environment, and brain function models, which are by definition less dependent on exogenous factors, we are seeking instruments that would be culture-free and yet reflect deviations produced by the endogenous factors subsumed by these models. For the developmental and learning-theory models, culture-fair techniques were sought in order to detect behavior that, though reflecting social-cultural factors in a given environment, could nevertheless be translated, their equivalents being

---

*It is, of course, dangerous to *assume* that interview methods identify deviations in behavior. Psychiatric and psychological interviews inquire into areas for which we have almost no population norms, and even where we have such norms—e.g., employment or marriage—they are statistical norms for which, for the most part, measures of variation are not available.

Furthermore, as Boas pointed out a long time ago, a category of facts can more easily yield to analysis when the social group in which it is manifested has not elaborated a conscious model to interpret or justify it. Consciously applied norms are by definition very poor, since they are not intended to explain but to perpetuate the phenomena—these inaccurate conscious models get in the way of evaluating the condition of the patient.

found cross-culturally. Examples of behaviors that can be analysed cross-culturally are communicative behavior, greeting behavior, bereavement behavior, etc. Deviation from the norm in such behaviors takes on the local coloration of the particular social-cultural environment, but their functional equivalence can be partially established. (True equivalence must also show that the behaviors are of comparable *importance* in two or more cultures.)

To describe psychopathology in terms of the ecological model and to test some of the hypotheses emanating from this model (e.g., inverse relation of socio-economic status to incidence of mental illness), the most useful tools are interviewing and observational methods. There are a variety of such techniques available (dyadic interviews, group interviewing, participant observation, stress interviews). There are also a variety of methods for analyzing these techniques (content analysis, scaling) and a variety of multivariate techniques for summarizing and dissecting the results. The most frequently used method, however, is the dyadic interview.

It soon became clear to us that such assessment of patients as mental

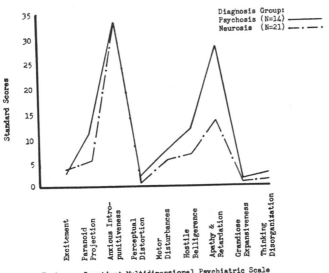

Mean Symptom Profiles of a Psychiatric Patient as Viewed
by Two Groups of Clinicians Who Differed on Diagnosis

Factors: Inpatient Multidimensional Psychiatric Scale

FIG. 2.

status examinations afford could be much improved if more systematic interviewing methods were introduced. To this end a series of structured interviews were constructed, which passed through several revisions and are now available in standard form: the Mental Status Schedule (Spitzer, Burdock and Hardesty), Structured Clinical Interview (Burdock and Hardesty), and Psychiatric Status Schedule (Spitzer, Endicott and Cohen). With the help of these instruments, and factor, cluster, and profile analytic methods, a fairly stable taxonomy of patient behavior began to emerge, reflecting less the behavior of the psychiatrist and more the behavior of the patient.

The usefulness of these systematic structured interviews in determining the basis on which diagnoses are arrived at is demonstrated in Fig. 2, reporting an experiment conducted by Martin Katz.[13] One of our structured interviews was videotaped so that it could be presented to groups of psychiatrists for their clinical judgment and diagnosis. In addition to the over-all diagnosis, the psychiatrists were asked to fill out ratings on an inventory for such factors as excitement, paranoid projection, anxious intropunitiveness, perceptual distortion, motor

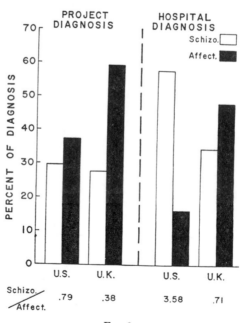

Fig. 3.

TABLE 2.—Diagnoses (%) of patients at U.S. and U.K. hospitals by the respective hospital and project staffs (Series 1: ages 35-59).

U. S.: Diagnoses:	N	Schiz.	Affect.	Other	Total	Schiz./Affect.
Project:	145	30.3	36.6	33.1	100	0.83
Hospital:	145	56.6	16.6	26.8	100	3.41
Project/Hospital:		0.54	2.20	1.24		

U. K.: Diagnoses:	N	Schiz.	Affect.	Other	Total	Schiz./Affect.
Project:	145	22.8	59.3	17.9	100	0.38
Hospital:	145	34.5	48.3	17.2	100	0.71
Project/Hospital:		0.66	1.22	1.04		

disturbances, hostile belligerence, apathy and retardation, grandiose expansiveness, and thinking disorganization.[15] The psychiatrists were all seasoned veterans of psychiatry; nevertheless, of the 35 participants, 14 diagnosed the patient as neurotic and 21 as psychotic. An examination of their ratings revealed, however, that the groups differed significantly only in one respect—the rating on apathy. Those who rated the patient high on apathy diagnosed him as psychotic, while those who rated him low on apathy diagnosed him as neurotic. We are planning an objective approach to the estimation of apathy independently of the interview.

An application of similar interviewing methods to two selected hospitals in the United Kingdom (Netherne) and the United States (Brooklyn) has yielded the following interesting results. In the U.K. there is a preponderance of patients diagnosed as suffering with affective disorders, while in the U.S. there is a preponderance of schizophrenics, according to the diagnoses of the local hospitals respectively as well as according to the diagnoses made by the project staff. (See Table 2 and Fig. 3, in which slightly different n's are involved.)

On the other hand, while the profiles on the structured interviews differentiated clearly the affective from the schizophrenic groups when the hospital clinicians' diagnoses in England were used, this difference did not appear as clearly when the hospital clinicians' diagnoses in the U.S. were used.

In general, an average reliability coefficient of at least .90 was obtained on the individual items of the interview.

A comparison of the profiles on the data gathered on the same patient by means of a structured interview and of an unstructured interview indicates that, for some factors, a greater amount of psychopathology was elicited on the structured interview while, for other factors, a greater amount appeared on the unstructured interview (Fig. 4).

In an informal study conducted by Barry Gurland and Martin Katz, a group of clinical psychologists who viewed a video tape of the structured interview found less pathology than a comparable group of psychologists who viewed the unstructured interview of the same patient (Fig. 5).

Culture-fair techniques which we have used for the developmental model are three in number: (1) delayed auditory feedback for children and adults; (2) friendship pattern evaluation for adolescents; and (3) measure of pre-admission isolation for residents of old-age homes and mental institutions.

The delayed auditory feedback technique was applied to children to determine at what age stuttering begins. This was found to be approximately age 5 to 7.[4] William Goldfarb[8] applied the same technique to schizophrenic children. From his study, it appears that his subjects behaved like normal children two or more years younger, not beginning to be affected until age 8 to 9. In adult schizophrenics, where we expected to find that they would be affected less than normals, we were surprised to find that they were affected more.

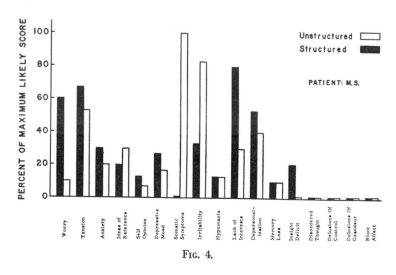

FIG. 4.

With regard to the friendship patterns of adolescent schizophrenics, it was found that even in their premorbid stage their capacity to make friends, hold friends and have intimate contacts was much less than that of a comparable group of normals.

In studies of the residents of old age institutions, an outstanding, consistent factor militating against good adjustment regardless of the type of institution was found to be preadmission isolation. This isolation was not correlated with mental disorders of the senium, but it did seem to lead to maladaptive behavior. Its effects may be reversible with resocialization techniques now being developed and tested.

In the learning area, reinforcement techniques were used to determine whether the verbal behavior of schizophrenics could be influenced. It was found that under reinforcement patients produced more affective utterances but, unlike the normal controls, failed to continue for as long a time to emit affective utterances when reinforcement was eliminated during the extinction period. The patients who showed greater effects of reinforcement had better prognoses. When the communicability of patient speech was examined with the cloze technique, it was found that it is more difficult to fill in gaps in a patient's speech than in the speech of

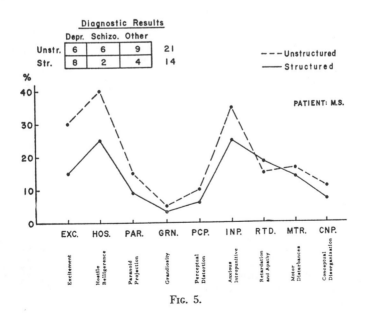

Fig. 5.

a normal and, furthermore, that the lower the intelligibility the longer the stay in the hospital.

Culture-Free Techniques

The rest of the chapter will be devoted to the culture-free techniques. In surveying the available experimental approaches to measuring patients' behavior that may be culture-free, we decided to limit ourselves to the responses of patients to controlled stimulation during the first 1000 milliseconds following stimulation, under the assumption that the response follows so quickly after the stimulus that culture cannot directly modulate it. Such responses may be designated as either physiological, sensory, perceptual, psychomotor, or conceptual.*

---

*The time epoch of 1000 milliseconds is obviously arbitrary, and there is nothing magical about this figure that can prevent culture from getting its licks in, so to speak. Two points might be made in this connection. One is that care must be taken to distinguish between primary physiological or sensory responses, of the sort that can be recorded directly by, for example, electrophysiological techniques (e.g., a single evoked potential, or a heart cycle) and a class of response that may be called reporting responses (direct responses or responses mediated through voluntary muscles). In the latter case, while the input of energy stimuli may be equally well controlled as in the former case, one may have to depend, for example, on a verbal report of flicker or apparent movement or on the pressing of a button whose reliability and latency may depend on factors not controlled by stimulus input in a given trial. In these cases, the validity of the measure must rest on experimental demonstrations that motivation is constant, or that a public language is being used, or that the use of a warning stimulus and a variable foreperiod drives reaction time down to an irreducible level. The correlation between primary or physiological responses and reporting responses is a persistent problem area, and one to which detection theory has made important contributions.

The other, more general, point to be made is that no measure can really be said to be culture-free, in that the subject always has a cultural history. No one disagrees that the nervous system is plastic, that even single cells can be "conditioned" (though perhaps in a rather special sense), that physiological levels can be shifted over time, that habituation occurs in sensory systems, that even the simplest "involuntary" reflexes can be facilitated or inhibited by complexly mediated means. As my anthropologist colleague, Dr. Muriel Hammer, points out, the fact that social reinforcement can affect the shape of the cortical evoked waveform, as Grey Walter and Samuel Sutton have reported, forces one to be cautious about "culture-free" measures. However, note that exactly the same considerations apply to psychophysical research. In both areas, the situation may be clarified by observing that, when experiments are properly done, these uncontrolled factors are presumably fairly *constant* and do not enter unpredictably or selectively into the data. That is, for example, the subjects' experience with the stimuli is approximately equal, motivation does not vary significantly trial by trial, the instructions as to the response or to the reception of the stimulus are standard and sufficient, different experimental conditions are counterbalanced, and so on.

One of the perennial findings in the field of schizophrenia is the retardation in reaction time that characterizes several types of schizophrenics. Impressed as we are with the finding, we have never felt comfortable with it, since it is relatively easy to find differences between patients and normals when motivation cannot be suitably controlled. In our own work we circumvented the problem of motivation by randomizing it—i.e., comparing the reaction time in the same patient under certain types of situations which do not alter his motivation. We found that the reaction time to ipsimodal sequences (where sound followed sound or light followed light) was faster than when a modality switch occurred.

Our first thought was that the reason for this delay in the schizophrenic was due to the fact that he developed certain expectancies, so that having just responded to a light he would expect another light, but the coming of a sound instead slowed him up. In order to eliminate this possibility, we told him what to expect each time and had him verbalize the expectation. The effect persisted. The patients exhibited greater retardation than normals in modality switches even when the basic level of response was equated by covariance techniques.

In a similar situation Dr. Harrington Gosling, one of our staff members, compared the effect of long and short preparatory periods on reaction time of mental retardates and normals. In general, the reaction time of retardates is always longer. However, while both groups respond more slowly when the preparatory interval is short, this effect is much greater for the retarded group. He also examined the effect on reaction time of the relative length of preparatory intervals in two successive trials (Figure 6). Regarding the second trial as the target trial, he found in both of the contrasted groups that when the preparatory interval to the first trial is shorter than the preparatory interval for the second or target trial, reaction time is unaffected by the relative duration of the two preparatory intervals. However, when the preparatory interval for the target trial is shorter than the preparatory interval of the immediately preceding trial, reaction time for the target trial increases as the difference between the preparatory intervals increases. Here again, the effect is greater for the retardates—i.e., their reaction time is more impaired than that of normals by longer preparatory intervals in the preceding trial. This finding, while also not accounted for by motivational variables, is consistent with an expectancy explanation. If one postulated that there is a tendency for subjects to assume that successive preparatory intervals will be of the same length, then a short preparatory interval coming after a long preparatory interval comes as a surprise and reaction time will be longer. The inverse order, however, would not disrupt reaction time, since with a *longer* interval in the target trial there is time to recover from the surprise.

In pupillographic research, we have established that:

a) There is a smaller initial diameter in the patient group. While this is a small effect, it has been found reliably in two studies.

b) There is less contraction of the pupil to light in the patient group. This is a large effect, which dramatically differentiates patients from normals. However, this effect has been prominent only in the most recent study.

On the basis of our knowledge of the pupil's neural pathways, it may be said that finding *a* is consistent with the interpretation of reduced sympathetic activity (smaller initial diameter). Finding *b* is consistent with either increased sympathetic activity (which contradicts the first statement) or reduced parasympathetic reactivity to light in the patient sample, or is due to a possible artifact. The source of the possible artifact is the report of corneal opacities due to phenothiazine intake by the patient. The results based on our sample, which was matched for initial diameters, do not support the interpretation of reduced sympathetic activity, and in fact they are consistent with either reduced parasympathetic reactivity or the artifact hypothesis.

For critical flicker fusion, it has been recently shown by investigators at the New York Psychiatric Institute that this technique is tapping the criterion that the subject utilizes in making a decision (a conceptual or motivational process) rather than his perception.[5] While differences in critical flicker fusion are to be found between schizophrenics and normals when tested with the classical psychophysical methods of limits and constant stimuli, the differences disappear when a temporal forced-choice psychophysical method is used. (In the latter method, the subject merely states which of several stimuli is different from the other in the set.)

We have been carrying out similar specifications and analyses with our other measures. We have, for example, been working with measures of binaural interaction and visual temporal integration and resolution. We have little to report as yet with respect to the functioning of mental patients on our more refined measures. Our preliminary findings suggest that when adequate care is taken to reduce or control the role of attitudinal, motivational, and criterion variables, and when the task that is constructed is based on close experimental analysis of the perceptual situation, the differences found between patients and normals are usually small. The large differences to be found between patients and normals are evidently results of factors other than sensory or perceptual ones. That the residual differences are small does not disturb us, except in the sense that we have to exercise infinite care with our equipment and procedures to prevent experimental artifacts from swamping small differences between groups. If we can establish such findings and be sure of their accuracy, we would have a sound basis for moving to theoretical formulations that might open the door to designing measures that would yield large differences between patients and normals. Of course, we may find instead that under these conditions of testing the differences between patients and normals will vanish altogether. Findings of this kind would lead us to give up the search on this level of organization, and we would concentrate on those variables—e.g., motivational, attentional, attitudinal, effects of prior reinforcement history—that we have striven so hard to exclude as factors in our perceptual experiments.

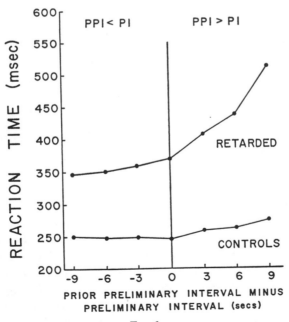

FIG. 6.

One may ask, what profit is there in investigating these partial and small-scale functions or their patterning in the mental disorders? What possible advantage can they offer for understanding the total disorder? Would it not be better to study the totality of the behavior—the total disorder? Our answer is that the total disorder is so encrusted with so much varying life experience that it defies analysis; all one can do is describe it. We have had 34 centuries of such descriptions, dating back to the Hindu Ayure-Veda text (*The Caraka Samhita*),[3] but understanding still eludes us. By dealing with behavior that is relatively free of prior experience and cultural influence, as we do when we limit ourselves to these brief laboratory tasks, we are attempting to obtain differentials between schizophrenics and normals that reflect a basic substrate of brain functioning in the processing of information. If the difference between schizophrenia and normality can be demonstrated to begin at the information-processing level, for example, we may be able eventually to understand why the world looks so different to the schizophrenic, and yet demonstrate that his behavior is consistent and predictable, though systematically deviant from normal expectancy in some basic substrate. Such differences may yield the culture-free indicators we so desperately need when studying subcultural groups or when making cross-cultural comparisons. By depending on interviewing methods or clinical tests alone, or on techniques highly dependent on prior reinforcement history, such as perceptual constancy or higher mental functions, we cannot escape the cultural bias inherent in such techniques. It is hoped that culture-free indicators may help us detect deviations that would be either falsely occluded or spuriously introduced when culture-dependent techniques are used.

Conclusions

In reviewing these 17 years of work it becomes clear that we must draw several important distinctions in its evaluation. We must first realize that in our search for aetiology we must not neglect or belittle the discovery of indicators that may not be causal in themselves but that may help detect deviation. Thus, we still do not know whether the presence of excess phenylalanine is the *cause* of PKU, but it certainly serves as a good indicator. Similarly, retardation in cross-modal reaction time or reduction in size of the pupil are probably not causes of schizophrenia but, again, they may prove to be indicators of a condition that has few if any objective indicators for its detection or for judging its severity or course.

If these objective indicators can be firmly established, there is hope that we can at the very least obtain more homogeneous groups of patients for testing the various aetiological hypothesis emanating from our models.

Work with aetiological models is only in its infancy, yet the weight of the evidence today may serve the purpose of rank-ordering the importance of each model in a given disorder. But it must be admitted that we are richer in models than we are in data.

Claude Lévi-Strauss, in his book *Structural Anthropology*, analyzes the search for a model or models in anthropology in a way that can serve as an epilogue to our own endeavor. He quotes von Neuman as saying: "An almost exact theory of a gas containing about 10^{25} freely-moving particles is incomparably easier than that of our solar system, made up of 9 major bodies." Psychopathology is presumably not at the level of unorganized complexity of gas theory, but it surely involves more variables than nine. In fact, we may regard it as a state of organized complexity to which neither Newtonian mechanics nor random statistical properties apply. However, we have a parallel, as Claude Lévi-Strauss points out, in linguistic analysis, which consists of a few thousand morphemes out of which significant regularities in phoneme frequencies and interaction can be obtained by limited counts. Psychopathology may be no more complex than language, but linguistic behavior has the advantage of being recordable with great fidelity and reliability. Thus, in our approach toward a scientific psychopathology, the ground seems to fail where it was expected to be firmest: the facts themselves are lacking, either not numerous enough or not collected under conditions insuring their comparability. Paraphrasing Lévi-Strauss: "Though it is not our fault, we have been behaving like amateur botanists, haphazardly picking up heterogeneous specimens, which were further distorted and mutilated by preservation in our herbarium. And we are, all of a sudden, confronted with the need of ordering complete series, ascertaining original shades, and measuring minute parts which have either shrunk or been lost. When we come to realize not only what should be done but also what we should be in a position to do, and when we make at the same time an inventory of our material, we cannot help feeling in a disheartened mood. It looks almost as if cosmic physics were asked to work with Babylonian observations.

The celestial bodies are still there, but unfortunately the. . . cultures from which we used to gather our data [for example, in our field, hospitals] are rapidly changing and that which they are being replaced by can only furnish data of a very different type. To adjust our techniques of observation to a theoretical framework which is far more advanced is a paradoxical situation, quite opposite to that which has prevailed in the history of sciences. Nevertheless, such is the challenge. . . ."

A review of the last 17 years of Biometrics Research indicates that though we have made some progress, the road ahead is still a long one. We have provided specific culture-bound, culture-fair, and culture-free techniques to assess deviant behavior. Structured interviews, verbal conditioning and perceptual, psychomotor, and neurophysiological techniques have been and are being adapted to assess psychopathology. We have focused on the need for specifying not only the response, as is done by the above-mentioned technique, but also the stimuli or aetiological agents which elicit the psychopathology. Thus, the parameters of the ecological forces which are associated with psychopathology need to be delineated and specified. It is not enough to speak of poverty, deprivation, low socio-economic status, migration, stress, etc. We must contrive methods for demonstrating how these factors impinge on the mental health of the person if we are not to merely join the ranks of the do-gooders and claim that elimination of these hazards will eliminate mental disorder. We must similarly analyze the parameters of the developmental model, the learning theory model, the internal environment model, and the neurophysiological model before we can develop a true understanding of the aetiology of any of the mental disorders. Sheer intervention may produce improvement, but it will be short-lived or will soon exhaust its benefit if we do not analyze the essential components involved.

REFERENCES

1. Bateson, G., Jackson, D. D., Haley, J., and Weakland, J. H.: Toward a theory of schizophrenia. Behav. Sci. 1:251-264, 1956.

2. Burdock, E. I., Sutton, S., and Zubin, J.: Personality and psychopathology. J. Abnorm. Psychol. 56:18-30, 1958.

3. The Caraka Samhita. Jamnagar, India: Shree Gulab-Kuniverba Ayurvedic Library, 1949.

4. Chase, R. A., Sutton, S., Zubin, J., and First, D.: A developmental study of

changes in behavior under delayed auditory feedback. J. Genet. Psychol. 99: 101-112, 1961.

5. Clark, W. C., Brown, J. and Rutschmann, J.: Flicker sensitivity of response bias in psychiatric patients and normal subjects. J. Abnorm. Psychol. 72:35-42, 1967.

6. Dohrenwend, B. P., and Dohrenwend, Barbara S.: The problem of validity in field studies. J. Abnorm. Psychol. 70:52-69, 1965.

7. Essen-Möller, Erik: Individual traits and morbidity in a Swedish rural population. Acta Psychiat. Neurol. Scand. Supplement 100:1-160, 1956.

8. Goldfarb, William: Childhood Schizophrenia. Cambridge, Harvard Univ. Press, 1961.

9. Hagnell, Olle:: A Prospective Study of the Incidence of Mental Disorder. Lund, Berlingska Boktryckeriet, 1966.

10. Hagnell, Olle: The premorbid personality of persons who develop cancer in a total population investigated in 1947 and 1957. Ann. N.Y. Acad. Sci. 125:846-855, 1966.

11. Jarvik, L. F., and Erlenmeyer-Kimling, L.: Survey of familial correlations in measured intellectual functions. In: Zubin, J. and Jervis, G. (Eds.): Psychopathology of Mental Development. New York, Grune and Stratton, 1967, pp. 447-459.

12. Kanfer, F. H., and Saslow, G.: Behavioral analysis. Arch. Gen. Psychiat. 12:529-538, 1965.

13. Katz, M. M., Cole, J. O., and Lowery, H. A.: Studies on the diagnostic process. Amer. J. Psychiat. 125:937-947, 1969.

14. Lévi-Strauss, Claude: Structural Anthropology. New York, Basic Books, 1963.

15. Lorr, M.: Multidimensional scale for rating psychiatric patients. Veterans Administration Technical Bulletin, 1953, 1, No. 10—507.

16. Mednick, Sarnoff: A learning theory approach to research in schizophrenia. Psychol. Bull. 55:316-327, 1958.

17. Salzinger, Kurt: An hypothesis about schizophrenic behavior. Paper presented at the IV World Congress of Psychiatry, Madrid, Spain, September 5-11, 1966.

18. Salzinger, K., Pisoni, S., Feldman, R. S., and Bacon, P.M.: The effect of drugs on verbal behavior. Paper presented at symposium, Control of Verbal Behavior, A.A.A.S., Denver, Colorado, 1961.

19. Sjöbring, H.: La Personnalité: Structure et Développement. Paris, Doin. 1963.

20. Wolf, Richard: The measurement of environment. In: Invitational Conference on Testing Problems, Educational Testing Service, 1965.

21. Zeaman, D., and House, B. J.: The role of attention in retardate discrimination learning. In: Ellis, N. R. (Ed.): Handbook of Mental Deficiency: Psychological Theory and Research. New York, McGraw Hill, 1963, pp. 159-223.

22. Zubin, J.: Paul H. Hoch's contribution to the American Psychopathological Association. Compr. Psychiat. 6:74-77, 1965.

23. Zubin, J.: Psychopathology and the social sciences. In: Klineberg, O. and Christie, R. (Eds.): Perspectives in Social Psychology. New York, Holt, Rinehart & Winston, 1965.

15

A CONSIDERATION OF BIOLOGICAL FACTORS IN SCHIZOPHRENIA

by MORRIS A. LIPTON, Ph.D., M.D.*

IN THEIR RECENT TEXTBOOK of psychiatry, Redlich and Freedman succinctly describe the problems in our understanding of schizophrenia by emphasizing that despite a half century of work and thousands of publications, "the important questions of diagnosis, prognosis, etiology and therapy are still unanswered and constitute psychiatry's greatest challenge."[1] Despite a vast amount of confusion engendered in part by failures in communication within and among different disciplines, there is by now a strong conviction that this illness arises from the interaction of biological and psychosocial factors. This essay attempts to summarize and to critically examine the strengths and weaknesses of the evidence for the biological factors which may predispose to or result in its development. While necessarily partisan, it in no way intends to minimize the psychosocial factors which lie in the research arena of clinicians and behavioral scientists, and emphasizes the need for joint efforts in the study of this complex condition.

The most persistent and persuasive evidence that there is a significant biological component in the etiology and pathogenesis of schizophrenia comes from genetic research. This has been the subject of frequent reviews.[2-7] Geneticists have used the strategies of examining the incidence of schizophrenia in various countries or cultures; examining the incidence in the pedigrees of specific families; and the twin method, in which the incidence of schizophrenia is compared in monozygotic twins and dizygotic twins. Their work permits certain conclusions. Apparently there are no known cultures devoid of schizophrenia, although the in-

*University of North Carolina School of Medicine

The work reported in this paper was supported in part by Grants AM-05062-05, 5-K3-MH-18,642-05, and 5-K02-MH-22536-08 from the U.S. Public Health Service, National Institute of Mental Health.

cidence in different communities may vary eightfold, as demonstrated in Germany and the Scandinavian countries.[8] Schizophrenia does run in families, although certainly not in classical Mendelian lines.[5] The incidence of schizophrenia in the children of schizophrenic couples is about 35 per cent, much higher than the incidence in the population at large.[9] The incidence in monozygotic twins has been studied for close to 50 years. Early studies showed a concordance rate of about 65 per cent; more recent studies with more critical methods indicate a range of 25 per cent to 42 per cent.[10,11]

All of the genetic evidence supports the view that a genetic diathesis is a major contributor to schizophrenia. In fact, it is the least equivocal evidence we have in this terribly complex field. None of the evidence supports the sufficiency of the gene in the development of this condition. The gene is certainly not all-powerful in the development of many other phenotypes or clinical illnesses.[12] Whether or not the environment can ever produce the illness with all of its symptoms and course in individuals not genetically predisposed cannot be answered at present because of our uncertainty as to whether schizophrenia is a single illness or a syndrome common to several illnesses. Certainly phenocopies of other genetic traits can be produced environmentally.[13] Even several genotypes may be encompassed within the same phenotype.[14] The behavioral changes resembling schizophrenia associated with porphyria, temporal lobe epilepsy, and chronic amphetamine psychosis may be examples of phenocopies without the existing genotypes. But even here we cannot be certain, because such changes do not occur in the majority of patients with these illnesses, and it is possible that schizophrenic symptoms may be the result of another illness superimposed upon a genetic predisposition. Whether or not such a predisposition is always absolutely essential, it would appear to be necessary in a very substantial number of cases. Meehl[15] has emphasized that the concept of etiology as a necessary but not sufficient condition is fully within the tradition of medicine and does not obviate the importance of environmental factors. Thus, in organic medicine etiologic factors need not produce illness, nor can the course of illness be altered only by agents directed against the specific etiology. Furthermore, the form and content of an illness is not derivable from the specific etiology alone, and not all persons showing the specific etiology need have a closely related history, symptomatology, and course. This seems to be true in schizophrenia.

The nature-nurture controversy is clearly obsolete in the study of schizophrenia, as Kety suggests.[16] Existing problems require greater focus on the nature and degree of interaction of the gene and the environment. The studies of monozygotic twins discordant for schizophrenia,[17] which show that the susceptible twin is almost always smaller at birth with a history of greater cyanosis and soft signs of central nervous system damage, demonstrate that the environmental contributions to this condition may even be intrauterine.

Conclusions from the genetic methods cited above are necessarily contaminated to an unknown degree by the effects of environment. The evidence that postnatal environmental factors can contribute to schizophrenia is as strong as that supporting a genetic theory, since about 60 per cent of schizophrenics show no family history of the illness and positive evidence for disturbances in family communication and interaction are impressive.[18-20] Only recently has Heston[21] reported a study in which 47 infants from schizophrenic mothers, separated from them in the first weeks of life and reared in foster or adoptive homes, were compared as adults with similar infants from normal mothers, also separated and reared in an identical situation. His data, showing an 11 per cent incidence of schizophrenia in the children of the schizophrenic mothers compared to none in the children of normal mothers, are very compelling support for a genetic theory. The additional finding that there was a higher incidence of other types of mental illness and antisocial behavior in the children also supports the concept that the diathesis may not be specific for schizophrenia. A similar conclusion is supported by the data of Gottesman and Shields,[10] who find a concordance rate for schizophrenia of 42 per cent in monozygotic twins but find the rate to increase to 79 per cent if the concordance criteria are loosened to include other types of mental illness or of psychiatric abnormality.

The complexity of the data derived from genetic studies does not presently permit an answer to the important questions of the type of genetic inheritance or the number of genes involved. There is agreement that the inheritance is not sex-linked, that it is not related to the age of the mother, and that there are no visible alterations in the chromosomes like in Down's syndrome. There are advocates of a single gene with incomplete penetrance[22] two genes (in which one is dominant and the other recessive),[5,8] and a polygenic inheritance[23,24] similar to that found in diabetes,[25] peptic ulcer,[26] or even height or intelligence. The question, though difficult, is hardly academic, for depending upon the answer, every individual, given an appropriate environment, may or may not harbor the potential of becoming schizophrenic. Of equal importance to biochemical research, at least, is the probability that if the interaction of a large number of genes is involved in creating the diathesis, the chances for a simple biochemical mechanism, though not eliminated, are diminished.

The search for biochemical abnormalities in schizophrenia which has been going on for about a half century has, until recently, been motivated primarily by two considerations. The first has been the consistent evidence from genetics that the illness has some hereditary component. The second has been the faith that so flourishing a field as biochemistry, which has been so successful in increasing our knowledge about other biological processes and so powerful in offering us tools for the treatment of other diseases, must ultimately make a significant contribution to this pervasive and malignant illness. Because of this faith, biochemical and biological research until the last decade has had a curiously fashionable quality. New techniques and concepts derived from the study of other processes or illnesses were immediately applied to schizophrenia without necessarily a critical examination of their relevance. Thus, there has been a long and basically unfruitful period when ptomaines, intoxications, vitamin deficiencies, endocrinopathies, viruses, and even infections were claimed as causative agents and later rejected.[27,28]

More recently, however, there has accumulated evidence which has moved the research from a shotgun type of empiricism to more focused studies and to the generation of relatively specific hypotheses. The relevant evidence in this regard comes from various sources. First, there has been the accumulating evidence that somatic intervention in the form of the phenothiazines or halogenated butyrophenones, when used early, controls symptoms and even promotes remission and re-entry into the community.[29] Concomitant with this there has been the increasing recognition that psychotherapy alone yields disappointing results.[30]

Second, there has been the increasing evidence that certain clearly organic syndromes like temporal lobe epilepsy, chronic amphetamine poisoning, and porphyria can sometimes produce conditions in some patients which are difficult or perhaps impossible to distinguish clinically from schizophrenia. Third, there has been the major impetus offered from the recognition that the administration of minute quantities of psychotomimetic drugs can produce dramatic disturbances of thought, feeling, and perception which in some ways resemble schizophrenia. The study of the chemical composition of these compounds and their structural similarities to serotonin and the catecholamines has led to the generation of hypotheses regarding aberrant metabolism of the neurohumors as being causative in the production of schizophrenia.

Finally, there have been a variety of naturalistic studies aimed at demonstrating an existing biological abnormality in the tissues or urine of the schizophrenic patient. None of these lines of evidence has produced conclusive results, but they have generated interesting hypotheses which have in turn yielded much useful information regarding the metabolic function of the black box known as the brain, particularly as it relates to behavior. They have also permitted the increasing recognition that the schizophrenic syndrome of thinking and behavior probably does not represent a single illness, and have pointed out the need for the characterization of specific subgroups.

As stated previously, treatment, especially if it is only partially successful, does not necessarily indicate etiology. Medicine is replete with examples of treatment, such as the use of aspirin in fever, which are not directly related to etiology. On the other hand, treatment may be related to etiology; and the more successful the treatment, the greater the likelihood that it taps into a mechanism which is fundamental to the illness. The concept of cure in medicine is vague. Cures by excision of an offending organ are very different from cures in which an etiologic agent is eliminated. Cures with permanent scars are common in tuberculosis and rheumatic heart disease even when the etiologic agent is eliminated. Cures without residual defect are achieved medically mainly in the infectious diseases, where specifics for the destruction of the pathogenic organism are available. This model is hardly appropriate to illnesses of multiple etiology and particularly not to illnesses such as schizophrenia, in which there is a learned or adaptive component. Hence, it does not seem likely that there will ever be a magic bullet which alone will render patients completely well. Since many illnesses, schizophrenia among them, may have profound consequences which remain even after the etiologic agent is removed, it is conceivable that if we had a specific chemotherapeutic agent, we might not recognize it except in the freshest and most acute cases. It is probable that for the treatment of the fully developed illness, pharmacological control will always need to be coordinated with psychotherapy, reeducation, or measures of social rehabilitation. While the empirical value of the phenothiazines in the treatment of schizophrenia is beyond doubt, there is a tendency to belittle their importance in aiding our understanding of the nature of this illness. Thus, it is frequently stated that they merely tranquilize or treat symptoms, because they do not fully cure the illness. Nonetheless, it is quite possible that they tap into a basic pathogenic mechanism, since they are most successful in acute cases and cause a reduction in most of the symptoms. Thus, in a large scale cooperative study[29] it was found that 95 per cent of the patients showed some improvement, and almost half of them did not show enough residual symptoms to be judged even mildly ill after six weeks of phenothiazine treatment. Analysis of the response showed that those symptoms relieved by drug treatment corresponded to a limited extent to Bleuler's fundamental symptoms, while placebo response was more random in nature. It is certain that phenothiazines exert their behavioral effects by acting on cellular processes. Although the crucial cellular mechanisms which they affect are not known, and many mechanisms of action have been proposed,[31] most of these relate to their action on the neurohumors, particularly upon monoaminergic receptors.[32]

The evidence from the syndromes produced by psychotomimetic drugs is intriguing if not conclusive. In this type of reasoning by analogy it is imperative that the analogy be sound. Whether this is so in the case of states induced by the psychotomimetics is open to question. Superficial similarities like disordered perception, labile affect, hallucinations, and anxiety may exist in both conditions. The significance of these has been strongly emphasized by Smythies and his co-workers,[33,34] who point out that one could not expect identical reactions because of the wide variations in schizophrenic symptomatology and the equally wide variations in individual responses to the psychotomimetics. Critical comparison of the drug-induced states with the clinical illness is very difficult for at least two reasons. First, almost all subjects who receive psychotomimetics for test purposes in a laboratory setting or even for the experience in a variety of social settings know that they are receiving the compound and are generally able to integrate the experience in relation to its cause. There are anecdotal reports of naive individuals receiving the drugs without knowing it, and there seems to be no doubt that it is a much more shattering experience under these conditions. Second, objective psychological indicators of schizophrenia around which one might make comparisons are lacking.

Klüver,[35] for example, pointed out that there are major qualitative differences between the hallucinations of mescaline and those of schizophrenia. Keeler[36,37] has pointed out that hallucinations are an inconstant feature of schizophrenia and are not particularly relevant to the diagnosis. He has demonstrated the complexity of the problem by noting that changes in the Minnesota Multiphasic Personality Inventory occur during the psilocybin reaction, and that these are primarily elevations in the hypochondriasis and schizophrenic scores. On the other hand, he has also compared schizophrenics and subjects receiving psilocybin using a reaction time test with regular and irregular intervals devised by Shakow.[38,39] Using this test, he has found that subjects receiving psilocybin have a prolonged reaction time, as do schizophrenics. However, when the preparatory interval is prolonged and irregular, schizophrenics show a decrement in performance which is not shown by subjects receiving psilocybin. The unique feature of schizophrenia emphasized by Shakow, i.e. the deficiency in maintaining general sets,[40] is not exhibited by drug subjects. Wikler et al.[41] also failed to find the differential effect on reaction time with regular and irregular preparatory intervals with subjects receiving LSD.

Whether or not the analogy is completely sound, there is no doubt that it has been fruitful. From it there have been developed several hypotheses which deal with endogenous toxic amines related to the catecholamines and indoleamines as contributing factors to the schizophrenic syndrome. These have been generalized to form the transmethylation hypothesis, which proposes that in schizophrenia there is faulty transmethylation of the biogenic amines, and that this can lead to "functional changes in neurones incompatible with their normal function, and, on the behavioral side, with the production of a psychosis. This fault might also lead to the production of abnormally methylated compounds . . . which might aggravate the situation by adding their own psychotoxic effects to the neuronal function already disordered by an abnormal transmethylating mechanism."[42]

This hypothesis and its supporting evidence have been the subject of recent reviews and will be only briefly summarized.[34,43-46]

The lines of evidence which support this hypothesis are as follows:

(1) All known psychotomimetics which do not cloud consciousness are chemically related to the presumed n e u r o t r a n s m i t t e r s, noradrenaline, dopamine, and serotonin. They are either O-methyl or N-methyl derivatives of these compounds.

(2) The normal degradation of the catecholamines involves O-methylation.[47,48] N-methylation of norepinephrine to epinephrine has also been demonstrated and is under the control of the adrenal cortex.[49,50]

(3) An enzyme capable of methylating serotonin and tryptamine to bufotenin and psychotomimetic dimethyltryptamine has been found in the mammal.[51]

(4) Exacerbation of symptoms in chronic schizophrenic patients has been produced by the oral administration of large quantities of the amino acid l-methionine.[52] This finding, which appears to be unique for methionine among the dietary amino acids, is shared by betaine.[53] Both methionine and betaine act as methyl donors. Administration of the former compound has been shown to result in an elevation of brain and liver S-adenosylmethionine, the active compound in transmethylation.[54]

(5) Homocystinuria is an inborn error of metabolism in which the normal metabolism of methionine through cystathione is blocked by the absence of the enzyme cystathione synthetase. One consequence of this defect is that there is an accumulation of blood and presumably tissue levels of methionine. Mental retardation and schizophrenia have been reported in at least two such families.[55,56]

(6) In 1962 Friedhoff and Van Winkle reported the occurrence of 3,4-dimethoxyphenylethylamine (DMPEA) in the urine of schizophrenics.[57] The discovery of this compound, which is a dimethylated derivative of dopamine (mescaline is the trimethylated derivative), excited a good deal of interest because it had been "predicted" by Harley-Mason and Smythies in their formulation of the transmethylation hypothesis. In his most recent report Friedhoff finds this compound to be present in the urine of 67 per cent of schizophrenics and 8 per cent of normals.[58] The compound is excreted in quantities not greater than 10 micrograms daily and therefore poses a formidable problem in chemical analysis. Both sensitivity and specificity are required for its analysis; and methodological variations may account for some of the divergent results from other laboratories.

The results of attempts to replicate these findings in a number of laboratories have been admirably summarized by Friedhoff.[58] The compound is certainly present in the pooled urine of at least two schizophrenics because it has been identified by mass spectrometry.[59] Friedhoff's results have been confirmed in several laboratories.[60,61] Other workers have failed to find it.[62-64] Still other workers have found its presence to depend upon diet.[65,66] This factor is not crucial to Friedhoff's thesis, since urinary phenyl pyruvic acid in phenylketonuria and urinary galactose in galactosemia also depend on diet. It has been reported in both normal and schizophrenic urine[67] and in a longitudinal study upon patients and controls it has been found to appear and disappear from the urine apparently at random.[68] The compound is apparently found only in the urine of acute and not chronic, schizophrenic, patients, and it disappears with chlorpromazine treatment.[58] The metabolism of DMPEA has been investigated by Friedhoff. Both normals and schizophrenics are able to oxidize this compound to the corresponding acid, and both excrete dimethoxyphenylacetic acid (DMPAA).[69,70] The existence of quantitiative differences between normals and schizophrenics in this regard has been denied.[69] DMPEA is also metabolized by acetylation to form N-acetyldimethoxyphenylethylamine (NADMPEA), a potent pharmacological agent in the rat which is rapidly demethylated to N-acetylmethoxytyramine (NAMT) which is pharmacologically inert. In a recent finding, Friedhoff reports that demethylation in the brain may occur via a different route than is present in other tissues. This may account for the action of methoxylated hallucinogens.[71] Since both normals and schizophrenics excrete DMPAA, it would appear that dimethylation of dopamine is a normal process. Whether this occurs in the brain, the periphery, or both is not known. The defect in the schizophrenic may lie in his inability to detoxify DMPEA by oxidizing it to DMPAA or by demethylating it.[71,72] Unfortunately, there is no evidence on these questions. It would appear to be important to determine whether differences exist in the quantitative and qualitative handling of administered DMPEA by schizophrenics and normals. Equally important would be the determination, by longitudinal studies, of the conditions under which the excretion of DMPEA is altered in individual schizophrenics.

In addition to the evidence suggesting the existence of abnormally methylated catecholamine metabolites in schizophrenia, there is also evidence suggesting a similar defect in the indoleamines. Thus, there are reports of increased free bufotenin excretion associated with active psychotic symptoms in schizophrenics.[73] Many of the methylated tryptamines are hallucinogenic.[74]

There is additional evidence, not directly related to studies of schizophrenia, which tends to support the transmethylation hypothesis. Recent studies have shown that there is increased synthesis and turnover of the catecholamines with sympathetic stimulation or stress.[75] Conceivably, when the system is operating maximally under stress, there may be a greater chance for "error" in the normal synthetic and degradative pathways. Other studies have shown that under special circumstances false transmitters—may be synthesized and stored in neurones in the periphery and brain.[76] The physiological consequences of such transmitters depend upon the properties of the substitute molecule as well as the decrease in endogenous transmitter release. In the brain they may influence synaptic efficacy. For example, phenylethylamine, which is pharmacologically similar to amphetamine, may be synthesized from phenylalanine in unusually high quantities in phenylketonuric subjects. It has been suggested as a neurotoxic substance which could irreversibly interfere with learning during the postnatal development of the brain and therefore be responsible for the mental retardation.[77] Finally, considerable evidence is accumulating that levels of both catecholamines and indoleamines may be important in the regulation of human mood.[78,79] It would be strange indeed if neurohumors which affect the biological substrates for mood did not also in some fashion relate to perception, thinking and social behavior.

Despite the attractiveness of the hypotheses dealing with aberrations in amine metabolism in schizophrenia, existing hypotheses, while not contradicted by other types of data, have difficulty in accommodating them. For example, tolerance to repeatedly administered exogenous p s y c h o t omimetics occurs rapidly in both normals and schizophrenics.[80,81] Why does it not develop to the presumed endogenous psychotogen? In this regard the finding of Vogel,[68] that DMPEA appears and disappears from the urine of both normals and schizophrenics, may be of value. Such an intermittent appearance would tend to minimize tolerance development, and if the apparently random appearance and disappearance were to be related to stress, it would be possible to construct a useful hypothesis integrating stress, a metabolic diathesis, and schizophrenia.

The problem is further confounded by the realization that no compound having psychotomimetic properties has ever been isolated from the urine of man. Bufotenin was initially reported to have such properties,[82] but this has been refuted.[83] DMPEA and NADMPEA, which have mescaline-like properties in rats, are also devoid of activity in man.[84,85] The appearance of DMPEA in the urine of 8 per cent of normals is puzzling because this figure is so much higher than the incidence of clinical schizophrenia. If this figure is not a product of adventitious artefacts, DMPEA might represent a genotypical characteristic which, though potentially useful to the study of heterozygote carriers, could at the very most be only a necessary but hardly a sufficient condition for clinical schizophrenia.

The absence of DMPEA from the urine of chronic schizophrenics and the disappearance of this compound from the urine when chlorpromazine is administered are also puzzling.[58] This is especially true since chlorpromazine accelerates the synthesis and turnover of dopamine.[86] The continuance of symptoms in the chronic patient and in the chlorpromazine-treated patient, neither of whom apparently excretes the compound, suggests that the relationship between the compound and the illness must be more complex and subtle than a 1:1 relationship. It may even be that the schizophrenic behavior patterns, once learned, may be perpetuated without any continuing metabolic abnormality.

Finally, the evidence from homocystinuria and from methionine loading of schizophrenics has recently been questioned. Thus, homocystinuric homozygotes have been found in whom there is evidence for neither mental deficiency or mental illness.[87] Whether the incidence of schizophrenia in homocystinuria is higher than in the population at large remains to be determined. Similarly, a recent report from Japan[88] states that the administration of methionine and an MAO inhibitor produces symptoms resembling a toxic psychosis superimposed upon the schizophrenia. More important perhaps was the failure to find any increase in the ratio of normally methylated catecholamine metabolites to the free amines, or any evidence for abnormally methylated metabolites such as DMPEA, bufotenin, or methylated tryptamines. Instead, marked changes were found in the patterns of urinary amino acids. The authors suggest that this and an associated ionic imbalance play a major role in the effects of methionine.

It should be apparent from the evidence cited above that for every piece of evidence favoring the toxic amine or transmethylation hypothesis there is also evidence which does not fit. Clearly, the story is far from complete.

The hypotheses based upon transmethylation and formation of psychotomimetic amines are by no means the only biochemical ones. Heath[89] finds an abnormal gamma globulin and considers schizophrenia to be an immunologic disease. Other workers have also obtained evidence for abnormal proteins but have focused upon beta globulins, and have raised the possibility that these are carriers for small molecules, perhaps similar to the toxic amines suggested by the advocates of the transmethylation hypothesis.[90] Most recently, Proctor[91] has found that when DMPEA is incubated with the plasma of untreated schizophrenics, the resulting product is more toxic to aggregated mice than DMPEA incubated with normal serum. This observation suggests that schizophrenic plasma may protect DMPEA from destruction or perhaps assist in its transport to crucial centers. If confirmed, it may reconcile the results of the advocates of the toxic amines with those of the abnormal proteins.

Kety[16] has pointed out that even if Koch's postulates cannot be fulfilled, certain minimum requirements are demanded of the evidence before special etiological significance can be ascribed to a finding. "The data should distinguish some or all of the schizophrenics from the rest of the population and preferably from those suffering from other mental illnesses. It should be capable of objective demonstration or at least free from the possibility of subjective bias. It should be found in other populations of schizophrenics by other investigators. Before etiological significance may be attributed to such a difference, however clear it may be, every possibility that it results from the presence of schizophrenia should be entertained and excluded." Obviously, we have not yet achieved even these minimal conditions, even though exciting possibilities exist.

Although it is an axiom of genetics that one gene should affect a specific protein or enzyme and thus a specific metabolic pathway, no such abnormality has been unequivocally demonstrated in schizophrenia. Lest this be too discouraging it is worth comparing our progress with other fields of medicine. Childs[92] has pointed out that biochemical mechanisms in the form of enzyme deficiencies are known in only 47 genetic illnesses, but the rate of discovery seems to be about 20 per cent per annum, and if continued, 1,000 such mechanisms should be known in the next twenty years. Of the 47 clinical illnesses presently known, 15 can be controlled by diet or by withholding injurious drugs. A therapeutic rate of 30 per cent offers reason for optimism because it demonstrates that phenotypic expression of the genotype can often be ameliorated by appropriate environmental measures. Perhaps this will be true in schizophrenia as well. Very little is currently known about the genetic control of sequences of development except in microbes. Since schizophrenia, like mental retardation, may profitably be viewed as a developmental defect, this increasing and important field in human genetics may yield promising leads.

Since most physical or behavioral traits and most genetic predispositions and illnesses cannot yet be described in biochemical terms, it is necessary to express them in appropriate anatomical, physiological, or behavioral ones. There are numerous findings relevant to schizophrenia in the literature of neurophysiology and clinical and experimental psychology. Thus, the research which has yielded data suggesting hypersynchronization,[93] hyperarousal,[94] disordered thinking,[95] disordered attention,[96] and the inability to maintain general sets[38,40] offers objective clues as to the nature of the disordered central nervous system function, which are still best described in language and concepts appropriate to the inquiring discipline. Correlation of these studies with physiological and biochemical investigations may establish their cellular and metabolic determinants. Meehl[15] in a highly imaginative article suggests several types of disordered neuronal function which might have a genetic basis.

There is not yet a unified theory of schizophrenia, and the evidence suggests that there may be subtypes similar to that found in diabetes, hypertension, thyrotoxicosis, mental retardation, and other illnesses of multiple etiology or polygenic inheritance. Despite this, common pathologic mechanisms amenable to treatment may exist, as they do in these somatic disorders. However, the problem is much more complex than even these illnesses because of the adaptive and learned components of schizophrenia. There is no hard evidence to answer whether some individuals are so heavily predisposed that they will inevitably develop the illness regardless of the environment, while others, lacking the genetic diathesis, will be immune. Judgment based upon genetic evidence and clinical experience suggests that the former probably occurs. Schizophreniform psychoses occur in adults exposed to prolonged life-threatening situations, but these are generally benign and reversible. Whether exposure of children to similar environments would produce the more classical picture with a protracted course and guarded prognosis is a matter for conjecture, since it is hardly likely to become a subject for active experimentation. It seems plausible that in extreme cases it could occur but that in most there is a genetic–environmental interaction. Whether there are genes specific for schizophrenia or whether there is a continuum of mental illness ranging from neurosis through antisocial behavior to schizophrenia is also not certain. The polygenic hypothesis and its supporting evidence tends to favor the continuum.[21,6,10]

The genetic–environmental interaction may begin at birth. The evidence from the invaluable studies on monozygotic twins discordant for schizophrenia supports this view.[17] The susceptible twin is more vulnerable at birth. His behavior may call forth special parental responses like overprotection or perhaps rejection. Heightened anxiety may induce pathological family tensions and fragmented communication among the parents and other siblings and between them and the susceptible child. These, in turn, may lead to fragile or pathological adaptation and defenses on the part of the potential patient, and, when these are threatened or broken, schizophrenic behavior may result.

Since the evidence for biological factors in the etiology of schizophrenia is incomplete and perhaps neither better nor worse than that derived from environmental studies, it is tempting to speculate that both points of view may have substantial elements of truth, and that schizophrenic behavior is the product of a final common path in the nervous system which can be brought into play from either direction. It is not difficult to conceive of possible mechanisms from the biological end. Most acute schizophrenic reactions are characterized in onset by a period of intense emotional turmoil. There is much evidence, recently reviewed by Hamburg,[97,98] that intense emotional distress results in massive outputs of adrenal steroids and epinephrine. The capacity of the adrenal to respond appropriately may be limited by genetic factors. Alterations in thyroid function also occur under stress, and these, too, may be limited by the genetic capacity of the individual. Finally, alterations in synthesis and turnover rates of noradrenaline under stress have been described.[75] Similar changes may occur with serotonin.[99] There is recent evidence which casts new light on the relationships between the adrenal and thyroid hormones and catecholamine metabolism. Thus, not only does cortisone enhance the methylation of noradrenaline to form adrenaline,[49] but both the thyroid hormone and the adrenal steroids control the rate of synthesis of noradrenaline at least in the peripheral sympathetic nervous system.[100,101] The evidence for this is the finding that adrenalectomy and thyroidectomy increase the rate of synthesis of norepinephrine in sympathetically innervated tissues. No effects of hypothyroidism have been demonstrated on synthesis or turnover in the brain, but hyperthyroidism diminishes it.[102] The mechanism for this control is not certain, but present evidence favors the view that the direct effects of the thyroid and adrenal hormones are to sensitize adrenergic receptors and that the effects on noradrenaline synthesis may be mediated through the nervous system in an attempt to compensate for the alterations in receptor sensitivity. We can, therefore, speculate that under stress, conditions may be optimum for slippage and error in the synthesis and degradation of the neurohumors among genetically susceptible individuals. This may result in the formation of endogenous psychotogens, or "false transmitters," which could generate considerable noise and instability in the many operations of the central nervous system in a fashion similar to that induced by exogenous psychotomimetics. The behavioral consequences of living with an unreliable nervous system might very well lead to hyperarousal, pan-anxiety, and compensatory efforts in the direction of seeking to achieve maximal stability by withdrawal from interpersonal, social, and environmental stimulation into the more certain schizophrenic world. Once this posture is assumed, stress may well be minimized, as Sachar has shown,[104] and metabolic defects may then not be apparent. If, however, attempts are made therapeutically to budge the patient from this position, stress is again encountered and the metabolic errors and their behavioral consequences may again ensue.

Despite the heuristic value of invoking specific biochemical mechanisms such as those described, those presently selected are undoubtedly incomplete and may even be incorrect. Perhaps they are not even necessary. Hamburg poses the hypothetical case of a child who is genetically limited in his capacity to respond with increased thyroid hormone production in the face of a stress-induced major central nervous system-thyrotropin stimulation, and delineates the possible detrimental consequences of persistent borderline-low levels of thyroid hormone upon behavior, interpersonal relationships, and styles of coping. It is curious that levels of thyroid activity are correlated with birth weight, and that in the discordant monozygotic twin study the susceptible twin apparently has lower thyroid activity.[104] It is also interesting that we have found the addition of thyroid hormone in combination with imipramine to markedly accelerate the therapy of retarded depression.[105] Perhaps, depending upon genetic limitations in the capacity to synthesize the hormone, and therefore its degree of deficiency, especially under stress, one may have consequences ranging from cretinism and its associated mental retardation to contributing factors in schizophrenia and depression.

Although it is difficult to extract a common ingredient from the work of the environmentalists, it seems plausible that ambivalence manifested in overprotectiveness or rejection, double bind instructions, and disordered communications might also create a world which is characterized by uncertainty and unreliability. Such a world must be incredibly stressful to a child and may readily interfere with central nervous system maturation and organization. To the potential schizophrenic it may not matter whether his central nervous system or his environment is unreliable. He would probably be unable to discriminate between them and would recognize only the anxiety and distress which he would try to alleviate by schizophrenic withdrawal and adaptation. This view, though highly speculative and lacking significantly in evidence, contains hypotheses which are testable and tenuously offers a mechanism by which the evidence and the perspectives of the biologists and the behavioral scientists might be reconciled.

It is a pity that technical and conceptual communication between biologists and behavioral scientists and even between different disciplines in the biological realm are so difficult. Because of this we cannot be certain whether crucial pieces of the puzzle are still missing or whether, perhaps like the schizophrenic, we have integrative difficulties in setting the vast mass of information into a meaningful whole. Interdisciplinary training of individuals and carefully controlled and systematic research by interdisciplinary teams would appear to offer the greatest hope for obtaining objective indices of the clinical illness, of preclinical characteristics of potential patients, of heterozygote carriers, and of the special characteristics of the environment required for the development of schizophrenia.

REFERENCES

1. Redlich, F. C., and Freedman, D. X.: The Theory and Practice of Psychiatry. New York, Basic Books, Inc., 1966.

2. Shields, J.: The genetics of schizophrenia in historical context. In: Coppen, A., and Walk, A. (Eds.): Recent Developments in Schizophrenia. Ashford, Kent, England, Headley Brothers, Ltd., 1967.

3. Gottesman, I. I., and Shields, S.: Contributions of twin studies to perspectives in schizophrenia. In: Maher, B. A. (Ed.): Progress in Experimental Personality Research, Vol. III. New York, Academic Press, 1966.

4. Rosenthal, D.: An historical and methodological review of genetic studies of schizophrenia. In: Romano, J. (Ed.): The Origins of Schizophrenia. Amsterdam, Excerpta Medica Foundation, 1967.

5. Karlsson, J. L.: The Biologic Basis of Schizophrenia. Springfield, Ill., Charles C Thomas, 1966.

6. Gottesman, I. I., and Shields, S.: Schizophrenia in twins: 16 years' consecutive admissions to a psychiatric clinic. Dis. Nerv. Syst. 27:11, 1966.

7. Kreitman, N., and Smythies, J. R.: Schizophrenia: genetic and psycho-social factors. In: Smythies, J. R., Coppen, A., and Kreitman, N. (Eds.): Biological Psychiatry: A Review of Recent Advances. New York: Springer-Verlag, 1968.

8. Böök, J. A.: Genetical etiology in mental illness. In: Causes of Mental Disorders: A Review of Epidemiological Knowledge. New York, Milbank Memorial Fund, 1959.

9. Rosenthal, D.: The offspring of schizophrenic couples. J. Psychiat. Res. 4:169, 1966.

10. Gottesman, I. I., and Shields, S.: Schizophrenia in twins: 16 years' consecutive admission to a psychiatric clinic. Brit. J. Psychiat. 112:809, 1966.

11. Kringlen, E.: Hereditary and social factors in schizophrenic twins: An epidemiological clinical study. In: Romano, J. (Ed.): The Origins of Schizophrenia. Amsterdam, Excerpta Medica Foundation, 1967.

12. Stern, C.: Genes and people. Perspect. Biol. Med. 10:500, 1967.

13. Goldschmidt, R. B.: Physiological Genetics. New York, McGraw-Hill, 1938.

14. Wright, S.: Complementary factors for eye color in drosophila. Amer. Naturalist 66:282, 1932.

15. Meehl, P.: Schizotaxia, schizotypy, schizophrenia. Amer. Psychol. 17:827, 1962.

16. Kety, S. S.: The relevance of biochemical studies to the etiology of schizophrenia. In: Romano, J. (Ed.): The Origins of Schizophrenia. Amsterdam, Excerpta Medica Foundation, 1967.

17. Pollin, W., Stabenau, J. R., Mosher, L., and Tupin, J.: Life history differences in identical twins discordant for schizophrenia. Amer. J. Orthopsychiat. 36:492, 1966.

18. Jackson, D.: Family rules. Arch. Gen. Psychiat. 12:589, 1965.

19. Lidz, T., Wild, C., Schafer, S., Rosman, B., and Fleck, S.: Thought disorders in the parents of schizophrenic patients, a study utilizing the Object Sorting Test. J. Psychiat. Res. 1:193, 1962.

20. Singer, M. T., and Wynne, L. C.: Thought disorder and family relations of schizophrenics. III. Methodology using projective techniques. Arch. Gen. Psychiat. 12:187, 1965.

21. Heston, L. H.: Psychiatric disorders in foster home reared children of schizophrenic mothers. Brit. J. Psychiat. 112:819, 1966.

22. Slater, E.: The monogenic theory of schizophrenia. Acta Genet. (Basel) 8:50, 1958.

23. Gottesman, I. I., and Shields, J.: A polygenic theory of schizophrenia. Science 58:199, 1967.

24. Rosenthal, D.: Theoretical overview. In: Rosenthal, D., et. al. (Eds.): The Genain Quadruplets: A Study and Theoretical Analysis of Heredity and Environment in Schizophrenia. New York, Basic Books, Inc., 1963.

25. Neel, J. V., Fajans, S. S., Conn., J. W., and Davidson, R. T.: Diabetes mellitus. In: Neel, J. V., Shaw, M. W., and Schull, W. J. (Eds.): Genetics and the Epidemiology of Chronic Disease. Washington, D.C., U.S. Department of Health, Education and Welfare, publication #1163, 1965.

26. Falconer, D. S., The inheritance of liability to certain diseases, estimated from the incidence among relatives. Ann. Human Genet. 29:51, 1965.

27. Kety, S. S.: Biochemical theories of schizophrenia, Part I. Science 129:1528, 1959.

28. Kety, S. S.: Biochemical theories of schizophrenia, Part II. Science 129: 1590, 1959.

29. National Institute of Mental Health Psychopharmacology Service Center Collaborative Study Group: Phenothiazine treatment in acute schizophrenia. Arch. Gen. Psychiat. 10:246, 1964.

30. May, P. R. A., and Tuma, A. H.: Treatment of schizophrenia: an experimental study of five treatment methods. Brit. J. Psychiat. 111:503, 1965.

31. Smythies, J. R., Coppen, A., and Kreitman, N.: Schizophrenia: Biochemical factors. In: Smythies, J. R., Coppen, A. and Kreitman, N. (Eds.): Biological Psychiatry: A Review of Recent Advances. New York, Springer-Verlag, 1968.

32. Da Prada, M., and Pletscher, A.: Acceleration of the cerebral dopamine turnover by chlorpromazine. Experientia 22:465, 1966.

33. Osmond, H., and Smythies, J.: Schizophrenia: A new approach. J. Ment. Sci. 98:309, 1952.

34. Smythies, J. R.: Recent advances in the biochemistry of schizophrenia. In: Coppen, A. and Walk, A. (Eds.): Recent Developments in Schizophrenia. Ashford, Kent, England, Headley Brothers, Ltd., 1967.

35. Klüver, H.: Neurobiology of normal and abnormal perception. In: Psychopathology of Perception. New York, Grune and Stratton, 1965.

36. Keeler, M. H.: Similarity of schizophrenia and the psilocybin syndrome as determined by objective methods. Int. J. Neuropsychiat. 1:630, 1965.

37. Keeler, M. H.: Similarities and differences in set and attention between the psilocybin reaction and schizophrenia. Int. J. Neuropsychiat. 3:434, 1967.

38. Shakow, D.: Psychological deficit in schizophrenia. Behav. Sci. 8:275, 1963.

39. Rodnick, E. H., and Shakow, D.: Set in the schizophrenic as measured by a composite reaction time index. Amer. J. Psychiat. 97:214, 1940.

40. Shakow, D.: Segmental set: A theory of the formal psychological deficit in schizophrenia. Arch. Gen. Psychiat. 6:1, 1962.

41. Wikler, A., Haertzen, C. A., Chessick, R. D., Hill, H. E., and Pescor, F. T.: Reaction time ("mental set") in control and chronic schizophrenic subjects and in postaddicts under placebo, LSD-25, morphine, pentobarbital and amphetamine. Psychopharmacologia 7:423, 1965.

42. Smythies, J. R.: Introduction. In: Himwich, H. E., Kety, S. S. and Smythies, J. R. (Eds.): Amines and Schizophrenia. Oxford, Pergamon Press, 1967.

43. Kety, S. S.: The relevance of biochemical studies to the etiology of schizophrenia. In: Romano, J. (Ed.): The Origins of Schizophrenia. Amsterdam, Excerpta Medica Foundation, 1967.

44. Smythies, J. R.: Schizophrenia: Biochemical factors. In: Smythies, J. R., Coppen, A. and Kreitman, N. (Eds.): Biological Psychiatry: A Review of Recent Advances. New York, Springer-Verlag, 1968.

45. Kety, S. S.: Summary. The hypothetical relationships betweeen amines and mental illness, a critical synthesis. In: Himwich, H. E., Kety, S. S. and Smythies, J. R. (Eds.): Amines and Schizophrenia. Oxford: Pergamon Press, 1967.

46. Kety, S. S.: Current biochemical research in schizophrenia. In: Hoch, P. and Zubin, J. (Eds.): Psychopathology of Schizophrenia. New York, Grune and Stratton, 1966.

47. Axelrod, J., Senoh, S. and Wittkop, B.: O-methylation of catecholamines in vivo. J. Biol. Chem. 233:697, 1958.

48. Armstrong, M. D., McMillan, A. and Shaw, K. N. F.: 3-Methoxy-4-hydroxy-d-mandelic acid: A urinary metabolite of norepinephrine. Biochem. Biophys. Acta 25:422, 1957.

49. Wurtman, R. J., and Axelrod, J.: Adrenaline synthesis: Control by the pituitary gland and adrenal glycocorticoids. Science 150:1464, 1965.

50. Blaschko, H.: The development of current concepts of catecholamine formation. Pharmacol. Rev. 11:307, 1959.

51. Axelrod, J.: Enzymatic formation of psychotomimetic metabolites from normally occurring compounds. Science 134:343, 1961.

52. Pollin, W., Cardon, P. V., and Kety, S. S.: Effects of amino acid feedings in schizophrenic patients treated with iproniazid. Science 133:104, 1961.

53. Brune, G. G., and Himwich, H. E.: Biogenic amines and behavior in schizophrenic patients. In: Recent Advances in Biological Psychiatry, Vol. 5. New York, Plenum Press, 1963.

54. Baldessarini, R. J., and Kopin, I. J.: Assay of tissue levels of S-adenosylmethionine. Anal. Biochem. 6:289, 1963.

55. Carson, N. A. J., Cusworth, D. C., Dent, C. E., Field, C. M. B., Neill, D. W., and Westall, R. G.: Homocystinuria: A new inborn error of metabolism associated with mental deficiency. Arch. Dis. Child. 38:425, 1963.

56. Spiro, H. R., Schminke, R. N., and Welch, J. P.: Schizophrenia in a patient with a defect in methionine metabolism. J. Nerv. Ment. Dis. 141:285, 1965.

57. Friedhoff, A. J., and Van Winkle, E.: The characteristics of an amine found in the urine of schizophrenic patients. J. Nerv. Ment. Dis. 135:550, 1962.

58. Friedhoff, A. J.: Metabolism of dimethoxyphenylethylamine and its possible relationship to schizophrenia. In: Romano, J. (Ed.): The Origins of Schizophrenia. Amsterdam, Excerpta Medica Foundation, 1967.

59. Creveling, C. R., and Daly, J. W.: Identification of 3,4-dimethoxyphenylethylamine from schizophrenic urine by mass spectrometry. Nature 216:190, 1967.

60. Kuehl, F. A., Hichens, M., Ormond, R. E., Meisinger, M. A. P., Gale, P. H., Cirillo, V. S. and Brink, N. G.: Para-o-methylation of dopamine in schizophrenic individuals. Nature 203:154, 1964.

61. Bourdillon, R. E., and Ridges, A. P.: 3,4-dimethoxyphenylethylamine in schizophrenia? In: Himwich, H. E., Kety, S. S. and Smythies, J. R. (Eds.): Amines and Schizophrenia. Oxford, Pergamon Press, 1967.

62. Bell, C. E. and Somerville, A. R.: Identity of the "pink spot". Nature 211: 1405, 1966.

63. Boulton, A. A., and Felton, C. A.: The "pink spot" and schizophrenia. Nature 211:1404, 1966.

64. Pind, K., and Faurbye, A.: Does 3,4-dimethoxyphenylethylamine occur in the urine from schizophrenics and normal persons? Acta Psychiat. Scand. 42:246, 1966.

65. Perry, T. L., Hansen, S. and Macintyre, L.: Failure to detect 3,4-dimethoxyphenylethylamine in the urine of schizophrenics. Nature 202:519, 1964.

66. Von Studnitz, W., and Nyman, G. E.: Excretion of 3,4-dimethoxyphenylethylamine in schizophrenia. Acta Psychiat. Scand. 41:117, 1965.

67. Takesada, M., Kakimoto, Y., Sano, I. and Kaneko, Z.: 3,4-dimethoxy-

phenylethylamine and other amines in the urine of schizophrenic patients. Nature 199:203, 1963.

68. Vogel, W., Ahlberg, C. D., and Horwitt, M. K.: Time study of the urinary excretion of 3,4-dimethoxyphenylethylamine and 3,4-dimethoxyphenylacetic acid by schizophrenic and normal individuals. Int. J. Neuropsychiat. 3:292, 1967.

69. Kuehl, F. A., Ormond, R. E. and Vanden Heuvel, W. J. A.: Occurrence of 3,4-dimethoxyphenylacetic acid in urines of normal and schizophrenic individuals. Nature 211:606, 1966.

70. Friedhoff, A. J. and Furiya, K.: 3,4-Dimethoxyphenylacetic acid in urine. Nature 214:1127, 1966.

71. Friedhoff, A.: Strategies for investigating biochemical aberrations in mental dysfunction. Presented at the 134th meeting of the American Association for the Advancement of Science, New York, New York, December 28, 1967.

72. Sargent, T. W., Israelstam, D. M., Shulgin, A. T., Landaw, S. A. and Finley, N. N.: A note concerning the fate of the 4-methoxyl group in 3,4-dimethoxyphenylethylamine. Biochem. Biophys. Res. Commun. 29:126, 1967.

73. Tanimukai, H., Ginther, R., Spaide, J., Bueno, J. R. and Himwich, H. E.: Occurrence of bufotenin (5-hydroxy-N,N dimethyl tryptamine) in urine of schizophrenic patients. Life Sci. 6:1697, 1967.

74. Szara, S.: Hallucinogenic amines and schizophrenia (with a brief addendum on N-dimethyl tryptamine). In: Himwich, H. E., Kety, S. S. and Smythies, J. R. (Eds.): Amines and Schizophrenia. Oxford, Pergamon Press, 1967.

75. Gordon, R., Spector, S., Sjoerdsma, A. and Udenfriend, S.: Increased synthesis of norepinephrine and epinephrine in the intact rat during exercise and exposure to cold. J. Pharmacol. Exp. Ther. 153:440, 1966.

76. Kopin, I. J.: False adrenergic transmitters. Ann. Rev. Pharmacol. 8:377, 1968.

77. Udenfriend, S.: Phenylketonuria. Amer. J. Clin. Nut. 9:691, 1961.

78. Schildkraut, J. J.: The catecholamine hypothesis of affective disorders: A review of supporting evidence. Amer. J. Psychiat. 122:509, 1965.

79. Coppen, A. J.: Depressed states and indolealkylamines. In: Garattini, S. and Shore, P. (Eds.): Advances in Pharmacology, Vol. 6, Part B. New York and London, Academic Press, 1968.

80. Abramson, H., Jarvik, M., Gorin, M. and Hirsch, M.: Lysergic acid diethylamide (LSD-25): XVII. Tolerance development and its relationship to a theory of psychosis. J. Psychol. 41:81, 1956.

81. Chessick, R., Haertzen, C., and Wikler, A.: Tolerance to LSD-25 in schizophrenic subjects. Arch. Gen. Psychiat. 10:653, 1964.

82. Fabing, H. D.: On going berserk: A neurochemical inquiry. Amer. J. Psychiat. 113:409, 1956.

83. Turner, W. J., and Merlis, S.: Effect of some indolealkylamines on man. Arch. Neurol. Psychiat. 81:121, 1959.

84. Friedhoff, A. J., and Hollister, L. E.: Comparison of the metabolism of 3,4-dimethoxyphenylethylamine and mescaline in humans. Biochem. Pharmacol. 15:269, 1966.

85. Friedhoff, A.: Personal communication.

86. Nyback, H., Sedvall, G. and Kopin, I. J.: Accelerated synthesis of dopamine-C^{14} from tyrosine-C^{14} in rat brain after chlorpromazine. Life Sci. 6:2307, 1967.

87. Graham, J. B., and Goyer, R.: Personal communication.

88. Kakimoto, Y., Sano, I., Kanazawa, A., Tsujio, T. and Kandko, Z.: Metabolic effects of methionine in schizophrenic patients pretreated with a monoamine oxidase inhibitor. Nature 216:1110, 1967.

89. Heath, R. G., and Krupp, I. M.: Schizophrenia as an immunologic disorder. Arch. Gen. Psychiat. 16:1, 1967.

90. Bergen, J. R.: Possible relationship of a plasma factor to schizophrenia. Trans. N.Y. Acad. Sci. 28:40, 1965.

91. Proctor, C. D., Cho, J. B., Potts, J. L., Ashley, L. G., Douglas, J. G., Amoroso, C. P., McGriff, J. E. and Eaton, H. E.: An influence of blood plasma from schizophrenics on an action of 3,4-dimethoxyphenylethylamine. Arch. Int. Pharmacodyn, 172:95, 1968.

92. Childs, B.: Genetics and child development. Amer. J. Dis. Child, 114:464, 1967.

93. Goldstein, L., and Beck, R. A.: Amplitude analysis of the electroencephalogram: Review of the information obtained with the integrative method. Int. Rev. Neurobiol. 8:265, 1965.

94. Kornetsky, C., and Mirsky, A. F.: On certain psychopharmacological and physiological differences between schizophrenic and normal persons. Psychopharmacologia 8:309, 1966.

95. McGhie, A.: Studies of cognitive disorder in schizophrenia. In: Coppen, A. and Walk, A. (Eds.): Recent Developments in Schizophrenia. Ashford, Kent, England, Headley Brothers, Ltd., 1967.

96. Lang, P. J., and Buss, A. H.: Psychological deficit in schizophrenia: II. Interference and activation. J. Abnorm. Psychol. 70:77, 1965.

97. Hamburg, D. A., and Lunde, D. T.: Relation of behavioral, genetic, and neuroendocrine factors to thyroid function. In: Spuhler, J. N. (Ed.): Genetic Diversity and Human Behavior. Chicago, Aldine Publishing Co., 1967.

98. Hamburg, D. A.: Genetics of adrenocortical hormone metabolism in relation to psychological stress. In: Hirsch, J. (Ed.): Behavior Genetic Analysis. New York, McGraw-Hill, 1966.

99. Diaz, P. M., Ngai, S. H. and Costa, E.: Factors modulating brain serotonin turnover. In: Garattini, S. and Shore, P. (Eds.): Advances in Pharmacology, Vol. 6, part B. New York and London, Academic Press, 1968.

100. Landsberg, L., and Axelrod, J.: Influence of pituitary, thyroid and adrenal hormones on norepinephrine turnover and metabolism in the rat heart. Circ. Res. 22:559, 1968.

101. Lipton, M. A., Prange, A. J., Jr., Dairman, W., and Udenfriend, S.: Increased rate of norepinephrine biosynthesis in hypothyroid rats. Fed. Proc. 27:399, 1968.

102. Meek, J. L., Prange, A. J., Jr., and Lipton, M. A.: Catecholamines: Diminished synthesis in rat brain and heart after thyroxine pretreatment. In preparation.

103. Sachar, E. J., Mason, J. W., Kolmer, H. S., and Artiss, K. L.: Psychoendocrine aspects of acute schizophrenic reactions. Psychosom. Med. 25:510, 1963.

104. Stabenau, J. R. and Pollin, W.: Maturity at birth and adult protein bound iodine. Nature 215:996, 1967.

105. Prange, A. J., Jr., Wilson, I. C., Rabon, A. M., and Lipton, M. A.: Enhancement of imipramine antidepressant activity by thyroid hormone. Amer. J. Psychiat., in press.

Discussion of Dr. Lipton's Paper

by ABEL LAJTHA, Ph.D.

New York State Research Institute for Neurochemistry and Drug Addiction

Dr. Lipton has beautifully summarized the most important aspects of a very big and somewhat controversial field, that of biochemical mechanisms that may lead to mental disorder, just as Dr. Heath discussed a somewhat different mechanism, also leading to mental disorder, this morning. Dr. Lipton concentrated on two major areas: the influence of the levels of amines on mental states, and the possible production of abnormal metabolites of amines. In my comments, I would like to speculate somewhat further on these two points, to add a little more to the various theories so concisely discussed by Dr. Lipton.

As far as the level of amines is concerned, I feel that such a simple quantitative fact as the level of a small compound is not likely to be responsible for such complex reactions. I think that we have to look for a more complex mechanism for the control of the emotional state, for example. I hardly need to emphasize to the present audience the complexity of the nervous system; the complex structural relationships of the nervous system have been very well documented with the latest techniques of histology and biology. I am not referring to the structural differences that were observed many years ago between various areas of the brain or various cell types, but the structural changes in the different parts of the membrane of a single mitochondrion, which have very much to do with the function of this particle. Modern neurochemistry has shown us that the structural complexity of the nervous system is paralleled by an equally complex biochemical dynamic equilibrium. By mentioning this complexity I do not want to suggest that the mechanisms are beyond possible approach; on the contrary, important recent advances clearly show that the processes in the brain are not beyond our understanding in biological terms. The various metabolic and other biochemical reactions are kept in a dynamic equilibrium by a great number of equally complex control mechanisms. These mechanisms do impart a stability to the brain, but equilibrium can be altered in a number of experimental as well as pathological situations.

We have already discussed a number of metabolic defects this morning—phenylketonuria, galactosemia, lipidoses, for example—which clearly show that in many areas of the metabolism of the brain—amino acid metabolism, carbohydrate metabolism, lipid metabolism, for example—an inbalance results in some form of mental pathology. I am sure that we can expect similar pathological results of imbalance in other aspects of metabolism: amine metabolism, as Dr. Lipton discussed; protein metabolism, perhaps, as Dr. Heath referred to; and other factors, such as ions. I would not exclude structural defects such as damage to membranes. In other words, it seems that every aspect of the chemical equilibrium and biological machinery operative in the brain is necessary for perfect function, and I would expect that the biochemical mechanism responsible for emotional state is also a complex interplay of a number of reactions, with control mechanisms above them, making this the possible area that should be investigated in the future.

The possibility of the production of abnormal metabolites that Dr. Lipton summarized perhaps illustrates the same point. I don't think that we need to expect the presence of harmful enzymes in the brain, which are inactive under normal conditions and are liberated only under pathological conditions. I do not think that we carry the seeds of damage in our organism in such a fashion. I think rather, that we should look at the control mechanisms of biological specificity. This specificity, although great, is not absolute in most biological reactions; in amine metabolism, for example, amine oxidase has broad substrate specificity, with not a separate enzyme oxidizing each separate amine present in the body, but, rather, few enzymes responsible for the metabolism of a number of compounds. Such relatively broad specificity occurs with a number of other mechanisms. In my own work, for example, I found not that there is a specific transport mechanism for each single metabolite in the brain, but that a group of compounds are transported by the same mechanism. In spite of this, the distribution and the level of the compounds within the group is well defined individually, and therefore we have to postulate additional control mechanisms that are necessary to insure further biological selectivity. The broadness of specificity is perhaps a safety factor in the organism, which makes it possible for the metabolic machinery to handle unusual or foreign compounds at times. A small change in the control mechanism that influences this specificity, for example the specificity of methylation, could then result in the production of pathogenic products.

The fact that often it is not the level of a compound, most of which may be in bound form, but its rate of turnover (and not in all parts, but only in a particular brain area), makes our task even more difficult.

All this complexity and difficulty, however, should not make us lose our optimism. I very much agree with Dr. Elkes, who mentioned at this symposium that he begins to see the outline of the mountains in the horizon. If I may borrow a rather simple analogy between brain research and space research: We are not commuting to the moon or Mars yet, but, with our present rate of advance in metallurgical, fuel and guidance technology, etc., we should be able to make it soon.

16

SOME IMPLICATIONS OF SLEEP RESEARCH FOR PSYCHIATRY

by I. FEINBERG, M.D.* and E. V. EVARTS, M.D.†

RESEARCH into the psychophysiology of sleep has implications for psychiatry on two levels. On an applied level, this research can shed new light on such questions as the nature and amount of dreaming in the mentally ill; the potential relation between dreams and waking hallucinations; and on the physiological description and measurement of insomnia and its relation to clinical state in a variety of behavioral disorders. Also of direct clinical relevance is the considerable expansion of normative data on electroencephalographic (EEG) patterns in man yielded by techniques of continuous monitoring of brain wave activity during nocturnal sleep.[41] The rich variety of these patterns has made possible the empirical discovery of new and hitherto unknown aberrations in the electrical activity of the brain.

However, present research into the mechanisms of sleep and dreaming has implications which go beyond the elucidation of currently recognized clinical problems, for this research also has relevance for such profound problems as the biological bases of consciousness and memory. The most significant advances in clinical understanding have often come about through clarification of basic physiological processes. In the present review, therefore, we shall attempt to consider, in addition to those findings with obvious clinical relevance, certain more basic data whose implications for the biological function of sleep may ultimately lead to a more general understanding of relationships between brain and behavior.

*Downstate Medical Center, State University of New York.
†Laboratory of Clinical Science, National Institute of Mental Health.
Some of the work described here was supported by Grant MH 10927 from the U.S. Public Health Service to I. Feinberg.
We are indebted to Dr. Alan Rechtschaffen for his careful review of this manuscript and his many valuable suggestions. Dr. Ralph Berger and Dr. Donald Goodenough also made useful comments.

This paper will be divided into four sections. Part I will review information regarding the frequency and nature of mental activity during sleep and will consider new facts pertinent to older hypotheses regarding the cerebral bases of dreams and hallucinations. Part II will describe the results of physiological sleep studies in the two major functional mental disorders, schizophrenia and psychotic depression. Part III will be concerned with those conditions for which there now is evidence that S-REM mechanisms may become dissociated from sleep and intrude into waking as manifest psychopathology: narcolepsy, delirium and chronic brain syndrome. Part IV will describe the alterations in sleep pattern associated with impairment in cognitive function, and will discuss the implications of these findings for a theory of the biological function of sleep.

Before beginning Part I, it may be useful to describe the EEG patterns of human sleep and the sequences of the two kinds of sleep across the night. Fig. 1 shows the EEG patterns observed in normal adults. The transition between waking (W) and sleep is associated with disappearance of alpha activity and its replacement by a low-voltage, fairly rapid, and irregular EEG (descending stage 1). This pattern is soon (in 3-5 min.) replaced by the spindles (S) and K-complexes (K) of stage 2 sleep. The voltage then increases and the frequencies slow further with the introduction of a moderate amount of high-voltage delta activity

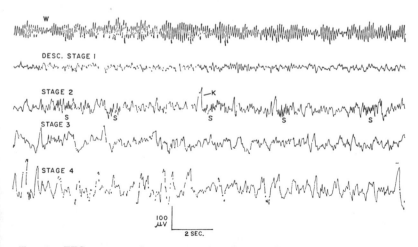

Fig. 1.—EEG patterns during relaxed waking and sleep in a young adult. W=waking, K=K-complex, S=sleep spindle. See text for further description.

(stage 3). This is followed by more intense and sustained delta activity (stage 4). The distinctions between stages 3 and 4, and, to a lesser extent, between stages 2 and 3, are quantitative and represent a somewhat arbitrary categorization of continuous variables. After about 70 min. in young adults, the EEG pattern gradually or abruptly changes (Fig. 2) to low-voltage, irregular activity (now "emergent" stage 1) which sometimes shows "saw-tooth" (ST) activity and is associated with rapid eye-movements and a variety of other changes in autonomic and central nervous system activity. The Dement and Kleitman[30] EEG stage-classification is employed here; it is similar to that proposed by Loomis, Harvey and Hobart.[96] S-REM usually refers to amounts of emergent stage 1 EEG, although some laboratories measure amount of eye-movement as well. S-SW comprises EEG stages 2-4. Fig. 3 shows the sequence of S-REM and S-SW found in 15 young normal adults, (mean age=26.6 yrs., range 19-36 yrs.), each subject having been studied for 4-5 consecutive nights. The sequences shown are considerably affected by age.[50]

1. Contributions to Knowledge of Dreaming

A. Mental activity during sleep.

The potential relationship between dreams and mental illness has been the subject of age-old speculation. Plato noted the similarity between dreams and hallucinations of madness, and Aristotle proposed that this

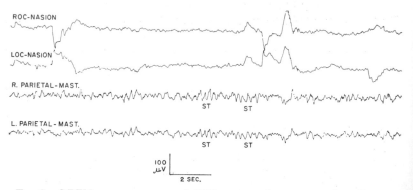

Fig. 2.—S-REM eye movement and EEG patterns in a young adult. Eye-movement activity is recorded as electro-oculogram (TC=0.3) between right and left outer canthi and nasion. Horizontal movements are therefore out-of-phase and vertical movements are in-phase. Right and left monopolar parietal EEG is shown. ST refers to "saw-tooth" waves.

similarity was based upon more than phenomenology, suggesting that
". . . the faculty by which . . . we are subject to illusion when affected by
disease is identical with that which produces illusory effects in sleep."[37]
Hughlings Jackson similarly viewed dreaming as "physiologic in-
sanity."[77] Freud, at the turn of this century, put forward the hypothesis
that dreaming carries out processes of need gratification and is
therefore vital to the integration of the mind.[61] He stated further that
"the mechanics of these (dream) processes is unknown . . . anyone who
seriously wishes to follow up these ideas must address himself to . . . getting a picture of the sequence of motions which ensues on the excitation
of the neurons."[61,p.534]

In view of the special interest of dreaming to both the psychiatrist
and neurologist, it is puzzling that the discovery of the relation of
dreaming to a specific pattern of physiological activity was made ac-
cidentally by physiologists concerned with identifying the basic features
of sleep rhythms. Indeed, in the hindsight of present knowledge, the
phenomena of sleep with rapid eye-movements (S-REM) are so prominent and easily detected that it seems incredible that their recognition
was so long delayed. That this delay occurred in spite of the emphasis

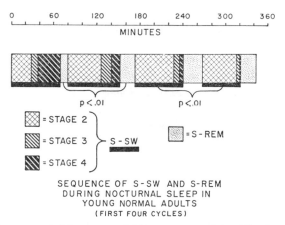

SEQUENCE OF S-SW AND S-REM
DURING NOCTURNAL SLEEP IN
YOUNG NORMAL ADULTS
(FIRST FOUR CYCLES)

FIG. 3.—Sequence of S-REM and S-SW in young adults. The first four cycles
are shown. Changes occurring with age and brain disease tend to alter the duration rather than the number of cycles. The first S-REM period is significantly
shorter than the others; the fourth period of S-SW is significantly shorter
than the first three periods. Shortening of the S-SW periods betweeen S-REM
episodes, rather than an increase in the durations of the latter stage, account for
the increased proportion of S-REM during the terminal hours of sleep.

given to an understanding of dreams by the observers noted above poses an interesting question for both the history and philosophy of science.

The discovery of the existence of S-REM by Aserinsky and Kleitman[8] and of its relationship to dreaming,[9] led quickly to a number of studies which attempted to elaborate this association. An early study reported that 80 per cent of awakenings from S-REM led to recall of dreaming, in contrast to a rate of only 7 per cent for awakenings from sleep with slow waves (S-SW). Subsequent work has shown this latter figure to be too low. Although all studies agree that frequency of recall from S-REM is greater than that from S-SW, figures for incidence of recall of *some* content on awakening from S-SW now include 72 per cent;[58] 57 per cent;[84] 35 per cent;[65] and 23 per cent.[120] Kamiya, Foulkes and others have suggested that these discrepant values result from differences in criteria for recall, in the set of the subject, in the rigor of interrogation during experimental awakenings, and in the duration of these latter periods. Goodenough et al.[64] have further shown that gradual as opposed to abrupt awakening leads to a change in the character of the recalled mental activity. Gradual awakenings from S-REM tend to yield "thought-like" mental content as opposed to the "dream-like" content obtained from abrupt awakening. Finally, Zimmerman[153] has found that "light" sleepers with low arousal thresholds more often report dreaming from S-SW than do "deep" sleepers. In view of the many factors which influence recall of mental content, data for relative recall rates from S-REM and S-SW must be assessed in light of the specific experimental procedures employed. Perhaps more important than the actual ratios of content retrieval from the two kinds of sleep is the general agreement of later investigators that absolutely typical and vivid dreams are sometimes reported upon awakenings from S-SW. Excellent discussions of the relation of EEG stage to dreaming may be found in Berger[12] and in Foulkes.[56]

Although these observations indicate that recall of subjective mental activity on awaking from S-SW is considerably more substantial than initially believed, data for differences in recall rate from the differing EEG stages of which S-SW is composed are still scanty and contradictory. Foulkes[55] found no differences in recall among awakenings from EEG stages 2, 3 and 4, whereas Kales et al.[80] in a study in which the experimenters served alternately as subjects, found the incidence of recall from stage 3-4 awakenings to be lower than from stage 2. This result seems plausible in view of the higher arousal thresholds of stage

3-4 sleep.[115] However, Hobson et al.[75] found mental content classified as dream-like was more frequent from stage 4 than from stage 2 awakenings, and Broughton[19] has found that nightmares usually occur on arousal from S-SW. This issue therefore requires further study.

Does the mental content elicited on awakening from S-REM differ qualitatively from that obtained from S-SW? Several excellent studies have yielded a clear-cut positive answer to this question. Foulkes[55] found that awakenings from S-REM yielded reports of mental experiences having high degrees of elaboration, affective involvement, frequent and intense visual imagery, and physical movement. Reports from S-SW tended to have fewer of these qualities, and also to be more "thought-like" and more contemporary in their temporal references than reports from S-REM. Rechtschaffen et al., in an independent study carried out at about the same time, found essentially the same differences between S-REM and S-SW mentation.[120] They noted in addition that S-REM yielded mental content which was more bizarre and implausible and less pleasant than that elicited from S-SW. Paradoxically, however, subjects awakened from S-REM considered that they were more "soundly" asleep than when awakened from S-SW. This finding, which is supported by the work of Goodenough et al.,[64] is somewhat surprising in view of the general belief that dream-filled sleep is disturbed and unsatisfactory. At least partly responsible for this belief must be the fact that the recall of dreams requires awakening and the recall of many dreams over a night's sleep implies frequent spontaneous awakenings. Rechtschaffen and his co-workers suggested that mentation from S-SW awakenings "resembles that large portion of our waking thought which wanders in seemingly disorganized, drifting, non-directed fashion whenever we are not attending to external stimuli or actively working out a problem or daydreaming" (ref. 120, p. 411). Monroe, Rechtschaffen, Foulkes and Jensen, using as criteria most of the differences described above, were able to discriminate mental content reports obtained from awakenings from S-REM and S-SW with a high degree of accuracy.[102] Antrobus and Antrobus using the concept-formation approach employed by Kamiya in training subjects to discriminate waking alpha periods, were able to train some subjects to distinguish REM from S-SW awakenings.[5] The successful subjects reported that they used as criteria the soundness of sleep and the presence of visual imagery.

Thus, recent research clearly indicates that more mental activity during sleep occurs than had previously been recognized. Dreaming is apparently a universal phenomenon, occurring frequently each night, both within and (less frequently) outside of periods of S-REM. As Monroe and co-workers concluded, ". . . there seems to be a continuum of sleep mentation ranging from relatively plausible, thought-like ideation to the hallucinatory, bizarre productions we generally think of as dreams. While full-blown dreams are sometimes reported on NREM (S-SW) awakenings, the kind of report generally elicited on NREM awakenings is easily distinguishable from the more dream-like reports elicited from matched REM awakenings."[102]

The large amount of mental activity which has been demonstrated to occur during sleep raises anew the question of why dreams are forgotten. Until quite recently, Freud's notion of repression has been the main hypothesis advanced to explain this amnesia. This hypothesis, rendered questionable by the ready reversibility of the "repression" with experimental awakenings and by the banal content of many evoked dream narratives, must now compete with an alternative view. Portnoff, et al. have shown that neutral words presented briefly on arousals from sleep are recalled the following morning if a substantial period (mean=18 min.) of waking followed the presentations.[113] In contrast, when the subjects were permitted to return to sleep (S-SW) immediately (mean=2.6 min.) after presentation of the stimuli, there was a marked reduction in later recall and recognition of these words. Portnoff et al. interpreted these data as indicating that consolidation of memory traces is impaired during S-SW, and that effective consolidation requires some minimum period of waking brain activity. Presumably the mental activity of S-REM also fails to be consolidated when it is followed, without an intervening period of waking, by S-SW. This interpretation, taken in association with the rapidly accumulating data on changes in neuronal activity during natural S-SW, S-REM, and waking in animals, points to new directions for the study of the brain mechanisms underlying engram formation.[46] Indeed, the study by Portnoff and associates must be regarded as a pioneer rather than as a definitive investigation of the complex relationship of sleep to the consolidation of memory traces. Thus, E. V. Shulman (personal communication) has pointed out that part of the recall difference in the two conditions may result from the fact that stimulus words followed by waking activity are also provided a context (lighted room, interpolated tasks) which may itself play a role in memory formation or retrieval.

Offenkrantz and Rechtschaffen[105] first noted that the temporal reference of the mental content elicited from periods of S-REM early in the night tends to be contemporary, whereas that elicited from later periods more often has reference to earlier memories of the subject. This finding was supported by a later, more systematic study by Verdone.[132] A similar analysis of changes during the night in the temporal reference of mentation elicited from awakenings from S-SW has not yet been reported, although, as noted above, S-SW reports as a group more frequently refer to contemporary matters than do S-REM reports. Further investigation and clarification of this question for both S-REM and S-SW would be of special interest for the information-processing theories of sleep to be described below.

Some of the physiological concomitants of S-REM have been found related to the nature of the mental content elicited on awakenings. S-REM periods with more intense eye-movement activity are more likely to yield reports of more intense imagery, especially of activities which would be expected during waking to be associated with scanning.[13] Increased respiratory rate and variability have been found positively correlated with vividness of dream imagery.[128,84,127,75] A recent study suggests that the respiratory rate and eye-movement activity are themselves related.[7,130]

A question of special interest is whether the direction of eye-movement activity is specifically correlated with the direction of the eye-movements expected from the dream imagery. Such a correlation would be the most convincing argument against the hypothesis that differences in mental content on awakenings from the different stages of sleep reflect differences in the nature of recall rather than in the ongoing mental activity at the time of awakening. This latter hypothesis, while rendered remote by the bulk of present evidence, cannot be definitively rejected in the absence of a demonstrated relation between some biological index (such as eye-movement) and the associated imagery. Dement and Kleitman[30] and Dement and Wolpert[32] first put forward evidence for such a relation. Roffwarg et al. carried out a systematic investigation of this problem.[124] They concluded that there was a high, and perhaps fundamentally a perfect, correspondence between recorded eye-movement and dream imagery. However, because the design of this study did not include "blind" matching of eye-movement records and dream reports, this conclusion cannot be regarded as established. The major evidence supporting the conclusion was indirect. It was found that dream narratives for which the subject was confident of his recall (the judges being unaware of these confidence levels) showed a better correspondence with the eye-movement records than did narratives for which the subject was less confident.*

At the very onset of sleep there occurs a period, variable in duration, but usually lasting 3 to 5 minutes, during which EEG alpha activity has been replaced by a low-voltage irregular EEG and slow, rolling, horizontal eye-movements occur. These changes mark the first appearance of behavioral sleep. However, mental content reports on arousal from this period, called "descending stage 1 EEG" by Dement and Kleitman,[30] have only recently been investigated. The findings[60,136,59] indicate that dream reports, although less common than from S-REM arousals, occur with substantial frequency on awakening from descending stage 1. This result sheds light on the fact that one may recall dreaming on awakening from periods of sleep too brief for the first episode of S-REM (see Fig. 3) to have occurred. Wide individual differences were found in the frequency of these hypnagogic reports. Dream-like narratives were given more often by subjects with higher waking ego strength and adaptive flexibility.[60,59] In contrast, there exist data which indicate that the tendency to recall dream-like episodes from awakenings from nocturnal S-REM is positively related to maladaptive personality features.[58]

The studies described above have been carried out with young adult volunteers, usually college students. Experimental investigations of dream content from other groups have been relatively few. Foulkes et al.,[57] in a study of boys aged 6-12 years, found that the percentage of dream recall from S-REM (72 per cent) was only slightly lower than that found in young adults, and that the word counts of narratives obtained 10 minutes after the onset of S-REM were strikingly similar for both the children and young adults. These investigators found no relation between chronological age or IQ and narrative length; however, the IQ range was quite narrow. The actual content of these narratives was of an everyday nature, consistent with the "major foci of juvenile and pre-adolescent social adjustment: parents, siblings, male peers, recreational or play settings and activities." This finding, which duplicates observations made in experimental studies of young adults, bears emphasis since it seems inconsistent with everyday experience. However, the extraordinary distortion and bizarre nature of spontaneously-recall-

---

*A recent study by E. Moskowitz and R. J. Berger, which employed "blind" matching of eye-movement records and dream reports, has failed to confirm the findings of Roffwarg and co-workers (personal communication from the authors).

ed dreams is relatively infrequent in the laboratory. This may result from constraining effects of the laboratory situation, or alternatively, this finding may indicate that bizarre dreams are themselves atypical, being remembered because they are more likely to be followed by awakening, and because they are more interesting and thus more often the subject of rumination. Although laboratory inhibition and an increased tendency of bizarre dreams to be followed by waking probably both play a role, we consider the latter to be the more potent explanation of the discrepancy between laboratory and home-recalled dreams. It would be of interest to determine the physiological concomitants of intensely affective dreams. Such investigations might profitably make use of patients suffering from traumatic neuroses, a condition whose clinical diagnosis depends upon the occurrence of intense, repetitive dreams of the traumatic event, usually leading to arousal.

Experimental studies of dream recall in the aged have recently been carried out by Kahn.[79] He found a low incidence of dream recall from S-REM, a result consistent with the widely recognized occurrence of subclinical memory impairment in elderly persons. In view of the possibility that dreaming involves activity in memory storage systems, and in view of the relative preservation of remote memory in the elderly, it is of special interest that four of Kahn's 19 elderly subjects had vivid dreams concerning events which occurred at the turn of the century. This observation also suggests that older subjects, perhaps those in late middle age, would prove a useful group in which to pursue the question of the temporal reference of dreams. Such subjects do not yet have gross memory impairment and their broader range of diverse memories might permit more ready determination of temporal origin.

Experimental studies of dreaming in psychiatric patients are also limited in number. In an early investigation, Dement found that schizophrenic patients reported dreams with little action or elaboration of narrative when awakened from S-REM.[24] This result is probably attributable to the negativism of schizophrenic patients, since the amount of eye-movement activity, which was noted above to be correlated with active dream imagery in the normal, is similar in both schizophrenic and normal subjects.[49] Leo Arey[6] found that acute schizophrenic subjects showed relatively little incorporation of elements of the laboratory situation into their dreams (such incorporation is common among normals). With clinical improvement these patients showed greater amounts of incorporation of the laboratory experiences.

This finding may plausibly be interpreted as indicating that at the height of the psychosis, nocturnal as well as daytime fantasy is more likely to be internally generated and independent of real events in the environment.

Only a few studies have examined relations among several dream narratives elicited by sequential awakenings from S-REM periods within a single night. Dement and Wolpert,[33] in a study of 38 nights of sleep in 8 normal adult subjects, found that "for the most part, each dream seemed to be a self-contained drama relatively independent of the preceding or following dream." Dreams which showed similar elements were most often contiguous, although on seven of the 38 nights of study, all of the dreams seemed to be related to a single theme. Offenkrantz and Rechtschaffen, studying a 36-year-old psychotherapy patient for 15 nights, concluded that in spite of variations of manifest content, "all the dreams of a given night were concerned with the same conflict or with a limited number of different conflicts."[105] Rechtschaffen et al.[121] studied relationships of mental content of reports obtained from S-REM and S-SW awakenings in two normal volunteers with good dream recall. They found the same images and themes appeared (sometimes repetitively) in both types of awakenings on a given night. Kramer et al., in a study of two patients undergoing psychotherapy, observed two types of sequential dream patterns obtained with experimental awakenings.[90] The first type, previously described by Offenkrantz and Rechtschaffen, demonstrated progressive attempts toward resolution of a conflict. The second type manifested repetitive statements of the same theme. The interpretations in these latter two studies included inferences based upon latent as well as manifest content. Since such inferences are necessarily speculative, the conclusions must be viewed with caution. In addition, the unavoidable effects of the awakening procedures in these studies may influence the content of subsequent dreams, a problem noted by each of the above authors. Although such work is very time-consuming, it is to be hoped that further studies of this problem will be carried out. Such data could clarify the clinical significance of dreaming, and in addition, might shed light on the nature of information-processing during sleep. Finally, it must be noted that experimentally evoked dream narratives have not yet shown themselves to be of value in clinical psychotherapy. This fact may seem surprising. However, the collection of such narratives in a somewhat artificial situation is laborious, time-consuming, and raises problems of transference. In addition, the amount of dream material elicited is too great to be efficiently analyzed or interpreted with existing techniques.

Despite the enormous expansion of knowledge concerning the frequency, timing, and certain formal characteristics of dreaming, many basic questions remained unanswered. We remain ignorant of whether the dream itself serves a role in the economy of mental function or whether it represents a mere epiphenomenon of more basic biological processes. While the narratives elicited from S-SW generally can be distinguished from those obtained from S-REM, it is not possible at this point to predict the content of either kind of report. In this latter respect, we have advanced little beyond the ancient Greeks, who knew that dreaming was often, but not invariably or exclusively, concerned with recent events and preoccupations.

The manner in which information is communicated in the course of active dreaming has been little studied. Although a recent report suggests that such communication is similar to everyday experience and includes auditory as well as visual modalities,[129a] there certainly do occur marked differences of special interest to the psychiatrist. Highly implausible events are often simply "known" and accepted by the dreamer. This suspension of disbelief and the general failure to recognize the unreality of ongoing dreams in spite of thousands of previous experiences has been emphasized by Rechtschaffen.[114] We would add that there appears to be a striking similarity between this aspect of dreaming

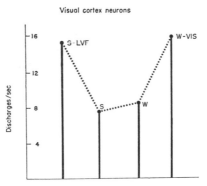

FIG. 4.—Activity of neurons in the visual cortex of the cat during S-REM (S-LVF), S-SW(S), waking in darkness (W) and waking with visual activity (W-Vis). The same neurons were studied under all four conditions. Neuronal activity is similar in S-SW and W, the values doubling for both S-REM and W-Vis. Reprinted from Evarts.[38]

and the acceptance, by the schizophrenic, of certain delusional ideas which are also experienced as "givens" and which compel the belief of the patient ("autochthonous delusions"[98]). This latter similarity between dreams and functional psychosis has not yet received the emphasis it merits.

Many investigators are currently attempting to delve more deeply into the mysteries of dream content by modifying the pre-sleep experiences of subjects and eliciting subsequent dream narratives from experimental awakenings,[58,148] and with other techniques. It is to be hoped that these and other investigations will shed further light on what has been referred to as a third level of existence.[129]

As noted earlier in this section, several early observers of human behavior suggested that common mechanisms underly dreams and hallucinations. We shall now briefly review some of the recent physiological evidence which is pertinent to this speculation.

B. Cerebral Basis for Dreams and Hallucinations

Three years after Aserinsky and Kleitman discovered the relation between S-REM and dreams in man,[9] Dement found that S-REM also occurs in the cat, and that feline S-REM has many properties in common with S-REM in man.[25] The discovery that S-REM occurs in mammals quickly triggered a number of neurophysiological studies of S-REM, and these studies have now provided us with clues as to the neurophysiological correlates of dreaming. One must, of course, be cautious in extrapolating from cat or monkey to man, but the similarity of the objective manifestations of S-REM in these three species is so striking that the extrapolations seem relatively safe, and it appears likely that one may actually learn a good deal about the cerebral basis of dreaming in man from neurophysiological studies of S-REM in laboratory animals. Furthermore, knowledge of the physiological bases of dreams may tell us something of the cerebral mechanisms underlying hallucinations during the waking state. Indeed (as will be pointed out later when we consider narcolepsy and delirium), at least some kinds of hallucinations during waking now appear to involve the same neural mechanisms which give rise to dreams during sleep.

Before reviewing the contributions of the current era of sleep research to our understanding of the cerebral basis for dreams, it may be useful to summarize some of the more classical views on this topic—views such as those formulated by Hughlings Jackson and William James toward the end of the 19th century. An earlier paper by one of the present authors[37] has already dealt with the ideas of James and Jackson in some detail, and it will be sufficient to summarize their views as put forward previously:

1. Dreams and hallucinations are similar in nature.

2. Both of these forms of mentation are correlative with activity of those brain centers involved in waking perception.

3. Hallucinations, dreams and waking perceptions are correlative with a "strong discharge" of the same nervous arrangements whose "weak discharge" is correlative with the corresponding thought, idea, or memory.

The three propositions listed above have certain implications for the cerebral processes underlying dreams and hallucinations, and lead to the formulation of three hypotheses:

I. The proposition that hallucinations are similar to dreams leads to the hypothesis that neurophysiologic processes associated with dreams (and hence with certain levels of sleep) are also associated with hallucinations occurring in the waking state.

II. The proposition that the central structures mediating perception also mediate hallucination leads to the hypothesis that those mechanisms underlying normal vision will be active in the course of dreams and visual hallucinations.

III. The third proposition, that a hallucination differs from the corresponding thought in the intensity of neuronal discharge, would lead to the hypothesis that hallucinations result from pathologically strong discharges. Jackson proposed that this strong discharge resulted from elimination of a controlling force, either in the "normal dissolution" of sleep or the "pathologic dissolution" of cerebral disease. In more modern terminology, this amounts to the hypothesis that dreams and hallucinations result from the elimination of an inhibitory process.

Recent sleep research has yielded an extraordinary degree of support for these ideas of James and Jackson, providing considerable evidence for the truth of all three of their general propositions:

I. Studies on patients with sleep hallucinosis, as this condition occurs in patients with narcolepsy, have shown that the neural processes associated with dreams will, if they extend into the waking state, give rise to hallucinations. Thus, on the basis of polygraphic studies of narcoleptic attacks, Dement et al.[31] concluded that hallucinations which occur in the waking moments of narcoleptic patients are probably dream phenomena—based on the persistence during waking of certain patterns of cerebral activity normally confined to S-REM. Furthermore, observations of Feinberg et al.[52] on the confusion, agitation, and disorientation occurring upon awakenings from S-REM in patients with chronic brain syndrome, and of Gross et al.[71] on subjects with delirium tremens, indicate that the cerebral processes underlying S-REM may extend into waking behavior of these groups of patients as well as of patients with narcolepsy. Additional observations, dealt with in greater detail in Part

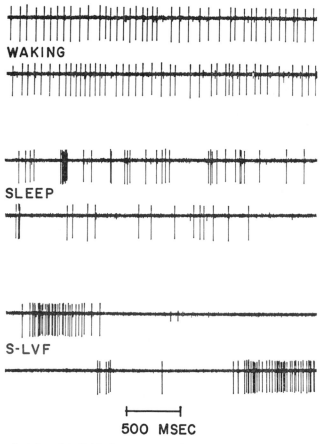

Fig. 5.—Activity of individual neurons in the pyramidal cortex of the monkey during waking, sleep (S-SW) and S-REM (S-LVF). Although the amount of activity is similar in waking and S-REM, the pattern of activity differs greatly under the two conditions.

III of this paper, now provide strong support for the hypothesis that *the neurophysiologic processes associated with dreams are also associated with some types of hallucinations occurring in the waking state.*

II. The second hypothesis put forth above holds that the visual components of dreams and hallucinations involve activity of the same structures which mediate waking vision. Now, literally centuries after this hypothesis was first set forth, neurophysiological studies of sleep in laboratory animals have provided definitive support for the hypothesis: studies of the activity of individual neurons during S-REM and waking vision have shown that the same neurons *are* involved in these two processes. Fig. 4 illustrates the results of these studies, and shows that S-REM is associated with heightened activity of neurons in visual cortex. Although their temporal patterns differ (Fig. 5), the amount of activity of visual cortex neurons during S-REM is approximately the same as during waking vision, and in both of these states activity is approximately twice as great as during S-SW or waking in the absence of visual experience. Here, then, we have evidence that during the dream the brain centers for vision are driven from *within,* and that this internal drive causes discharges whose intensity parallels that which is initiated from without during waking.

III. The third hypothesis set forth at the beginning of this section suggested that dreams and hallucinations involve the elimination of an inhibitory process. According to this view, the inputs to sensory regions which are set up by memories are relatively weak, and during waking these inputs fail to evoke sensations. This idea was well expressed by David Hume.[76] "Here therefore we may divide all the perceptions of the mind into two classes or species, which are distinguished by their different degrees of force and vivacity." Hume felt that thoughts and imaginations were on a continuum with perceptions, differing only in intensity or "vivacity," and that the difference in intensity between these two forms of mental activity was such that imagination was not confused with its antecedent perception "except the mind be disordered by disease or madness . . ."

To Hume's statement, "madness," might be added sleep. The hypothesis thus proposes that the hallucinations of sleep and madness occur when inhibitory controls are lost—when weak inputs which normally engender only thoughts and memories acquire the capacity to evoke sensory experience.

A number of neurophysiological studies have now shown that sleep, and especially S-REM, is associated with numerous manifestations of disinhibition at the level of the cerebral cortex. The number and variety of these studies preclude their individual consideration here; the interested reader is referred to one of several recent volumes on the neurophysiological correlates of sleep.[4,78,85,88] In essence, studies in these volumes show that for a given input, the cortex responds much more vigorously during S-REM than *at any other time*. *Weak* inputs reaching the cortex during S-REM evoke *strong* discharges. Furthermore, there is considerable evidence that the cause of this heightened responsiveness during S-REM is, in fact, disinhibition.[c.f.38,39]

Disinhibition at the cortical level is associated with heightened inhibition at the level of the spinal cord motoneuron[112]—and as a result the strong discharges of the cortical motor centers during S-REM usually fail to evoke somatic movements, for the anterior horn cells are practically uncoupled from higher levels of the CNS. It is only with extremely intense, almost convulsive, cortical discharges of S-REM that the excitation reaching the spinal cord motoneuron is sufficient to overcome the tonic inhibition of S-REM and initiate a movement.

In summary, the current era of sleep research has already revealed considerable knowledge of the neural bases of dreams and strongly implicates these same mechanisms in their waking counterpart, hallucinations. It seems reasonable to expect that further studies will extend this knowledge, leading to new insights into the neural mechanisms underlying the perceptual and cognitive disorders occurring in psychosis.

II. EEG SLEEP PATTERNS AND MENTAL DISORDERS

Insomnia is the only physiological change known to occur with some consistency in severe mental disorder. EEG recordings of sleep provide a measure of this insomnia and, in addition, a description of the amounts and temporal sequences of the EEG stages of whatever sleep is obtained. A number of studies have now been carried out in which the EEG and eye-movement patterns of psychiatric patients were continuously monitored. In this work, patients are usually studied for several consecutive nights in the absence of experimental intervention with the expectation of obtaining information regarding the effects of the psychiatric illness upon the naturally occurring sleep pattern. Before discussing these investigations, it may be worthwhile to note certain methodological problems which often act to restrict the inferences which may be drawn from such data.

Participation in the experimental procedure, which involves attachment of electrodes and prolonged electronic monitoring, is often viewed as threatening by normal subjects. This distress is reflected by decreased total sleep time with a disproportionate reduction of S-REM on the first night in the laboratory in normal subjects ("first-night effect").[119,29] It is therefore not surprising that psychiatric patients are especially disturbed by these procedures; indeed, many subjects simply refuse to participate. Such refusals may be minimized by study of patients on their home wards, rather than in special laboratories, and by combining responsibility for clinical care and experimental work in the same persons. Nevertheless, even under optimal circumstances, a substantial number of patients refuse cooperation, thus introducing inevitable sampling biases. Such errors might be especially prone to occur in the selection of chronic schizophrenic patients because the large number of available subjects in this diagnostic group may lead investigators to select only cooperative patients. In addition, sampling biases may occur to different degrees in different illnesses. Thus severely ill depressive patients, who are frequently quite passive, may more readily participate in sleep research than severely ill, negativistic schizophrenic subjects. In part, some of these sampling errors may be avoided by use of systematic behavioral observations which are independent of the cooperation of the subject.[47] However, such observation provides only gross information regarding behavioral sleep.

A second source of uncertainty stems from the effects of previous or concurrent drug intake. Acute administration of phenothiazines and antidepressants has profound effects on the sleep cycle of normal subjects and of psychiatric patients. These effects, which may conceivably differ in the two groups, have not yet been fully explored. The effects of chronic administration of these drugs and of recent abstinence are largely unknown. Equally unknown is the duration of abstinence required to eliminate effects of previous drug intake. For these reasons it appears especially hazardous to draw conclusions regarding the nature of sleep processes in the natural illnesses from studies of patients under active or recent drug treatment. Since clinical responsibility requires that severely ill patients be given adequate drug therapy, a further selection factor favoring the less severely ill is introduced.

A third difficulty stems from the uncertainties which arise in the scoring of the sleep EEG. Although physiological techniques afford considerable advantage in precision over behavioral observations, it must be emphasized that EEG sleep tracings are by no means entirely unequivocal. These ambiguities, which are usually slight in normal subjects, are often greatly increased in patients with disturbed sleep. For these reasons, scoring of the sleep records may permit intrusion of unconscious bias. Such bias may be eliminated by "blind scoring," in which tracings of control and experimental groups are not identified as such. Blind evaluations have not often been carried out, and their absence poses a restriction upon the interpretation of certain studies which claim differences between patients and control populations.

The subjective criteria by which emergent stage 1 and stage 4 EEG are judged vary somewhat for different raters trained in the same laboratory, and this variation is doubtless greater among raters from different laboratories. In addition, while most investigators employ modifications of Dement's scoring scheme,[27] these modifications themselves often differ substantially. These differences render inter-laboratory comparisons difficult and uncertain. For example, present variation in scoring techniques would appear to preclude comparing the results of patient groups studied in one laboratory with the results of a control group studied elsewhere, yet such comparisons are sometimes reported.

Inter-laboratory comparisons of sleep data obtained on psychiatric patients may also be affected by the heterogeneity existing within diagnostic groups. Both schizophrenic and depressed patients vary widely in their symptomatology, and this variation may contribute discrepant results, especially when small samples are employed. A related problem is posed by variations in severity of illness within a given nosological group. Such variation covers an extremely broad range and can be evaluated only after special training. In the absence of adequate clinical descriptions of severity, discrepancies could arise, for example, by considering as equivalent a sample composed of excited catatonic patients and one composed of apathetic schizophrenic subjects.

Related to this latter issue are questions regarding the nature of appropriate control groups. In addition to the obvious need for matching control with experimental subjects on age, sex, and perhaps, socio-environmental status and intelligence, there arises the question of whether one should not also attempt matching for degree of distress or agitation. If one is interested in the effects of psychosis *per se*, rather than in less specific changes due to anxiety or agitation, the appropriate controls for disturbed psychotic patients would be severely anxious but non-psychotic normal subjects. The sleep patterns of such groups have not yet been reported.

Further uncertainties in the interpretation of sleep studies in psychiatric patients stem from the fact of institutionalization. One of us has found that mere living in an institution does not seem to produce abnormal sleep patterns. Thus, the nocturnal sleep of a group of sociopathic subjects was entirely normal (Feinberg, unpublished observations). However, the fact of institutionalization may affect the recorded patterns of those patients who, because of insomnia, take daytime naps. If such naps have become habitual, and are then prevented during periods of physiological recording, results may be contaminated by the need for adaptation to this changed schedule. Telemetric recording over prolonged periods could provide a solution to this problem by permitting registration of the spontaneous sleep patterns of institutionalized subjects. However, such recording would be quite expensive and would itself pose special problems for obtaining appropriate control groups.

In addition to increased opportunity for daytime naps, other factors, such as the level of physical activity, are likely to differ in institutionalized patients. We are inclined to view this problem as being minor, since effects on the sleep pattern of chronically differing levels of activity have not yet been demonstrated and because of the normal sleep patterns found in the small group of institutionalized, inactive, sociopathic patients cited above. However, it has been speculated that increased physical activity is associated with increased stage 4 EEG during sleep;[123] and some evidence supporting this view exists.[11] Until more conclusive data are available, some uncertainty on this question must remain.

No study carried out thus far has controlled all of these variables. It is therefore all the more striking that considerable agreement exists regarding sleep patterns found in the major functional psychoses. We shall now direct our attention to investigations of the physiological sleep pattern in schizophrenia and depressive psychoses, the two conditions which have been most intensively studied.

A. Schizophrenia

Dement (1955) carried out the first EEG study of sleep in schizophrenic patients.[24] He monitored the sleep of 17 chronic patients, four of whom had undergone recent somatic treatment. He found the amount and pattern of S-REM in this group to be similar to that of a control group composed of medical students. Fisher and Dement[54] reported the case of a single "borderline" patient who was studied within a day of the onset of florid psychosis characterized by visual and auditory hallucinations and paranoid delusions. However, on the first night of study this patient was treated with a large dose (20 mg.) of Stelazine. On this night, the patient showed what was interpreted as 50 per cent level of S-REM as measured by emergent stage 1 EEG; and various hypotheses regarding the relationship to psychosis of S-REM were advanced on this basis. However, subsequent work suggests early schizophrenia is associated with low rather than high S-REM levels,[49] and the findings in this one case appear attributable to the drugs administered.[42]

Koresko et al.[89] compared the physiological sleep pattern of seven hallucinating schizophrenic patients with that of four non-hallucinating patients. Four of the patients included in this study had recently been treated with tranquilizing drugs. Total sleep time was similar in the two groups, as was the amount of S-REM as reflected by measurements of both emergent stage 1 EEG and rapid eye-movement activity. However, these authors noted certain apparently atypical features of S-SW in both groups. These included an apparent diminution of sleep spindles and relatively long periods of low-voltage EEG, generally occurring at the conclusion of S-REM periods. This low-voltage activity was unaccompanied by rapid eye-movement, and showed occasional bursts of alpha, spindles or K-complexes.

Expanded studies[49,48] described the sleep patterns of 22 schizophrenic patients, of whom 18 were actively ill and 4 in states of remission. Nine of the actively ill patients were classified as short-term (ill less than one year) and nine as long-term (continuously ill for over two years). Ten of the 18 were experiencing hallucinations at the time of study. The results obtained were compared with those found in a control group (N=10) consisting of four hospitalized patients suffering from character disorders and six non-hospitalized control subjects. All subjects in this investigation were studied for at least four consecutive nights, care being taken to prevent daytime sleep. The subjects were drug-free during the period of study, and with the exception of four patients, had received no medication during the preceding three weeks. Again, it was found that the total sleep time of the actively ill schizophrenic group did not differ from that of the control subjects, although sleep latency was significantly longer for the patients. Absolute and percentage stage 1 EEG did not differ in the two groups. However, the patients showed significantly lower values for another index of S-REM, the amount of rapid eye-movement activity. This difference was due to low values in the short-term subgroup of patients. Latency to the first eye-movement was significantly more variable in the schizophrenic subjects as a result of the occurrence of both longer and especially shorter latencies as compared with control values. In addition, there was a tendency for hallucinating patients to show a higher density of eye-movement activity during periods of S-REM. Feinberg and associates concluded that the neurophysiological mechanisms underlying dreaming sleep were fundamentally normal in schizophrenia. The fact that recent onset of illness appeared associated with a slight diminution of S-REM was interpreted as indicating that this stage of sleep, already known to be reduced under the initial stress of laboratory recording, is generally sensitive to disturbed states of the organism. In a later review of these data, taken in association with further study of both schizophrenic and control subjects, Feinberg[42] noted that the variability of S-REM onset was attributable mainly to the occurrence of very short latencies in some schizophrenic subjects.* Also the previously noted tendency of hallucinating patients to show a higher density of eye-movements during S-REM did not receive further support. Again, it was concluded that S-REM mechanisms appeared fundamentally intact in schizophrenia and that there was no evidence to implicate a disturbance of S-REM mechanisms in the waking hallucinations of schizophrenic patients. Rechtschaffen et al.[118] came to a similar conclusion on the basis of waking recordings of EEG, eye-movement and chin-muscle activity in a small group of schizophrenic subjects.

---

*Since the two types of sleep are in dynamic interaction, it should be noted that the early onset of S-REM in some schizophrenic subjects may reflect an abnormality of S-SW rather than of S-REM itself. We think this explanation to be probable because disturbances in S-W occur more consistently than disturbances of S-REM in schizophrenia, and because there appears to be an inverse correlation between the amount of stage 4 EEG and S-REM onset.[50] Thus, the early onset of S-REM may be a reflection of the decrease in stage 4 EEG frequently found (see below) in schizophrenic patients. Similarly, the lengthened first S-REM period observed in some groups of schizophrenic patients[137] may represent decreased pressure of S-SW rather than an abnormality of S-REM mechanisms. Whatever their cause, there is no basis for attributing early S-REM onset or prolonged first S-REM periods to schizophrenia. Both phenomena occur in other conditions.[42,50]

Subsequent studies have corroborated the conclusion that basal S-REM levels are within normal limits in schizophrenia. Thus, Onheiber et al.[106] and Ornitz et al.[107,108] found normal amounts and patterns of S-REM in small samples of schizophrenic and autistic children. Caldwell and Domino found the mean time spent in S-REM in 25 chronic schizophrenic patients to be almost identical to the value found in 10 medical student volunteers.[20] The observation that early stages of illness are associated with a reduction rather than an increase in the proportion of S-REM has also received some further support.[91,152] However, in contrast to the results of Feinberg et al.,[49] who found normal sleep patterns in four recovered *acute* schizophrenic patients, Gulevich et al.[72] reported that a group of 13 chronic schizophrenic patients "at or approaching a state of clinical remission" showed significantly higher values in amount and percentage of S-REM when compared with seven non-psychotic controls. This discrepancy may be due to differences in the nature of the patients studied. Also of possible relevance is the fact that Gulevich had withdrawn tranquilizing drugs from eight of the patients 4 to 30 days prior to study. However the latter authors rejected this possibility, since their analysis showed the mean values for S-REM in the five patients who were drug-free for a period of six months prior to study to be as high as those found in the more recently medicated group. Further investigation appears required to reconcile this discrepancy.

A variety of abnormalities of S-SW have been noted to occur in the EEG sleep tracings of schizophrenic patients. In addition to the apparent reduction in abundance of sleep spindles mentioned above,[89] S-SW is delayed in its onset and shows decreased abundance of its high-voltage slow component (stage 4 EEG). Lairy et al.[91] found that stage 4 EEG was often diminished at the onset of delusional episodes, although this result was not documented statistically. Caldwell and Domino[20] reported significantly lower values for stage 4 EEG in 25 chronic schizophrenic patients when compared with 10 medical student control subjects. However, the controls were younger in age (mean=24 yrs.) than the patients (mean=32 yrs.). Since stage 4 EEG declines steadily over this age range,[45] some of the difference between patients and controls in this study may have been due to their difference in age. However, comparing the sleep tracings of the 18 actively ill patients described above with those of an equal number of control subjects, precisely matched with the patients for age, Feinberg et al. (unpublished data) found a reduction in stage 4 EEG (6.3 per cent vs. 12.6 per cent; $p<.02$). In addition, they found the regression of stage 4 EEG on successive periods of S-SW to be significantly flatter in slope for the schizophrenic than for the control subjects. However, it should be noted that mean values for stage 3 EEG in the schizophrenic patients were not significantly reduced compared with those of the control group (9.1 per cent vs. 9.6 per cent), and normal or even high stage 4 values occurred in some patients.

Stage 4 EEG, as scored in one laboratory,[50] represents high-voltage ($>50/uV$), slow ($<4cps$), activity occurring with a stipulated density (>16 waves per 20-sec. interval). Low values may result from a failure to meet any of these three criteria. Thus, if bursts of delta waves are shorter but more frequent throughout the night, delta activity could occur in normal amounts although stage 4 scores would be drastically reduced. The differences in regression of stage 4 EEG scores across non-REM periods, as cited above, suggests that part of the difference between schizophrenic and control subjects on this measure may result from alterations in the distribution of high-voltage slow activity.

In an attempt to investigate further the apparent reduction in stage 4 EEG in schizophrenic patients found by Caldwell and Domino, Luby and Caldwell carried out 85 hours of total sleep deprivation in four chronic subjects (mean age 32 yrs.).[97] Three of the four subjects showed no scorable stage 4 EEG prior to study, and the remaining patient showed rather high values on this measure. On the first recovery night following deprivation, the three schizophrenic patients without scorable stage 4 failed to show the compensatory increase in stage 4 activity previously reported by Berger and Oswald[14] in normals, and also found by Luby and Caldwell in their own control subjects. Stage 3 EEG values were not reported. The subject with high basal values for stage 4 EEG (20 per cent) showed a curious decline on this measure on the first recovery night (2 per cent). This finding, taken in association with the fact that the baseline recordings for these subjects had been carried out several months prior to the deprivation study, raises the possibility that a "first-night effect" (perhaps coupled with the development of increasing anxiety during the deprivation period) affected the sleep patterns on the recovery night. If such an effect was present, the maximum stage 4 response might have been delayed to the second recovery night. The sleep patterns on this night were not monitored, although tracings obtained on the third night again showed low stage 4 values. In view of this latter difficulty in interpretation, and in view of the small number of subjects studied, one hesitates to accept the suggestion of Luby and Caldwell that the stage 4 deficit found in some schizophrenic subjects is irreversible. In this regard it is pertinent to note that Lester et al.[95] recently reported that examination stress in students reduces stage 4 EEG and that one of their subjects, who had recently had an upsetting life experience, showed no scorable stage 3 or 4 EEG on three consecutive nights of study despite the fact that he had undergone some amount (unspecified) of sleep deprivation.

We consider that the most parsimonious interpretation of changes in both S-REM and S-SW found in some schizophrenic patients is that such changes represent a generalized increase in arousal level. Increased arousal, in addition to delaying sleep onset, seems associated with disproportionate reductions in S-REM and of the spindling and sustained delta phases of S-SW.* However, schizophrenia is neither a necessary nor a sufficient condition for these changes. Some severely ill schizophrenic patients whose symptomatology is entirely typical show physiological sleep patterns that are normal in all respects. Furthermore, some of the changes observed in schizophrenia have been noted to occur in non-psychotic subjects who complain of poor sleep,[101] and it remains possible that the sleep tracings of severely disturbed but nonpsychotic subjects might prove indistinguishable from those of the most agitated schizophrenic patient.

The significance of the increased arousal level in schizophrenia and other severe mental illnesses remains unknown. While behavioral observations of insomnia have been found positively correlated with severity of symptoms in a group of chronic patients,[47] the exceptions to this relationship are often quite striking. It remains for future investigation to determine whether the high levels of arousal found in some schizophrenic patients are intrinsic or secondary to the illness, and to discover whether these levels are of significance for prognosis and treatment.

Physiological systems whose basal levels are within normal limits may nevertheless reveal aberrant function when put under stress. The glucose tolerance test represents a familiar clinical example of this phenomenon. Attempts have now been made to stress S-REM systems in schizophrenic

---

*The sensitivity of S-REM to organismic disturbance, as shown by its disproportionate reduction on the first night in the laboratory and in schizophrenia and other conditions indicates that, in spite of its relatively low arousal threshold[115] this stage of sleep cannot be regarded as "light" sleep in any simple sense.

patients in an attempt to detect pathological function not otherwise apparent. Azumi et al.[10] compared the effects of four to five nights of S-REM deprivation (accomplished by awakenings at the onset of S-REM periods) in three chronic schizophrenic patients and four normal control subjects. The patients had been without somatic therapy during the previous year, although one patient had a previous course of insulin and another, a course of ECT. During the period of S-REM deprivation, the investigators noted no exacerbation of psychotic symptoms in the patients. On the recovery nights, when sleep was permitted without interruption, two of the three patients showed compensatory increases in S-REM smaller than those found in the control group. These results are difficult to interpret because of the high baseline values in two of these patients. Thus, although their increment was less, the mean percentage of S-REM on the first recovery night was greater for the three schizophrenic patients than for the three control subjects who underwent the same deprivation procedure (29.2 per cent vs. 27.8 per cent). Since the schizophrenic patient with the lowest baseline values showed the highest increment, the difference between schizophrenic and control subjects in this study may have been a function of the differences in initial values. The interpretation of these findings is further complicated by the uncertain consequences of the previous somatic therapy and by the fact that two of the three schizophrenic subjects (aged 45 and 55 years) were considerably older than the oldest control subject (36 years). Vogel and Traub,[137] in a similar experiment, deprived five chronic schizophrenic patients of S-REM over a period of seven consecutive nights, employing a combination of dextroamphetamine[116] and awakenings to reduce the amount of S-REM. These investigators also failed to observe exacerbations of symptoms during the period of deprivation. When deprivation was discontinued, the patients manifested a compensatory increase in S-REM quite similar in magnitude to that previously reported for normal subjects. Vogel and Traub interpreted their data as indicating that S-REM deprivation is not harmful to schizophrenic patients and that the mechanisms underlying this stage of sleep are normal in schizophrenia. Zarcone et al.[152] in a third study of this problem, carried out deprivation of S-REM by repeated awakenings in six schizophrenic patients in remission, three actively ill patients, and four control subjects suffering from character disorders. These investigators found that, compared with the control group, compensation of S-REM after the two-night deprivation period was greater for the patients in remission and smaller for the actively ill patients. On the basis of these observations, these authors concluded that "at the very least . . . we have demonstrated a dramatic association between a physiological variable (the REM deprivation-compensation response) and clinical state." In addition, they suggested that "the CNS changes associated with REM sleep deprivation may directly underly psychotic disintegration." This latter conclusion is difficult to reconcile with the failure of Vogel and Traub and of Azumi et al. to find any exacerbation of symptoms during the longer periods of S-REM deprivation in their schizophrenic subjects. In view of the evidence that anxiety and agitation tend to diminish S-REM, it seems probable that some severely ill patients would show diminished compensatory responses to deprivation, as was the case for three subjects in the study of Zarcone et al. In such subjects, responses might be limited to some minimal biological requirement. However, one cannot attribute the limited responses of these highly agitated subjects to psychosis itself in the absence of study of disturbed nonpsychotic subjects.

Although their results differed, the findings of both Vogel and Traub and of Zarcone et al. may have been influenced by the fact that patients were maintained on therapeutic dosages of tranquilizing medication during these investigations. It is true that the baseline sleep patterns of these subjects were generally within normal limits despite ingestion of these drugs. Nevertheless, the possibility remains that the drugs might affect the response to deprivation and might do so differently for patients whose illnesses differ in severity. Finally, since there is now general agreement that S-REM may vary in intensity as well as in duration, each of the above studies might have benefited by inclusion of some presumptive measure of intensity, such as the density of eye-movements during S-REM periods.

In citing certain limitations of these extremely time-consuming and difficult clinical studies we do not wish to minimize their value. In view of the vital importance of discovering physiological correlates of schizophrenia, it certainly seems worthwhile to go beyond basal studies in this condition and to seek aberrant responses of sleep mechanisms to a variety of stresses, including partial and total deprivation. Nevertheless, again in view of the importance of the issue, one hesitates to accept positive findings which are based on small numbers and which do not control for the effects of anxiety or other potentially confounding variables.

B. Depressive Illness

Diaz-Guerrero et al.[34] in 1946 carried out the first known EEG recordings of the nocturnal sleep of psychiatric patients in a group of six manic-depressive patients, depressed type. This work was done prior to the discovery of S-REM in 1952 by Aserinsky and Kleitman. The patients, all under 40 years of age, were studied for two consecutive nights in the absence of the sedative drugs. Compared with data available in the literature and with the findings in a small control group, the patients displayed longer sleep latencies, more frequent wakefulness, and a decrease in the high-voltage phases of S-SW. Diaz-Guerrero et al. also observed increased fluctuations of EEG stage and an overall increase in the amount of low-voltage EEG in their depressed subjects. This latter finding is difficult to interpret, for, since eye-movement activity was not recorded, it is impossible to distinguish the amount of low-voltage EEG which represents arousal from that due to S-REM.

Zung et al.[154] found EEG arousal thresholds to auditory stimuli lower in 11 hospitalized depressed patients than in controls; this difference disappeared with clinical improvement of the patients. These investigators concluded that their findings supported the view of Diaz-Guerrero et al. that the sleep of depressed patients is lighter than that of normals. Oswald et al.[109] studied the effects of placebo and 400 mg. of heptabarbital on the sleep patterns of six depressed and six control subjects. On placebo nights, the patients showed increased wakefulness, which was prominent in the early hours of the morning but was not specifically related to the time of occurrence of S-REM periods. Oswald and co-workers did not observe the increased number of EEG stage fluctuations noted by Diaz-Guerrero et al. in their depressed patients. The former authors also reported an *increase* in stage E (stage 4) EEG in their depressed patients as compared with the controls. This anomalous finding differs from the results of Diaz-Guerrero et al. and from later investigations. It may result from the fact that the patients were previously deprived of this stage of sleep, and, under the hypnotic drug, were able to obtain a compensatory increase. In general, the design of the Oswald study renders it difficult to distinguish basal sleep differences between patient and control from the effects of drug intake. However, the drug effects themselves were quite clear. Heptabarbital decreased the amount of time spent in S-REM and reduced the density of eye-movements within this stage of sleep. It also decreased the amount of wakefulness (especially in the depressed patients), the frequency of EEG stage changes, and the number of body-movements during sleep.

Gresham et al.[69] and Hawkins and Mendels[73,99,100] have carried out the most detailed investigations of uninterrupted sleep patterns in depressed patients. Gresham and co-workers reported that the sleep patterns of eight patients showed more wakefulness and a tendency to decreased stage 4 EEG when contrasted with those of eight control subjects. These subjects were studied for four consecutive nights after three days without drug treatment. Four patients were restudied after treatment and prior to discharge from the hospital. Compared with values obtained when actively ill, these latter subjects showed significantly increased amounts of stage 4 and S-REM sleep.

These findings suggested that in depression, as well as in schizophrenia, active illness is associated with reduced levels of both stage 4 EEG and S-REM. The data of Mendels and Hawkins[99,100] further support this view. These investigators found increased wakefulness and decreased percentages of stage 4 EEG and S-REM in 19 depressed patients compared with 15 normal control subjects. After "significant clinical improvement" and prior to discharge, 13 of these patients showed increases in total sleep time, S-REM and stage 4 EEG and decreased awakenings. However, in spite of these changes toward a more normal pattern, the improved patients still showed greater wakefulness and somewhat less stage 4 EEG than did the controls. Mendels and Hawkins also noted that the severity of sleep disturbance tended to be positively correlated with the severity of symptoms, and they emphasized the importance of this latter variable in evaluation of sleep studies in depressed patients. They interpreted changes in sleep pattern in depressed patients as reflecting the existence of a generalized increase in arousal level, an interpretation similar to that put forward for findings in schizophrenic patients. In both conditions the question of whether the increased arousal levels are basic or secondary to the illness remains unanswered. These findings further emphasize the need for control studies of highly aroused but non-psychotic subjects.

Vogel et al.[138] carried out studies of S-REM deprivation in five depressed patients. They hypothesized on a variety of grounds that such deprivation might be beneficial in depression. Two of their patients showed the normal responses to deprivation, including both a progressive increase in the number of awakenings required to prevent S-

REM during the deprivation period, and a compensatory increase in this stage of sleep on recovery nights. These patients showed clinical improvement and were discharged from hospital without further treatment. The remaining three patients showed little evidence of increased pressure for S-REM (manifested by the number of awakenings necessary to prevent S-REM) during deprivation and little compensation on recovery nights. Vogel and associates interpreted these findings as indicating that S-REM deprivation is not harmful to depressed patients and may be therapeutic for some. Their observations are also consistent with the view that more severely ill patients are less likely to show S-REM compensation.

Although available data suggest that the physiological sleep pattern of many typical schizophrenic and depressed patients differs only slightly from normal, one may still wonder whether partial sleep deprivation or selective deprivation of one or another phase of sleep plays a role in the production of psychotic symptoms. This question is raised by the observations of certain psychotic-like phenomena in recent studies of prolonged sleep deprivation, and by the claims that marked personality changes occur in subjects selectively deprived of S-REM.

According to West et al.,[141] psychotic-like phenomena are usually observed after 100 hours of total sleep deprivation. These phenomena include disorientation, visual illusions and hallucinations, and paranoid thinking. This description is more suggestive of toxic delirium than functional psychosis. The hallucinatory experiences are usually related to brief periods of sleep (lapses, microsleep) and often seem to represent snatches of dreams. In most cases, subjects can, upon demand, be mobilized to behave appropriately and to perform a variety of simple tasks with a high degree of success. Except in occasional instances, the psychotic-like phenomena are completely reversed by a single night of sleep. Instances of more prolonged effects, such as residual paranoid suspicions, cannot be attributed to specific effects of sleep deprivation. Such cases may parsimoniously be interpreted as resulting from the effects of non-specific stress upon a volunteer population of less than optimal mental health. Finally, it remains possible that suggestion and expectation play a role in the production of some of these symptoms. On the basis of observations of four subjects undergoing 200 hours of sleep deprivation, Pasnau et al.[111] concluded that the psychopathological changes observed in sleep deprivation should not be classified as psychotic.

In view of the rapid reversibility of symptoms produced by sleep deprivation and in view of their phenomenological differences from those of schizophrenia and depression, it seems improbable that sleep deprivation itself plays a causal role in these latter conditions. Furthermore, while total sleep time is drastically reduced in some patients, there is no evidence that this insomnia ever reaches the levels (100-200 hours of sustained wakefulness) associated with the occurrence of psychopathology in the experimental situation. Thus, mean sleep time in 18 actively ill schizophrenic patients was 6 hrs. 23 min.[49] and in 19 depressed subjects, 5 hrs. 28 min.[99] Occasional patients may show considerably lower levels. For example, a mean sleep time over five nights of 3 hrs. 40 min. was recorded in an acute schizophrenic subject.[49] This insomnia still does not approach the level associated with the production of symptoms in non-psychotic volunteers.

One may question whether the moderate but prolonged insomnia found in some patients plays a causal role in their psychopathology. In the absence of studies of the effects of prolonged partial sleep deprivation, the answer to this question must remain unknown. Our own best estimate is that minimal biological requirements for sleep are fulfilled in the overwhelming majority of psychiatric patients.

A recent study by Monroe[101] in non-psychotic subjects is relevant to the general question of insomnia and psychiatric illness. He found that 16 subjects, recruited on the basis of complaints of poor sleep (Poor Sleep Group—PSG), showed less sleep time, markedly less S-REM, longer sleep latencies, and more frequent awakenings than 16 subjects recruited on the basis of statements of good sleep (GSG). An important limitation of this study is that recordings were carried out for only a single night. Although an habituation night was included, its value was limited by the fact that one or two nights of non-laboratory sleep intervened between adaptation and experimental nights. Thus, a severe "first-night effect" in the PSG on the habituation night might have been followed by unrecorded compensatory increases in total sleep with the experimental night becoming, in effect, another "first night." It would also seem that, on this type of group comparison, "blind" scoring would have been especially useful.

We discuss these methodological issues in detail because of the importance of the findings in this study. For example, the amounts of S-REM recorded in the PSG were as low as those observed in patients with senile brain disease.[50] This observation, if truly representative of the sleep requirements of the PSG subjects, would pose a crucial objection to the hypothesis for the biological function of sleep suggested below. A further interesting finding in Monroe's study was that the PSG scored higher on questionnaire indices of psychopathology than the GSG. However, this result, as the author points out, may signify the presence of response bias, the PSG responding affirmatively to questions regarding the presence of symptoms generally. Even if it were established that PSG showed a genuinely higher level of personality disturbance than the GSG subjects, one could not conclude on this basis alone that a causal relation (only one of several possibilities suggested by Monroe) between sleep disturbance and psychopathology exists. Thus, it would seem likely that subjects who complain of severe eating or elimination difficulties might also prove to have higher levels of psychopathology than the general population. In view of the importance of Monroe's observations for a variety of issues in sleep research and in psychiatry, it is to be hoped that further, more extensive investigation of non-psychotic subjects with sleep difficulties will soon be carried out.

The question of whether selective deprivation of S-REM plays a role in the production of psychotic phenomena has aroused considerable interest because of claims that marked personality changes and increased anxiety can be produced by such deprivation.[26,28] The data pertinent to this question have been thoroughly reviewed by Vogel.[135] He concluded that the positive findings in these studies were "probably a result of uncontrolled factors such as the expectations of the experimenters and the subjects." On the basis of several lines of evidence, Vogel goes on to state, "It is doubtful that the necessary conditions for the presumed harm—long and continuously complete REM deprivation—ever occur in the natural state outside the laboratory. This suggests that REM deprivation is not a cause or a contributor to clinical illness in man."

Although sleep loss does not seem to produce symptoms similar to those of the main functional psychoses, it does produce distinct changes in cognitive function.[143] Some of these changes are the consequences of brief sleep attacks ("lapses," "microsleeps"), whereas others seem to represent alterations in the efficiency of the cognitive processes themselves. Of these latter changes, deficits of memory are of special interest in view of the sleep-cognition hypothesis to be considered in Part IV of this paper. Thus, Williams et al.[142] havs shown that total sleep deprivation leads to impairment of short-term verbal recall which is not attributable to failure of sensory registration during lapses. It seems possible, in view of the results of Portnoff et al.[113] cited earlier, that this impaired recall results from effects of lowered arousal level on consolidation. However, it also seems possible that the memory impairment is the consequence of depletion of certain neuronal constituents during the prolonged waking. Williams et al.[142] also observed that memory for pictures presented during sleep loss was unaffected by an additional 24 hours of wakefulness but was then reduced after one night of recovery sleep. This latter finding suggests a role for sleep in the erasure of "weak" engrams, a possibility discussed by us in greater detail elsewhere.[46]

Although the cognitive as well as the emotional changes following sleep loss may be secondary phenomena unrelated to the biological function of sleep under natural conditions, we think it more likely that at least some of the former phenomena are intrinsically related to the role of sleep in maintaining the integrity of brain function. Our understanding both of sleep and of the central nervous system mechanisms which underlie cognition might be furthered by more systematic assessment of those cognitive functions which are "sensitive"[143] to sleep loss and recovery. Once such a catalogue is established, the selective deprivation of the different EEG stages of sleep may further specify the physiological functions involved. An especially useful design in this latter approach would be within-subject comparisons of the effects of stage 4 and S-REM deprivation. This technique might permit recognition of more subtle changes than are detectable with across-group designs. However, the latter approach has already yielded results of some interest. Thus, Agnew, et al.[3] found that deprivation of stage 4 EEG led to a "depressive outlook," whereas deprivation of S-REM led to irritability and lability.

III. Sleep Patterns in Narcolepsy, Chronic Brain Syndrome and Acute Brain Syndrome (Delirium)

We shall turn now to those conditions for which there exists evidence that S-REM mechanisms may become dissociated from sleep and may intrude into waking with resultant psychopathology: narcolepsy, and acute and chronic brain syndrome. The data on narcolepsy provide the most unequivocal support for this assertion. Findings in the latter two conditions are scanty and the implication of S-REM mechanisms in their psychopathology is considerably more inferential. It remains possible that these inferences will prove incorrect and that true instances of

dissociated S-REM mechanisms during wakefulness represent rare oc-
currences in the small proportion of the population which suffers from
specific sleep disturbances. Nevertheless, the available data for chronic
brain syndrome and delirium seem to us so promising, and the importance of these conditions to psychiatry so great, that they will be considered here in some detail. In view of the discussion in the last section,
it may be worthwhile to state at the outset that there is no strong reason
to suspect that prior deprivation is the underlying cause of the abnormal
S-REM phenomena to be considered below.

A. Narcolepsy

The term *narcolepsy* was introduced by Gelineau in 1880, though
several previous papers[94] had described the essential features of the syndrome. In its full-blown form, narcolepsy involves a tetrad of
symptoms:

(1) *Irresistible sleep attacks* of sudden onset and brief duration, often
recurring several times daily;

(2) *Cataplectic attacks* characterized by flaccid paralysis and muscular
atonia, commonly precipitated by laughter, excitement, or anger, and
associated with intact sensorium;

(3) *Sleep paralysis*, a condition characterized by loss of capacity to
move, and occurring either before sleep or immediately upon awakening;
and

(4) *Sleep hallucinosis*, in which auditory and/or visual hallucinations
may occur during waking periods immediately before or after sleep.

It is to be noted that any one of these four symptoms may occur in
isolation. Thus, in a series of 100 patients reported by Daly and Yoss,[23]
sleep attacks alone occurred in only 15 per cent of the group. In the remaining 85 per cent of the patients the sleep attacks were associated
with one or more additional elements of the syndrome—the most frequent combination being sleep and cataplectic attacks (37 per cent).
The full tetrad of symptoms was present in 16 per cent of the patients.
Narcolepsy was a subject of great interest in the early part of this century, and the works of Adie[1] and Wilson[147] still stand as the
authoritative references. From 1930 to 1960 progress in understanding
of narcolepsy was relatively slow, and it was not until the recent upsurge
of sleep research that a new chapter could be added to the narcoleptic
story.

Vogel[134] was one of the first investigators to obtain EEG and eye
movement records during three successive sleep episodes of a single

narcoleptic patient. In two of these episodes, S-REM occurred eight and four minutes after sleep onset; upon being awakened from these episodes, the subject reported that he had been dreaming. The early onset of S-REM in this narcoleptic subject was in sharp contrast to the delayed onset of S-REM in normal subjects. Vogel's observation raised the possibility that the sleep attacks of narcolepsy might actually be episodes of S-REM.

The first definitive study of S-REM in narcoleptics was carried out by Rechtschaffen et al.[122] These authors reviewed previous EEG studies (which had failed to reveal any remarkable findings) and noted that several patients studied by earlier investigators had been reported to have unusually long EEG stage 1 periods at sleep onset. Since eye movements were not recorded in these earlier studies, however, it had not been possible for S-REM to be recognized.

The work of Rechtschaffen et al.[122] showed that narcoleptics usually have S-REM at sleep onset (rather than at approximately 70 minutes after sleep onset, as is characteristic of normals; cf. Fig. 3), and indicated that narcoleptics have a special susceptibility to the occurrence of REM sleep. With this discovery several aspects of the narcoleptic syndrome became understandable in terms of what had been learned about S-REM during the preceding few years. Thus, Rechtschaffen et al. pointed out that ". . . the narcoleptic symptoms of cataplexy and sleep paralysis with hypnagogic hallucinations . . . may be . . . the attributes of REM periods during the waking state. Although the normal circumstances for the occurrence of REM periods may be a preceding period of NREM sleep, in narcoleptics the propensity for their onset may be so great that REM periods occur not only at the initiation of sleep but during wakefulness itself." Finally, the authors noted that benzedrine and dexedrine, long known to be useful in control of narcolepsy, caused selective reductions of S-REM—inhibiting the appearance of REM periods without interfering with the other stages of sleep.

Demonstration that at least some diurnal *narcoleptic attacks* represent episodes of S-REM soon followed. Hishikawa and Kaneko[74] recorded EEG and eye movement activity during the diurnal sleep of narcoleptics. S-REM was found to occur at sleep onset or within several minutes of sleep onset, and it was noted that patients often experienced sleep paralysis and/or hallucinations in the sleep-onset REM period. It was concluded that the basic disturbance of narcolepsy was a persistent and intense inclination to fall directly from wakefulness into S-REM.

Dement et al.,[31] whose earlier work on the nocturnal sleep of narcoleptics has already been referred to,[122] independently came to essentially similar conclusions as to the nature of the narcoleptic sleep attack. These investigators studied 34 narcoleptics, of whom 24 gave a history of sleep and cataplectic attacks. Of these 24 patients, 20 had sleep episodes characterized by the immediate onset of S-REM. Dement et al. pointed out that the identification of narcoleptic attacks as S-REM periods could account for the associated symptoms of cataplexy, sleep paralysis, and hypnagogic hallucinations, and stated that, "Following the view now proposed, cataplexy and sleep paralysis are seen as dissociative manifestations of the motor inhibitory process which is an essential part of normal REM periods, and hypnagogic hallucinations are viewed as dream phenomena."

The comment of Dement et al. on the existence of "dissociative manifestations" of S-REM has important implications f o r psychopathology, for the existence of certain components of the narcoleptic syndrome in the absence of others may give rise to disorders of behavior which may at times be difficult to recognize. Thus, many patients with narcolepsy give a history of severe night terrors with resultant insomnia; these complaints often antedate the onset of full-blown narcoleptic-cataplectic attacks by many years. It seems likely that certain patients may have *only* these aspects of the disturbed S-REM mechanism, and may never go on to develop classical narcolepsy. Since narcolepsy is not an all-or-none disease (but a more or less severe exaggeration of certain processes which occur normally), it is important for the psychiatrist to be aware of the less obvious manifestations of the syndrome—for these manifestations are more likely to lead the patient to the psychiatrist than to the neurologist. Thus, trance-like states, hypnagogic hallucinations, and even episodes of paranoid panic may in fact occur early in the course of the narcoleptic syndrome. The severity of the psychopathological disorders in these patients is illustrated by one of Wilson's (1928) cases:

Of the greatest interest is the fact that when he has been asleep and dreaming, *the emotional content of the dream has precipitated an attack of powerlessness.* The worst he has ever experienced lasted for about a quarter of an hour, and occurred under the following circumstances. He had fallen asleep and was dreaming of a murder. The emotion experienced in association therewith brought on one of the 'loss of power' attacks, so that he at once awoke and was fully conscious but was utterly unable to move a single finger. He thought he heard his brother and sister coming up the stairs; he tried to call to them but could not make a single sound;

the more he tried the more intense became his emotion and the more absolute his helplessness; he lay thus, flat on the floor, motionless but suffering acute mental distress, for some fifteen minutes ere the attack dissolved itself spontaneously. Similar but less severe attacks have occurred when he has been dreaming of 'terrible happenings' on other occasions.[147]

Even more dramatic as regards psychopathological manifestations are the cases described by Brain (1939):

Thus a patient of mine, a married woman aged 34, who suffered from narcolepsy, would awaken every night in a state of terror in which external stimuli, such as the reflection of the street lamp on the wall or the wail of a cat, would appear to have a sinister meaning. She was also subject to terrifying nightmares. Another patient, an unmarried woman of 24 who also suffered from narcolepsy, had hallucinatory attacks which she described as nightmares and which preceded the narcolepsy by six months. As soon as she laid her head on the pillow she found that she could not move, but she would hear people whispering all round her head and 'horrible laughter like that of the witches at pantomimes.' She could feel ghosts coming into the bedroom and leaning over her, though she could not see them. Even more dramatic were the effects of these hallucinations on a man of 22, a commercial traveller, who had suffered from bad dreams since childhood. On three occasions his nocturnal hallucinations led to violent conduct on his part. All three of these attacks occurred when he was staying in a hotel in the course of his travels. He went to bed and to sleep at the usual time, but wakened about 2 A.M. to find himself standing by the bed. He experienced extreme anxiety, as if there was someone in the room creeping towards him and that it was imperative for him to get out. In this state he would shout, and, if no one came, give way to panic. Twice he broke a window, and on the third occasion he kicked a hole three feet wide between his own room and the next. As soon as someone came he became normal and retired to bed again. This man had always been subject to hypnagogic hallucinations when falling asleep in the twilight. In this state any object in the room would take on an alarming form as of something moving towards him. Similarly a noise would cause a sharp pang of fear and an acceleration of his heart rate.[17]

S-REM normally involves a) loss of awareness of the external environment, b) flaccid paralysis, and c) dreaming. The clinical reports which have been cited show that dissociation of these three states may give rise to a number of different, but related, behavioral aberrations. For example, b without a or c is cataplexy. State c without a or b expresses itself as waking hallucinosis. It is clear that the capacity for separate elements of the sleep complex to extend into waking behavior has highly significant implications for psychopathology. As Brain[17] has pointed out, "We are temporarily insane during sleep, and our waking moments are but lucid intervals." But what if waking is only partial? The importance of the new results on narcolepsy and S-REM lies in the unequivocal demonstration that the psychopathology of waking behavior may in certain cases result from a persistence of cerebral processes which are normally restricted to sleep.

Before leaving the general topic of narcolepsy, it may be of interest to mention one additional disorder, the "Kleine-Levin" syndrome (or, in Critchley's words, "periodic hypersomnia and megaphagia in adolescent males"). This syndrome is especially relevant to the central theme of this paper because, as Critchley[22] pointed out, "Psychiatric features may dominate the scene and obscure the recognition of the syndrome." Critchley summarized details of the syndrome as follows:

Somnolency represents the most conspicuous clinical symptom, and the patient may be asleep throughout most of the attack. The sleep does not differ in any obvious fashion from the normal pattern except for its immoderate duration. The ordinary appearances of sleep are present and there is no good reason to suspect any morbid aberration of consciousness or awareness. Some observers have explicitly noted flushing or congestion of the face; others however have remarked upon pallor. Heavy sweating has been observed. While asleep the patient may dream, often vividly. The patient is always rousable, even readily so at times. He wakes spontaneously to empty his bladder or bowel, and incontinence does not occur. Moreover he may naturally wake up for meals though this is not always so. In the great majority of cases, the patient when awake is intensely irritable and resentful. Abnormal mental reactions are often observed during the period of hypersomnia, especially when the patient is aroused, or wakes spontaneously. These symptoms may indeed endure longer than any others, in that they may both antedate and follow the attack itself. The commonest psychiatric features of an attack are truculence and confusion. The irritability when well marked, shows itself in a motor unrest; an excitement; and a veritable aggressiveness—particularly when disturbed. He may turn away and curl up in an uncooperative manner. A few patients are actively hostile in their behavior. Considerable hypermotility may complicate both the sleep and the wakeful intervals. Fidgeting from one position to another, the patient may disarrange the bedclothes and even unwittingly tear the sheets. At the same time there is usually a state of agitation which is dimly remembered afterwards as a vague affect of fear or unease. In milder cases the confusion comprises a depersonalization. When more intense there is a difficulty in thinking; a disorientation; forgetfulness; upset in the judgment of time; and incongruous speech. More positive symptoms comprise vivid imagery and visual and auditory hallucinations. Very typical are waking fantasies, which are sometimes difficult for the patient to disentangle from his vivid dreams. Often these have a bizarre and crudely sexuo-sadistic character. Sometimes there are grandiose, even megalomanic, ideas. The psychiatric manifestations may have a distinctly schizophrenic patterning. Though usually short-lived, mental symptoms occasionally continue for days or weeks after the period of hypersomnia has come to an end. The schizoid picture is also confirmed by the comportment and behavior of the patient. Should circumstances prevent him from taking to his bed as the hypersomnia develops, his appearance and turn-out will suffer, and he will become unkempt, slovenly and dishevelled. In his attitude towards others he may be uninhibited, insolent, and quarrelsome, in a fashion which is quite unexpected.[22]

Unfortunately, patients exhibiting this syndrome have not yet been studied with simultaneous EEG and eye movement recordings, although they continue to arouse the interest of psychiatrists.[16,35] Such studies are clearly indicated and may permit distinction of functional and organic components of this fairly diffuse condition. The theoretical interest of this syndrome is considerable, for, at the present time, we know of no pathological state in which a significant increase in the amount of *normal* sleep has been demonstrated. In narcolepsy, both total sleep time and total S-REM are within normal limits in spite of the premature onset of the latter stage of sleep. While moderately long sleep time has been observed in hypersomniacs,[117] the value obtained (8.8 hrs.) does not clearly exceed the normal range. It is of interest to note that the hypersomniacs in this latter study showed essentially normal EEG patterns.

B. Chronic Brain Syndrome

A second condition in which S-REM mechanisms appear related to waking psychopathology is chronic brain syndrome (CBS). In addition to cognitive deficit, especially manifested in recent memory impairment, CBS patients have long been known to become confused and agitated at night. At these times their behavior often resembles that of acute delirium. An important component of the latter episodes is nocturnal wandering. The patients dress themselves during the night, leave their homes and are usually found the next morning some distance away, lost and disoriented, and unable to recall or explain their activities during the night. Nocturnal agitation and wandering are often the main causes of hospitalization of elderly senile patients.

As will be discussed in greater detail in the next section, EEG studies of the sleep of CBS patients reveal frequent awakenings and a decrease in total sleep time with a disproportionate reduction in the amount of S-REM. In the course of these investigations, Feinberg and co-workers[50,52] noted that four of 20 CBS subjects awoke repeatedly from S-REM in states of extreme agitation and disorientation. These patients often leaped out of bed, tearing off their electrodes, stating that it was urgent that they leave for work or to carry out some other errand. Whereas awakenings from S-SW occurred with equal frequency, only one subject, on a single occasion, demonstrated such behavior on an awakening from apparent S-SW. These findings suggested that nocturnal confusion and wandering in CBS patients result from an intrusion of S-REM into the waking state, or, alternatively, from an inability of these cognitively impaired subjects to distinguish dream from reality. The latter interpretation seems the less plausible one, since it is unlikely that dream *recall* would persist so vividly and over such prolonged periods in patients with severely impaired memory. Whatever the correct interpretation, these findings have direct implications for the clinical management of geriatric subjects. They raise the possibility that drugs which can reduce the intensity of S-REM without (as do barbiturates) further depressing cognitive function would be useful in curtailing nocturnal confusion. Such treatment might thus permit retention in the community of many patients who would otherwise require hospitalization.

C. Delirium

Delirium, or acute brain syndrome, is a reversible, diffuse disturbance of brain function caused by a wide variety of agents and characterized by visual and auditory hallucinations, disorientation and confusion, changes in affect, transient and ill-systematized delusions (usually paranoid) and diverse physiological changes including insomnia, tremor, fever, sweating, tremulousness and, not uncommonly, grand mal convulsions. An excellent description of the syndrome was given by Wolff and Curran.[149] Clinicians have long recognized the similarity between delirium and dreaming, especially emphasizing the prominence of visual hallucinations in the two conditions. It might be noted in passing that the infrequent visual hallucinations of schizophrenic patients are markedly different in character from those occurring in delirium. In schizophrenia, these hallucinations are far less vivid and sustained, are usually monochromatic rather than colored, of normal size rather than microptic, and are seldom of animals, being more frequently concerned with human or parahuman creatures closely related to delusional preoccupations.[40] Diurnal variation in the intensity of hallucinations is not apparent in schizophrenia, whereas it is common in delirium. This latter phenomenon is of special interest in the context of our present thesis, for if some of the psychopathology of delirium results from intrusion of S-REM mechanisms into waking, such intrusion might be expected to occur most frequently at night because of persistent diurnal rhythms.[42] Evidence of the persistence of these rhythms despite prolonged insomnia has been provided by studies of experimental sleep deprivation. The suggestion that increased pressure for S-REM plays a role in the nocturnal exacerbation of symptoms in delirium is intended to supplement rather than replace the traditional view[21] that this exacerbation results from decreased social stimulation and more ambiguous sensory input at night: the importance of these factors has been convincingly supported by clinical observation.

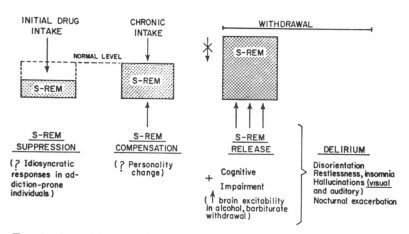

PROPOSED MECHANISM FOR DRUG-WITHDRAWAL DELIRIUM

FIG. 6.—A model proposed to account for the delirium which ensues upon withdrawal of certain REM-suppressant drugs. Initial administration leads to a suppression of REM. It is hypothesized that certain idiosyncratic responses may occur during this period in addiction-prone individuals. With chronic administration, S-REM returns to normal levels as a result of the development of compensatory mechanisms. Personality changes, particularly of a paranoid nature, may occur at this time. Withdrawal of the suppressing drug leads to high levels of REM since the compensatory mechanisms are now unopposed. If brain dysfunction sufficient to permit intrusion of REM processes into waking is also present, delirium results. This brain dysfunction is characterized by cognitive impairment, disorientation, and increased brain excitability.

Nevertheless, there is also some evidence that when room illumination and social stimulation are kept high, symptoms continue to be worse at night. A systematic study on this question has not yet been done. Many of the hallucinations in delirium are brief, encapsulated experiences, superimposed upon the veridical environment. Others, however, are more complex and elaborate. The dreamlike nature of the following excerpt, taken from Gross et al.[71] is apparent. The patient, who was suffering from delirium tremens, felt that his hallucinatory experience might have begun as a nightmare.

It started with his meeting a married couple accompanied by a young blonde woman, and they invited him for some drinks. They stopped at the couple's home for the woman to change clothes. While there, the man suddenly died and the young woman said it was murder and they'd best run away. They couldn't leave, were arrested and put into jail. While in jail, he was joined by two small fantastic creatures who threw dice and were playful. He also saw a dog performing cunnilingus on several women and a young girl. Then he was out of jail and met a woman who said she had money and invited him to join her for a drink. They went someplace and it caught fire. He was arrested, blamed for the fire and jailed. He bought a screwdriver and jimmied open the jail door. He was about to leave when the woman told him she had sixty dollars in a hole of the lock and asked him to jimmy it out, which he did. Then they went to her apartment and drank. At this point he actually turned on the light in his room and the hallucination ended.

In spite of the clinical and theoretical interest of the delirious states, only two EEG studies (both of delirium tremens) of sleep patterns in these conditions have been reported. Gross and his colleagues[71] monitored EEG, eye-movement and chin-muscle activity for 14 to 17 hours in four patients admitted for treatment of delirium tremens. Only one subject received medication (I.M. paraldehyde) during the period of recording. Two of the four subjects obtained some sleep during the recording period. Both showed high proportions of S-REM (185 min. of 395 min. of sleep in one case, and 91 min. of 91 min. of sleep in the second). A valuable feature of this study was the careful and extensive behavioral observation carried out by the investigators. On some occasions, they noticed that phasic miming movements which occurred during S-REM were continued, apparently in response to the same hallucinatory experiences, into waking. The S-REM patterns in one of their patients was characterized by unusually intense eye-movement activity ("REM storms"). Two patients who failed to sleep, nevertheless at times showed rapid eye-movement activity while lying with eyes closed.

On some of these occasions, these subjects reported experiencing hallu-cinations.

A second study of patients with delirium tremens was carried out by Greenberg and Pearlman.[67] These authors also noted considerable rapid eye-movement activity in their patients while awake. The five patients with severe delirium tended to have higher levels of S-REM than the seven patients who had been drinking variable amounts of alcohol but who did not develop delirium after admission to the hospital. Some of these levels were extraordinarily high—e.g., 300 min. S-REM out of a total of 300 min. of sleep. The data from these two studies may be sup-plemented by a single case report. Feinberg et al.[51] described results of four nights of sleep recording in a 79-year-old man who had developed marked auditory and visual hallucinations in the presence of a mild degree of cognitive impairment. Both the auditory and visual ex-periences were intensely vivid. The patient's symptoms were consistently

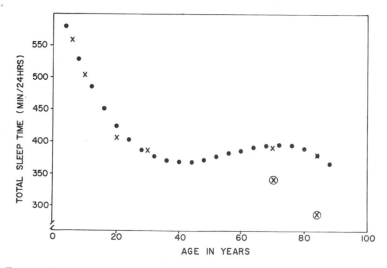

Fig. 7.—Total sleep time as a function of normal aging and in elderly chronic brain syndrome (CBS) patients. In this figure and in Fig. 8-11, data points for the normal subjects are represented by X's; the successive values for mean ages 6, 10, 21, 30, 69 and 84 years being based on N's of 4, 4, 6, 9, 7 and 8 subjects respectively. Circled points represent mean values for two groups of CBS patients (N's=6, 9). The dots represent an outline of the best-fitting theoretical curve which significantly reduces the deviations from regression of the next lower order function (Carlson and Feinberg, 1968). In this case, a cubic curve was indicated. See text for further discussion.

worse at night. The mean absolute amount (138 min.) and the percentage (41 per cent) of S-REM activity in this patient were extremely high and especially so in light of his age. The eye-movement activity was unusually intense; on the basis of measurement of the amount of eye-movement in successive four-second intervals of record, this patient showed levels twice as high as the highest recorded in a control subject (Feinberg, unpublished observations). Dr. Donald Goodenough, who examined the tracings of this patient, found them strikingly similar to those of the delirious patients in the study of Gross *et al.*

Thus, these findings suggest that delirium and perhaps other organic brain changes may produce psychopathology by permitting intrusion into waking of S-REM processes. A detailed interpretation of the role of alcohol withdrawal in producing delirium is not possible since research into the effects of drugs on physiological sleep pattern has been limited, the variables of dosage, duration and rate of administration not yet having been thoroughly explored. However, the available data on the effects of alcohol[70,150,67] and barbiturates[109,53] on sleep, taken in association with well-established clinical data, enable us to propose a tentative model for deliria which occur on withdrawal of alcohol, barbiturates

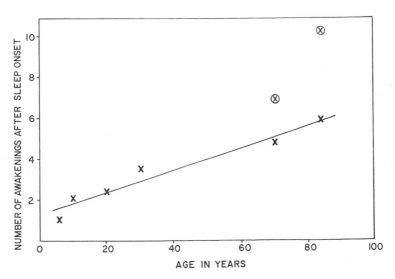

Fig. 8.—Number of EEG arousals as a function of age. These arousals were not necessarily associated with behavioral awakening, and, as they could be quite brief, did not necessarily affect total sleep times.

and similar drugs. As shown in Fig. 6, acute ingestion of these drugs reduces S-REM below normal values. There appear to be marked individual differences in initial response to these drugs. Thus, Feinberg et al.[53] found 200 mg. of phenobarbital to cause immediate onset of S-REM in a sociopathic patient, whereas in most subjects, this drug delays onset of S-REM. Kales et al.[82] noted that severe nightmares* occurred in a subject in withdrawal after only three nights of ingestion of a sedative drug in normal clinical dosage. These idiosyncratic reactions may be related to individual differences in propensity to develop addiction.

With chronic intake, S-REM returns to baseline levels. Apparently, the underlying S-REM mechanisms undergo compensatory changes which successfully overcome the suppressing effects of the drugs. It seems probable that such compensation permits normal S-REM requirements to be met. However, there is some reason to suspect that the alteration of CNS processes which permits this compensation may itself predispose to paranoid reactions. Such reactions are common in amphetamine and (especially) methedrine addicts. When S-REM suppression is abolished as a result of drug withdrawal, very high levels ensue as a result of the now-unopposed compensatory processes. However, these high levels are not in themselves sufficient to penetrate waking and to cause delirium. Thus, amphetamines[110,116] and other drugs[93] produce initial S-REM suppression and quite high S-REM levels upon withdrawal. Nevertheless, these drugs do not produce clinical deliria upon withdrawal. We suggest that in addition to high pressure for S-REM, clinical delirium requires a second alteration of brain function, one which permits intrusion of S-REM into waking. This alteration seems to involve diffuse impairment of brain processes and is thus associated with cognitive disturbances and disorientation. In addition, barbiturate and alcohol withdrawal are characterized by high levels of brain excitability. This feature is of special interest in light of the role postulated for disinhibition in the neurophysiological theories of hallucinations cited above.

We would propose that a balance between "pressure" for S-REM and the degree of overall cerebral competence determines whether or not clinical delirium occurs. Under this interpretation, the nocturnal delirium of some chronic brain syndrome patients can be understood as

---

*That the subjects of Kales et al.[82] experienced frequent nightmares during drug withdrawal is interesting in view of the prominence of nightmares in the histories of alcoholic[71] and narcoleptic[17,147] patients.

the result of pathological vicissitudes leading to marked cognitive impairment (apparently associated with reduction in inhibitory activity) in the presence of lesser damage to S-REM systems in these subjects.

Delirium is, of course, produced by a wide variety of agents. It is striking that its clinical picture appears relatively constant no matter what the specific etiology. Is it possible that the deliria caused by infection, atropine poisoning, or cerebral anoxia would also fit the present model? No systematic data on these other conditions are available at present. However, Zarcone et al.,[151] studying a schizophrenic patient who developed an acute brain syndrome during a course of electroconvulsive therapy, found extremely high levels of S-REM and noted that intense eye-movement activity was similar to what Gross and his colleagues had observed in delirium tremens. This intriguing finding appears consistent with our model.* However, much additional study of deliria produced by other conditions, as well as further work on delirium tremens itself, is required before the value of the present model can be determined.

IV. CONTRIBUTIONS OF SLEEP RESEARCH TO THE DEMONSTRATION OF EEG CORRELATES OF COGNITIVE DEFICIT IN MAN

Changes in the sleep EEG are the most pronounced age-related changes demonstrated thus far in the physiological activity of the brain. Figs. 7 to 11 illustrate age functions for the main sleep variables based on work done in one laboratory.[50,45,43]

Data points for two groups of CBS patients matched for age with the two oldest normal groups are also included in these figures. The CBS patients were selected for study on the basis of a premorbid history of normal cognitive function from which there had been a noticeable decline. These patients showed symptoms of general cognitive impairment with special deficits of recent memory. They did not manifest delusions or hallucinations.

For each of the sleep variables illustrated in Figs. 7 to 11, except

---

*It should be noted that the interpretation of this observation by Dement and his co-workers was different from our own. They consider the high levels of S-REM in their delirious patient to represent a therapeutic compensation for prior sleep deprivation. We suggest that these high levels of S-REM themselves produce certain aspects of the psychopathology of delirium. We interpret these levels as the result of abnormal pressure for S-REM caused by altered mechanisms rather than as an attempt of normal mechanisms to compensate for prior S-REM deprivation.

stage 4 EEG, CBS patients showed in significantly more extreme form the changes from young adult levels found in the aged normal (AN) subjects. Stage 4 EEG, which declines hyperbolically with age, reaches its asymptote at about 50 years. For this reason, these older AN and CBS groups would not be expected to differ on this measure. Within the group of 15 aged normal (AN) subjects (mean age 77.0 yrs., range 65-96 yrs.) significant positive correlation coefficients were obtained between the amount of S-REM (as estimated by emergent stage 1 EEG) and Wechsler Adult Intelligence Scale (WAIS)[139] Performance scores. These latter scores are known to be especially sensitive to the effects of brain damage. The magnitude of the relationship observed ($r=.72$) is especially striking in view of the previous failures of other physiological measures of brain function [e.g., waking EEG;[104] cerebral oxygen uptake (CMRO$_2$)[15]] to demonstrate significant relationships with intellectual function within groups of normal aged subjects.

The amount of wakefulness in the normal aged subjects was strikingly increased compared with that found in young adults (Figs. 10, 11). This finding documents the frequent complaints of insomnia in the

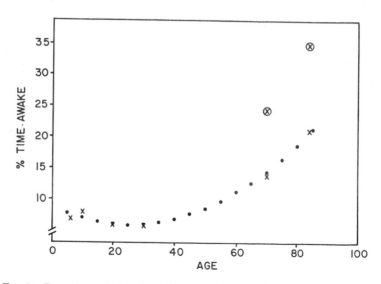

FIG. 9.—Percentage of time in bed spent awake as a function of age. This curve shows a positively accelerated (parabolic) increase beginning in late middle age. It is probably the best index of subjective insomnia. Higher values on this measure in the aged are associated with poorer intellectual function.

elderly. Increased wakefulness tended to be correlated negatively with WAIS Performance scores in the aged normal group, the correlation coefficients not quite achieving statistical significance.

Within the chronic brain syndrome group, significant correlation coefficients ($r=.72$) were again found between S-REM (stage 1 EEG) and WAIS Performance scores in the 10 subjects who were able to complete this test. Greater wakefulness (per cent of time awake) showed a significant negative correlation with psychometric performance in these subjects ($r=.64$; $p<.05$). A more detailed description of the relations of sleep variables to age and intellectual function in these AN and CBS subjects is given by Feinberg et al.[50]

The finding that increased levels of S-REM were associated with better intellectual performance, in patients suffering from the mild cognitive impairment of normal aging and the more severe deficits of chronic brain syndrome, led us to seek a similar relationship in patients with mental retardation.[44,43] Fig. 12 shows preliminary results of this investigation. The rank-order correlation coefficient between amount of rapid eye-movement during sleep and scores on the Wechsler Preschool

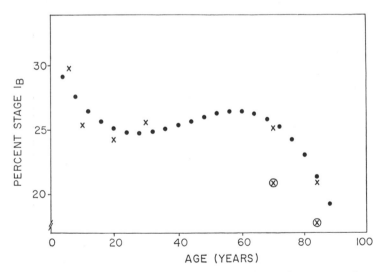

FIG. 10.—Percentage of stage l_B as a function of age. Stage l_B is the total emergent stage 1 EEG recorded during sleep. This is the most frequently employed measure of REM sleep. The data are best described by a cubic equation; values on this measure in the aged are positively correlated with level of intellectual function.

and Primary Scale of Intelligence (WPPSI)[140] as shown in this scattergram is rho=+.67. The special sensitivity of the sleep EEG to cognitive impairment in man was strikingly demonstrated in the mongolian subjects. These patients, whose waking EEGs are generally normal,[63] invariably showed grossly abnormal sleep patterns.

Thus these data indicate that in conditions of intellectual deficit caused by a variety of illnesses, S-REM appears positively correlated with level of intellectual function. The basis for this relation remains unknown. One possibility is that both intellectual level and S-REM are sensitive to brain disease and vary jointly as a function of its severity. A more interesting hypothesis suggests that this correlation results from an intrinsic relation between sleep and cognitive processes. Hughlings Jackson[77] appears to have been the first to propose such an hypothesis; he suggested that during sleep the brain carries out such functions as consolidation or erasure of memories and might also "sweep clean" certain neuronal organizations established during problem-solving activities of the previous day. According to this view, a relation between

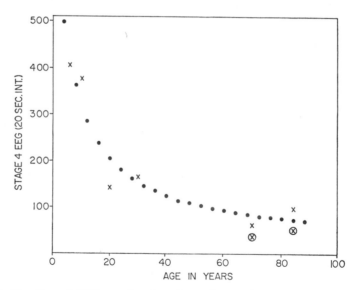

FIG. 11.—Stage 4 EEG as a function of age. Stage 4 EEG is the sustained high voltage slow activity which predominates in the early part of nocturnal sleep. Whereas total sleep time and its REM and NREM components essentially show a plateau during maturity, stage 4 EEG shows a substantial decline during this period.

sleep and intellectual function is expected because sleep processes must vary to complement the level of cognitive activity during waking. If such a complementary relation exists, the amount or intensity of nocturnal sleep should be correlated with the intensity of waking brain activity. An overall estimate of the latter variable is provided by the rate of cerebral oxygen uptake ($CMRO_2$). Fig. 13 shows that total sleep time appears strikingly correlated with waking $CMRO_2$. Other investigators have also proposed that sleep is involved in memory processes or information processing,[18,36,62,66,103] and this question has recently been reviewed in detail.[46]

The sleep-cognition hypothesis can be extended to interpret the striking changes in sleep time which occur between childhood and adolescence (cf. Figs. 7-11). Thus, Moruzzi[103] suggested that the high level of sleep during childhood occurs because this is a period of intense acquisition of new habits and knowledge with correspondingly high rates of synaptic activity. Information acquisition and total sleep time decline during adolescence to a plateau level maintained during maturity. In old age, both information acquisition and sleep show a further

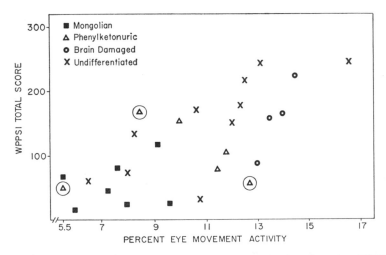

FIG. 12.—Percentage eye-movement activity (% EM_{20}) plotted against WPPSI total scores. The relation between these variables is clear for the retardate group as a whole. Among subgroups, this relation is most clear-cut among the UNDIFF subjects, who also showed the widest range in both measures. Data points for subjects over 50 years of age are circled. It may be seen that these data do not contribute disproportionately to the correlation.

decline. However, while total sleep time and its component S-REM and S-SW moieties fit this model, other aspects of sleep, such as stage 4 EEG, and number of awakenings, do not. It has been suggested that the former variable may be related to the decrease in plasticity of brain function and the loss of intellectual power which seems to occur during adulthood, and that the latter reflects changes in the intensity or pressure of sleep processes.[45,46]

There exists a rapidly accumulating body of data on changes in sleep with age. These findings[145,2,123,125,81,83,146] are generally consistent with the observations presented above. Although a few studies have been carried out in patients with cognitive deficit due to aging or other causes,[92,126] there have not yet been further attempts to demonstrate correlations between independent assessments of intellectual function and the sleep pattern. A recent report of the physiological sleep patterns in Korsakoff's psychosis is of special interest in view of the potential importance of sleep for memory function. However, this work[68] is difficult to interpret because of the absence of a control group and of statistical

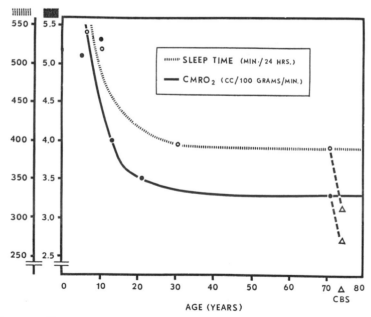

FIG. 13.—Total sleep time and rate of cerebral oxygen uptake (CMRO₂) measured across age and in chronic brain syndrome. The two curves are strikingly similar. (Reprinted from Feinberg, 1967.)

assessment of the results. It would seem especially important to include in future investigations of this condition sufficient psychometric testing to ensure that a specific impairment of memory exists in the presence of relatively intact cognitive function.[133,131] Finally, Williams and Williams[144] have recently put forward evidence that differences in sleep pattern may be related to cognitive function in apparently normal persons. These workers found subjects with "restless" sleep (less stage 4, more body movements, awakenings, and EEG stage fluctuations) showed greater impairment of memory under acute sleep loss than did "quiet" sleep subjects.

In summary, the investigation of physiological sleep patterns in cognitively impaired patients has demonstrated abnormalities of the electrical activity of the brain which were previously unknown. These findings may ultimately prove of diagnostic or prognostic significance. Of equal importance, in our view, are the implications of these discoveries for an understanding of the neurophysiological mechanisms which underlie cognition.

REFERENCES

1. Adie, W. J.: Idiopathic narcolepsy: a disease sui generis; with remarks on the mechanism of sleep. Brain 49:257-306, 1926.

2. Agnew, H. W., Webb, W. B., and Williams, R. L.: Sleep patterns in late middle-aged males: an EEG study. Electroenceph. Clin. Neurophysiol. 23:168-171, 1967.

3. Agnew, H. W., Webb, W. B., and Williams, R. L.: Comparison of Stage IV and 1-REM sleep deprivation. Percept. Motor Skills 24:851-858, 1967.

4. Akert, K., Bally, C., and Schadé, J. P.: Progress in Brain Research. Vol. 18, Sleep Mechanisms. Amsterdam, Elsevier, 1965.

5. Antrobus, J. S., and Antrobus, J. S.: Discrimination of two sleep stages by human subjects. Psychophysiology 4:48-55, 1967.

6. Arey, L. B.: Reference to the experimental situation in the first-night dreams of acute reactive schizophrenics, chronic schizophrenics and neurotics. Paper presented at the meeting of the Association for the Psychophysiological Study of Sleep, Washington, D.C., March 1965.

7. Aserinsky, E.: Periodic respiratory pattern occurring in conjunction with eye movements during sleep. Science 150:763-766, 1965.

8. Aserinsky, E., and Kleitman, N.: Regularly occurring periods of eye motility, and concomitant phenomena, during sleep. Science 118:273-274, 1953.

9. Aserinsky, E., and Kleitman, N.: Two types of ocular motility occurring in sleep. J. Appl. Physiol. 8:1-10, 1955.

10. Azumi, K., Takahashi, S., Takahashi, K., Maruyama, N., and Kikuti, S.: The effects of dream deprivation on chronic schizophrenics and normal adults: a comparative study. Folia Psychiat. Neurol. Jap. 21:205-225, 1967.

11. Baekeland, F., and Lasky, R.: Exercise and sleep patterns in college athletes. Percept. Motor Skills 23:1203-1207, 1966.

12. Berger, R. J.: When is a dream is a dream. Exp. Neurol. 19 (Monogr. Suppl. 4), p. 15-28, 1967.

13. Berger, R. J., and Oswald, I.: Eye movement during active and passive dreams. Science 137:601, 1962.

14. Berger, R., and Oswald, I.: Effects of sleep deprivation on behavior, subsequent sleep, and dreaming. J. Mental Science 108:457-465, 1962.

15. Birren, J. E., Butler, R. N., Greenhouse, S. W., Sokoloff, L., and Yarrow, M. R.: Interdisciplinary relationships: Interrelations of physiological, psychological and psychiatric findings in healthy elderly men. In: Birren, J. E., Butler, R. N., Greenhouse, S. W., Sokoloff, L., and Yarrow, M. R. (Eds.): Human Aging: A Biological and Behavioral Study. U.S. Dept. of Health, Education and Welfare; PHS Publication 986 (undated).

16. Bonkalo, A.: Hypersomnia: a discussion of psychiatric implications based on three cases. Brit. J. Psychiat. 114:69-75, 1968.

17. Brain, W.: Sleep: normal and pathological. Brit. Med. J. 2:51-53, 1939.

18. Breger, L.: Function of dreams. J. Abnorm. Psychol. 72:(2, Whole No. 641), 1967.

19. Broughton, R. J.: Sleep Disorders: Disorders of arousal? Science 159:1070-1078, 1968.

20. Caldwell, D., and Domino, E. F.: Electroencephalographic and eye-movement patterns during sleep in chronic schizophrenic patients. Electroenceph. Clin. Neurophysiol. 22:414-420, 1967.

21. Cameron, D. E.: Studies in senile nocturnal delirium. Psychiat. Quart. 15:47-53, 1941.

22. Critchley, M.: Periodic hypersomnia and megaphagia in adolescent males. Brain 85:627-656, 1962.

23. Daly, D. D., and Yoss, R. E.: Electroencephalogram in narcolepsy. Electroenceph. Clin. Neurophysiol. 9:109-120, 1957.

24. Dement, W.: Dream recall and eye movements during sleep in schizophrenics and normals. J. Nerv. Ment. Dis. 122:263-269, 1955.

25. Dement, W.: The occurrence of low voltage, fast, electroencephalogram patterns during behavioral sleep in the cat. Electroenceph. Clin. Neurophysiol. 10:291-296, 1958.

26. Dement, W.: The effect of dream deprivation. Science 131:1705-1707, 1960.

27. Dement, W. C.: A manual for scoring dream time. Paper presented at the meeting of the Association for the Psychophysiological Study of Sleep, Chicago, March 1962.

28. Dement, W., Henry, P., Cohen, H., and Ferguson, J.: Studies on the effects of REM deprivation in humans and animals. In: Kety, S. S., Evarts, E. V., and Williams, H. L. (Eds.): Sleep and Altered States of Consciousness. Baltimore, Williams & Wilkins, 1967, p. 456-468.

29. Dement, W. C., Kahn, E., and Roffwarg, H. P.: The influence of the laboratory situation on the dreams of the experimental subject. J. Nerv. Ment. Dis. 140:119-131, 1965.

30. Dement, W., and Kleitman, N.: Cyclic variations in EEG during sleep and

their relation to eye movements, body motility, and dreaming. Electroenceph. Clin. Neurophysiol. 9:673-690, 1957.

31. Dement, W., Rechtschaffen, A., and Gulevich, G.: The nature of the narcoleptic sleep attack. Neurology 16:18-33, 1966.

32. Dement, W., and Wolpert, E. A.: The relation of eye-movements, body motility, and external stimuli to dream content. J. Exp. Psychol. 55:543-553, 1958.

33. Dement, W., and Wolpert, E. A.: Relationships in the manifest content of dreams occurring on the same night. J. Nerv. Ment. Dis. 126:568-578, 1958.

34. Diaz-Guerrero, R., Gottlieb, J. S., and Knott, J. R.: The sleep of patients with manic-depressive psychosis, depressive type. An electromyographic study. Psychosom. Med. 8:399-409, 1946.

35. Duffy, J. P., and Davison, K.: A female case of the Kleine-Levin syndrome. Brit. J. Psychiat. 114:77-84, 1968.

36. Evans, C. R., and Newman, E. A.: Dreaming: an analogy from computers. New Scientist 24:577-579, 1964.

37. Evarts, E. V.: A neurophysiologic theory of hallucinations. In: West, L. J. (Ed.): Hallucinations. New York, Grune & Stratton, 1962, pp. 1-13.

38. Evarts, E. V.: Neuronal activity in visual and motor cortex during sleep and waking. In: Jouvet, M. M. (Ed.): Neurophysiologie des états de sommeil. Paris, Centre National de la Recherche Scientifique, 1965, pp. 189-209.

39. Evarts, E. V.: Activity of individual cerebral neurons during sleep and arousal. In: Kety, S. S., Evarts, E. V., and Williams, H. L. (Eds.): Sleep and Altered States of Consciousness. Baltimore, Williams & Wilkins, 1967, pp. 319-336.

40. Feinberg, I.: A comparison of the visual hallucinations in schizophrenia with those induced by mescaline and LSD-25. In: West, L. J. (Ed.): Hallucinations. New York, Grune & Stratton, 1962, pp. 64-76.

41. Feinberg, I.: Discussion of papers by Drs. Pierce and Dement. Amer. J. Psychiat. 122:408-410, 1965.

42. Feinberg, I.: Sleep electroencephalographic and eye-movement patterns in patients with schizophrenia and with chronic brain syndrome. In: Kety, S. S., Evarts, E. V., Williams, H. L. (Eds.): Sleep and Altered States of Consciousness. Baltimore, Williams & Wilkins, 1967, pp. 211-240.

43. Feinberg, I.: Eye movement activity during sleep and intellectual function in mental retardation. Science 159:1256, 1968.

44. Feinberg, I., Braun, M., and Shulman, E.: Electrophysiological sleep patterns in mongolism and phenylpyruvic oligophrenia (PKU). Psychophysiology 4:395 (Abstract), 1968.

45. Feinberg, I., and Carlson, V. R.: Sleep variables as a function of age in man. Arch. Gen. Psychiat. 18:239-250, 1968.

46. Feinberg, I., and Evarts, E. V.: Changing concepts of the function of sleep. Paper presented at the meeting of the Society for Biological Psychiatry, Washington, D.C., June 1968 (to be published).

47. Feinberg, I., Heller, N., Steinberg, H. R., and Stoeffler, V.: The relationship of sleep disturbance to behavior pathology in a group of schizophrenic patients. Compr. Psychiat. 6:374-380, 1965.

48. Feinberg, I., Koresko, R. L., and Gottlieb, F.: Further observations on electrophysiological sleep patterns in schizophrenia. Compr. Psychiat. 6:21-24, 1965.

49. Feinberg, I., Koresko, R. L., Gottlieb, F., and Wender, P. H.: Sleep electro-encephalographic and eye-movement patterns in schizophrenic patients. Compr. Psychiat. 5:44-53, 1964.

50. Feinberg, I., Koresko, R. L., and Heller, N.: EEG sleep patterns as a function of normal and pathological aging in man. J. Psychiat. Res. 5:107-144, 1967.

51. Feinberg, I., Koresko, R. L., Heller, N., and Steinberg, H. R.: Unusually high dream time in an hallucinating patient. Amer. J. Psychiat. 121:1018-1020, 1965.

52. Feinberg, I., Koresko, R. L., and Schaffner, I.:: Sleep electroencephalographic and eye-movement patterns in patients with chronic brain syndrome. J. Psychiat. Res. 3:11-26, 1965.

53. Feinberg, I., Wender, P. H., Koresko, R. L., Gottlieb, F., and Piehuta, J. A.: Current studies of sleep and dreaming in psychiatric patients. Paper presented at the meeting of the Association for the Psychophysiological Study of Sleep, Palo Alto, California, March 1964.

54. Fisher, C., and Dement. W.: Studies on the psychopathology of sleep and dreams. Amer. J. Psychiat. 119:1160-1168, 1963.

55. Foulkes, D.: Dream reports from different stages of sleep. J. Abnorm. Soc. Psychol. 65:14-25, 1962.

56. Foulkes, D.: Nonrapid eye movement mentation. Exp. Neurol. 19 (Monogr. Suppl. 4): pp. 28-38, 1967.

57. Foulkes, D., Pivik, T., Steadman, H. S., Spear, P. S., and Symonds, J. D.: Dreams of the male child; an EEG study. J. Abnorm. Psychol. 72:457-467, 1967.

58. Foulkes, D., and Rechtschaffen, A.: Presleep determinants of dream content: the effects of two films. Percept. Motor Skills 19:983-1005, 1964.

59. Foulkes, D., Spear, P. S., and Symonds, J. D.: Individual differences in mental activity during sleep onset. J. Abnorm. Psychol. 71:280-286, 1966.

60. Foulkes, D., and Vogel, G.: Mental activity at sleep onset. J. Abnorm.. Psychol. 70:231-243, 1965.

61. Freud, S.: The Interpretation of Dreams. In: Brill, A. A. (Ed.): The Basic Writings of Sigmund Freud. New York, Modern Library, 1938, pp. 181-552.

62. Gaarder, K: A conceptual model of sleep. Arch. Gen. Psychiat. 14:253-260, 1966.

63. Gibbs, F. A., and Gibbs, E. L.: The electroencephalogram in mental retardation. In: Carter, C. H. (Ed.): Medical Aspects of Mental Retardation. Springfield, Ill., Charles C Thomas, 1965, pp. 112-134.

64. Goodenough, D. R., Lewis, H. B., Shapiro, A., Jaret, L., and Sleser, I.: Dream reporting following abrupt and gradual awakenings from different types of sleep. J. Personality Soc. Psychol. 2:170-179, 1965.

65. Goodenough, D. R., Shapiro, A., Holden, M., and Steinschriber, L.: A comparison of "dreamers" and "nondreamers": eye movements, electroencephalograms, and the recall of dreams. J. Abnorm. Soc. Psychol. 59:295-302, 1959.

66. Greenberg, R., and Leiderman, P. H.: Perceptions, the dream process and memory: an up-to-date version of notes on a mystic writing pad. Compr. Psychiat. 7:517-523, 1966.

67. Greenberg, R., and Pearlman, C.: Delirium tremens and dreaming. Amer. J. Psychiat. 124:133-142, 1967.

68. Greenberg, R., Pearlman, C., Brooks, R., Mayer, R., and Hartmann, E.: Dreaming and Korsakoff's psychosis. Arch. Gen. Psychiat. 18:203-209, 1968.

69. Gresham, S. C., Agnew, H. W., and Williams, R. L.: The sleep of depressed patients. Arch. Gen. Psychiat. 13:503-507, 1965.

70. Gresham, S. C., Webb, W. B., and Williams, R. L.: Alcohol and caffeine: effect on inferred visual dreaming. Science 140:1226-1227, 1963.

71. Gross, M. M., Goodenough, D., Tobin, M., Halpert, E., Lepore, D., Pearlstein, A., Sirota, M., Dibianco, J., Fuller, M., and Kishner, I.: Sleep disturbances and hallucinations in the acute alcoholic psychoses. J. Nerv. Ment. Dis. 142:493-514, 1966.

72. Gulevich, G. D., Dement, W. C., and Zarcone, V. P.: All-night sleep recordings of chronic schizophrenics in remission. Compr. Psychiat. 8:141-149, 1967.

73. Hawkins, D. R., and Mendels, J.: Sleep disturbance in depressive syndromes. Amer. J. of Psychiat. 123:682-690, 1966.

74. Hishikawa, Y., and Kaneko, Z.: Electroencephalographic study on narcolepsy. Electroenceph. Clin. Neurophysiol. 18:249-259, 1965.

75. Hobson, J. A., Goldfrank, F., and Snyder, F.: Respiration and mental activity in sleep. J. Psychiat. Res. 3:79-90, 1965.

76. Hume, D.: An Enquiry Concerning Human Understanding. Chicago, The Open Court Publishing Co., 1935.

77. Jackson, J. H.: Selected Writings. In: Taylor, J., Holmes, G., and Walshe, F. M. R. (Eds.): Selected Writings of Hughlings Jackson. New York, Basic Books, 1958,, Vol. 2.

78. Jouvet, M. M.: Neurophysiologie des états de sommeil. Paris, Centre National de la Recherche Scientifique, 1965.

79. Kahn, E.: The sleep and other characteristics of the aged. Ph.D. Dissertation in preparation, Yeshiva University, 1968.

80. Kales, A., Hoedemaker, F. S., Jacobson, A., Kales, J. D., Paulson, M. J., and Wilson, T. E.: Mentation during sleep: REM and NREM recall reports. Percept. Motor Skills, 24:555-560, 1967.

81. Kales, A., Jacobson, A., Kales, J. D., Kun T., and Weissbuch, R.: All-night EEG sleep measurements in young adults. Psychonomic Science, 7:67-68, 1967.

82. Kales, A., Ling Tan, T., Scharf, M. B., Kales, J. D., Malmstrom, E. J., Allen, C., and Jacobson, A.: Sleep patterns with sedative drugs. Paper presented at the meeting of the Association for the Psychophysiological Study of Sleep, Denver, March 1968.

83. Kales, A., Wilson, T., Kales, J. D., Jacobson, A., Paulson, M. J., Kollar, E., and Walter, R. D.: All-night sleep measurements in normal elderly subjects: effects of aging. J. Amer. Geriat. Soc. 15:405-414, 1967.

84. Kamiya, J.: Behavioral, subjective, and physiological aspects of drowsiness and sleep. In: Fiske, D. W. and Maddi, S. R. (Eds.): Functions of Varied Experience. Homewood, Ill., Dorsey, 1961, pp. 145-174.

85. Kety, S. S., Evarts, E. V., and Williams, H. L. (Eds.): Sleep and Altered States of Consciousness. Baltimore, Williams & Wilkins, 1967.

86. Kety, S. S.: Relationship between energy metabolism of the brain and functional activity. In: Kety, S. S., Evarts, E. V. and Williams, H. L. (Eds.):

Sleep and Altered States of Consciousness. Baltimore, Williams & Wilkens, 1967, p. 39.

87. Knopf, N. O.: A study of heart and respiration rates during dreaming. Unpublished master's thesis, University of Chicago, 1962.

88. Koella, W. P.: Sleep. Springfield, Ill., Charles C Thomas, 1967.

89. Koresko, R. L., Snyder, F., and Feinberg, I.: "Dream time" in hallucinating and non-hallucinating schizophrenic patients. Nature 199:1118-1119, 1963.

90. Kramer, M., Whitman, R. M., Baldridge, B. J., and Lansky, L. M.: Patterns of dreaming: the interrelationship of the dreams of a night. J. Nerv. Ment. Dis. 139:426-439, 1964.

91. Lairy, G. C., Barte, H., Goldsteinas, L., and Ridjanovic, S.: Sommeil de nuit des malades mentaux, étude des bouffées délirantes. In: Le sommeil de nuit normal et pathologique: études électroencéphalographiques. Paris, Masson & Cie., 1965, pp. 353-381.

92. Lairy, G. C., Cor-Mordret, M., Faure, R., and Ridjanovic, S.: Etude EEG du sommeil du vieillard normal et pathologique. Rev. Neurol. (Paris) 107:188-202, 1962.

93. LeGassicke, J., Ashcroft, G. W., Eccleston, D., Evans, J. I., Oswald, I., and Ritson, E. B.: The clinical state, sleep and amine metabolism of a tranylcypromine ('Parnate') addict. Brit. J. Psychiat., 111:357-364, 1965.

94. Lennox, G.: Thomas Willis on narcolepsy. Arch. Neurol. Psychiat. 41:348-351, 1939.

95. Lester, B. K., Burch, N. R., and Dossett, R. C.: Nocturnal EEG-GSR profiles: the influence of presleep states. Psychophysiology 3:238-248, 1967.

96. Loomis, A. L., Harvey, E. N., and Hobart, G. A.: Cerebral states during sleep as studied by human brain potentials. J. Exp. Psychol. 21:127-144, 1937.

97. Luby, E. D., and Caldwell, D. F.: Sleep deprivation and EEG slow wave activity in chronic schizophrenia. Arch. Gen. Psychiat. 17:361-364, 1967.

98. Mayer-Gross, W., Slater, E., and Roth, M.: Clinical Psychiatry. London, Cassell, 1960.

99. Mendels, J., and Hawkins, D. R.: Sleep and depression. Arch. Gen. Psychiat. 16:344-354, 1967.

100. Mendels, J., and Hawkins, D. R.: Sleep and depression. Arch. Gen. Psychiat. 16:536-542, 1967.

101. Monroe, L. J.: Psychological and physiological differences betweeen good and poor sleepers. J. Abnorm. Psychol. 72:255-264, 1967.

102. Monroe, L. J., Rechtschaffen, A., Foulkes, D., and Jensen, J.: Discriminability of REM and NREM reports. J. Personality Soc. Psychol. 2:456-460, 1965.

103. Moruzzi, G.: The functional significance of sleep with particular regard to the brain mechanisms underlying consciousness. In: Eccles, J. C. (Ed.): Brain and Conscious Experience. New York, Springer, 1966, pp. 345-388.

104. Obrist, W. D., and Busse, E. W.: The electroencephalogram in old age. In: Wilson, W. P. (Ed.): Applications of electroencephalography in psychiatry. Durham, N. C., Duke Univ. Press., 1965, pp. 185-205.

105. Offenkrantz, W., and Rechtschaffen, A.: Clinical studies of sequential dreams. I. A patient in psychotherapy. Arch. Gen. Psychiat. 8:497-508, 1963.

106. Onheiber, P., White, P. T., DeMyer, M. K., and Ottinger, D. R.: Sleep and dream patterns of child schizophrenics. Arch. Gen. Psychiat. 12:568-571, 1965.

107. Ornitz, E. M., Ritvo, E. R., and Walter, R. D.: Dreaming sleep in autistic twins. Arch. Gen. Psychiat. 12:77-79, 1965.

108. Ornitz, E. M., Ritvo, E. V., and Walter, R. D.: Dreaming sleep in autistic and schizophrenic children. Amer. J. Psychiat. 122:419-424, 1965.

109. Oswald, I., Berger, R. J., Jaramillo, R. A., Keddie, K. M. G., Olley, P. D., and Plunkett, G. B.: Melancholia and barbiturates: a controlled EEG, body, and eye movement study of sleep. Brit. J. Psychiat. 109:66-78, 1963.

110. Oswald, I., and Thacore, V. R.: Amphetamine and phenmetrazine addiction: physiological abnormalities in the abstinence syndrome. Brit. Med. J. 2:427-431, 1963.

111. Pasnau, R. O., Naitoh, P., Stier, S., and Kollar, E. J.: The psychological effects of 205 hours of sleep deprivation. Arch. Gen. Psychiat. 18:496-505, 1968.

112. Pompeiano, O.: The neurophysiological mechanisms of the postural and motor events during desynchronized sleep. In: Kety, S. S., Evarts, E. V., and Williams, H. L. (Eds.): Sleep and Altered States of Consciousness. Baltimore, Williams & Wilkins, 1967, pp. 351-423.

113. Portnoff, G., Baekeland, F., Goodenough, D. R., Karacan, I., and Shapiro, A.: Retention of verbal materials perceived immediately prior to onset of non-REM sleep. Percept. Motor Skills, 22:751-758, 1966.

114. Rechtschaffen, A.: Discussion of Dr. Wm. Dement's paper, "Experimental dream studies." In: Masserman, J. (Ed.): Science and Psychoanalysis: Scientific Proceedings of the Academy of Psychoanalysis, Vol. 7. New York, Grune & Stratton, 1964, pp. 162-170.

115. Rechtschaffen, A., Hauri, P., and Zeitlin, M.: Auditory awakening thresholds in REM and NREM sleep stages. Percept. Motor Skills, 22:927-942, 1966.

116. Rechtschaffen, A., and Maron, L.: The effect of amphetamine on the sleep cycle. Electroenceph. Clin. Neurophysiol. 16:438-445, 1964.

117. Rechtschaffen, A. and Roth, B.: Nocturnal sleep of hypersomniacs. Paper read at International Symposium on Sleep, Marianske Lazne, Czechoslovakia, 1967 (to be published).

118. Rechtschaffen, A., Schulsinger, F., and Mednick, S. A.: Schizophrenia and physiological indices of dreaming. Arch. Gen. Psychiat. 10:89-93, 1964.

119. Rechtschaffen, A., and Verdone, P.: Amount of dreaming: effect of incentive, adaptation to laboratory, and individual differences. Percept. Motor Skills, 19:947-958, 1964.

120. Rechtschaffen, A., Verdone, P., and Wheaton, J. V.: Reports of mental activity during sleep. Canad. Psychiat. Ass. J. 8:409-414, 1963.

121. Rechtschaffen, A., Vogel, G., and Shaikun, G.: The interrelatedness of mental activity during sleep. Arch. Gen. Psychiat. 9:536-547, 1963.

122. Rechtschaffen, A., Wolpert, E. A., Dement, W. C., Mitchell, S. A., and Fisher, C.: Nocturnal sleep of narcoleptics. Electroenceph. Clin. Neurophysiol. 15:599-609, 1963.

123. Roffwarg, H. P., Dement, W. C., and Fisher, C.: Preliminary observations of the sleep-dream patterns in neonates, infants, children, and adults. In: Harms,

E. (Ed.): Problems of Sleep and Dream in Children. International Series of Monographs on Child Psychiatry, Vol. 2. New York, Macmillan, 1964.

124. Roffwarg, H. P., Dement, W. C., Muzio, J. N., and Fisher, C.: Dream imagery: relationship to rapid eye movements of sleep. Arch. Gen. Psychiat. 7:235-258, 1962.

125. Roffwarg, H. P., Muzio, J. N., and Dement, W. C.: Ontogenetic development of the human sleep-dream cycle. Science 152:604-619, 1966.

126. Schwartz, Betty A., and Guilbaud, Giselle.: L'EEG du sommeil nocturne en neuro-chirurgie: problemes d'interpretation. Rev. Neurol. (Paris) 110:307-308, 1964.

127. Shapiro, A., Goodenough, D. R., Biederman, I., and Sleser, I.: Dream recall and the physiology of sleep. J. Appl. Physiol. 19:778-783, 1964.

128. Snyder, F.: Dream recall, respiratory variability and depth of sleep. Paper presented at the meeting of the American Psychiatric Association, May 1960.

129. Snyder, F.: The new biology of dreaming. Arch. Gen. Psychiat. 8:381-391, 1963.

129a. Snyder, F., Karacan, I., Tharp, V. K., Jr., and Scott, J.: Phenomenology of REMS dreaming. Psychophysiology 4:375 (Abstract), 1968.

130. Spreng, L. F., Johnson, L. C., and Lubin, A.: Autonomic correlates of eye movement bursts during stage REM sleep. Psychophysiology 4:311-323, 1968.

131. Talland, G. A.: Deranged Memory; a Psychonomic Study of the Amnesic Syndrome. New York, Academic Press, 1965.

132. Verdone, P.: Temporal reference of manifest dream content. Percept. Motor Skills 20:1253-1268, 1965.

133. Victor, M., Talland, G. A., and Adams, R. D.: Psychological studies of Korsakoff's psychosis: I.. General intellectual functions. J. Nerv. Ment. Dis. 128: 528-537, 1959.

134. Vogel, G.: Studies in psychophysiology of dreams. III. The dream of narcolepsy. Arch. Gen. Psychiat. 3:421-428, 1960.

135. Vogel, G. W.: REM deprivation. III. Dreaming and psychosis. Arch. Gen. Psychiat. 18:312-329, 1968.

136. Vogel, G., Foulkes, D., and Trosman, H.: Ego functions and dreaming during sleep onset. Arch. Gen. Psychiat. 14:238-248, 1966.

137. Vogel, G. W., and Traub, A. C.: REM deprivation. I. The effect on schizophrenic patients. Arch. Gen. Psychiat. 18:287-300, 1968.

138. Vogel, G. W., Traub, A. C., Ben-Horin, P., and Meyers, G. M.: REM deprivation. II. The effects on depressed patients. Arch. Gen. Psychiat. 18:301-311, 1968.

139. Wechsler, D.: Manual for the Wechsler Adult Intelligence Scale. New York: Psychological Corp., 1955.

140. Wechsler, D.: Manual for the Wechsler Pre-School and Primary Scale of Intelligence. New York: Psychological Corp., 1967.

141. West, L. J., Janszen, H. H., Lester, B. K., and Cornelisoon, F. S., Jr.: The psychosis of sleep deprivation. Ann. N. Y. Acad. Sci. 96:66-70, 1962.

142. Williams, H. L., Gieseking, C. F., and Lubin, A.: Some effects of sleep loss on memory. Percept. Motor Skills 23:1287-1293, 1966.

143. Williams, H. L., Lubin, A., and Goodnow, J. J.: Impaired performance with acute sleep loss. Psychol. Monogr. 73:(14, Whole No. 484), 1959.

144. Williams, H. L., and Williams, C. L.: Nocturnal EEG profiles and performance. Psychophysiology, 3:164-175, 1966.

145. Williams, R. L., Agnew, H. W., and Webb, W. B.: Sleep patterns in young adults: an EEG study. Electroenceph. Clin. Neurophysiol. 17:376-381, 1964.

146. Williams, R. L., Agnew, H. W., and Webb, W. B.: The normative characteristics of EEG sleep patterns as a function of age. Paper presented at the meeting of the Association for the Psychophysiological Study of Sleep, Denver, March 1968.

147. Wilson, S. A.: The narcolepsies. Brain 51:63-109, 1928.

148. Witkin, H. A., and Lewis, H. B.: The relation of experimentally induced presleep experiences to dreams: A report on method and preliminary findings. J. Amer. Psychoanal. Ass. 13:819-849, 1965.

149. Wolff, H. G., and Curran, D.: Nature of delirium and allied states: the dysergastic reaction. Arch. Neurol. Psychiat. 33:1175-1215, 1935.

150. Yules, R. B., Freedman, D. X., and Chandler, K. A.: The effect of ethyl alcohol on man's electroencephalographic sleep cycle. Electroenceph. Clin. Neurophysiol. 20:109-111, 1966.

151. Zarcone, V., Gulevich, G., and Dement, W.: Sleep and electroconvulsive therapy. Arch. Gen. Psychiat. 16:567-573, 1967.

152. Zarcone, V., Gulevich, G., Pivik, T., and Dement. W.: Partial REM phase deprivation and schizophrenia. Arch. Gen. Psychiat. 18:194-202, 1968.

153. Zimmerman, W. B.: Psychological and physiological differences between "light" and "deep" sleepers. Psychophysiology, 4:387 (abstract) 1968.

154. Zung, W. W. K., Wilson, W. P., and Dodson, W. E.: Effect of depressive disorders on sleep-EEG responses. Arch. Gen. Psychiat. 10:439-445, 1964.

Discussion of
Dr. Feinberg's and Dr. Evart's Paper

by FRITZ A. FREYHAN, M.D.

St. Vincent's Hospital, New York

DR. FEINBERG has presented original data as well as theoretical considerations on the function of sleep. If my discussion consists primarily of raising questions, this should be regarded as a tribute to the authors' original experiments and sophisticated theorizing. I should state at the outset that I have some reservations, not directed at the work of the authors, but regarding the current state of sleep research generally.

To start with I do not know whether we have sufficient knowledge to determine what constitutes normal sleep. For example, do we have adequate longitudinal studies to assess the variability of sleep patterns in the same individual? Do we have data to correlate sleep patterns with the varieties of individual physiques and personality types? Does sleep, as studied in the artificial setting of the laboratory, fully resemble sleep under what pass as normal conditions for given individuals? Without a comprehensive body of knowledge on sleep variation and variability, it may be difficult, if not premature, to formulate theories regarding the function of sleep.

The question may be raised whether dreams are hallucinatory in nature. While dreams are normal phenomena, hallucinations are indicative of disorders of perception. A person's attitude toward a dream is fundamentally different from that of a patient who experiences hallucinations. The idea of a dissociation of sleep processes is highly intriguing. There are some problems regarding the assumption of a S-REM intrusion into waking.

Since deliria represent syndromes consisting of hallucinations, confusion and clouding of consciousness, they do not seem to resemble dreams. The quality of hallucinations in delirium tremens differs substantially from ordinary nightmares or sleep terrors. I would therefore hesitate to describe delirium tremens in terms of "a waking dream." If deliria, or for that matter delirium tremens, represent an intrusion of S-REM or dreaming sleep into waking behavior, the question arises why some alcoholic patients develop delirium tremens and others

394

chronic hallucinosis or a Korsakoff psychosis? To complicate matters further, delirium tremens may, but need not, occur during withdrawal. As a matter of fact, there is no agreement in the literature as to what part withdrawal plays in the development of delirium tremens. Manfred Bleuler and others have pointed out that delirium tremens is rarely seen when severely alcoholic patients are involuntarily admitted to hospitals for abrupt withdrawal and treatment.

It may be unfortunate for sleep research that there are today very few patients with residuals of the post-World War I epidemic of encephalitis. The sleep disturbances associated with chronic encephalitis and sleep inversion in particular may offer important information for the understanding of sleep disturbances in relation to mental functions. In some instances, patients were reported to have suffered a sustained inability to sleep, without evident damage to mental performance.

The authors submit a challenging hypothesis on the relationship of sleep disturbance to cognitive impairment. A significant decline in sleep occurs with pathological aging as manifested in chronic brain syndromes. Comparing levels of intellectual functions of normal aged subjects with chronic brain syndrome patients, they found that the amount of S-REM was in both groups positively and significantly correlated with intelligence levels as measured by WAIS scores. These findings are to support the assumption that the brain carries out certain positive functions required for the cognitive activities of waking. The amount of sleep is therefore related to the intensity of brain activity during waking.

This intriguing hypothesis also leaves room for some interesting questions. If we are to put any faith in general impressions as documented by reported observations, autobiographies and historical literature, some of the most creative writers, artists and political personalities suffered from insomnia problems throughout life.

Our current investigation of the effects of magnesium pemoline on memory impairment seems relevant in this connection. In a double-blind study we compared the effects of dextro-amphetamine, placebo and magnesium pemoline on intellectual and memory functions of aged patients with evidence of brain syndromes. The first results indicate significant gains with both drugs as measured by the WAIS and Wechsler Memory Scales. During the five-week treatment period, most patients slept poorly on account of the stimulant effects of the two active drugs. However, this temporary decline in sleep did not interfere with significant improvement of intellectual and memory functions.

The main questions in regard to the proposed hypothesis concern the role of sleep in the genesis of mental dysfunctions. We will need more specific evidence before we can determine whether sleep patterns, mental functions and mental disorders are concomitant, interdependent or causally linked phenomena. Furthermore, it does not seem quite clear to me why REM sleep tends to be considered more important than non-REM sleep. That sleep researchers are fascinated by REM sleep, and the unraveling of the mysteries of dreams can be easily understood. But how do we explain what seems to be an unproportional pressure to establish primary functions for sleep and especially REM sleep?

I have been privileged to discuss a paper that represents an imaginative and challenging contribution to sleep research. It will require time before the various discoveries of sleep phenomena can be integrated into psychiatric theory on mental function and illness. At the risk of being too cautious, too critical, or both, I believe that we will get there faster without the ballast of teleological commitments on the meaning of dream and sleep.

17

ELECTROLYTES AND MENTAL ILLNESS

by ALEC COPPEN, M.D. D.P.M.*

I MUST START by delimiting the scope of this review. I will be dealing with work carried out, for the most part in the past decade, into electrolytes and the affective disorders, for it is in this area that most work has been recently devoted.

Electrolytes have an extraordinarily central place in biological processes. Physiological research has shown the fundamental importance of electrolytes in the functioning of the cell. According to the ionic theory, the resting and action potentials of nerve and muscle cells depend on potassium, sodium, chloride and other ions having a different concentration inside the cell from the concentration they have in the extracellular fluid. The cell membrane is freely permeable to potassium and chloride, but is much less permeable to sodium, and there is active transport of sodium which keeps the sodium concentration within the cell at about 1/10 of the concentration of sodium in the extracellular space. Because of this uneven distribution of sodium and the presence within the cell of impermeable anions (such as glutamic acid), potassium and chlorine are also unevenly divided between the cell and the extracellular fluid; potassium has a very high intracellular concentration and chlorine a low intracellular concentration compared to their concentration in the extracellular space.

Investigations over the last 20 years on invertebrate giant nerve fibers have shown the role of electrolytes in the nervous system. Although the study of the giant axon of the squid seems remote from any investigation that we may be able to carry out on our patients, radioactive-isotope techniques enable us to study the intra- and extracellular concentrations of electrolytes in man. In the clinical field the study of disturbances of intracellular ions is still in its early stage. We do not yet know the physiological processes controlling the intracellular

*Medical Research Council, Surrey, England.

concentration of sodium and other electrolytes, nor do we know the functional consequences of alterations in their distribution, except that in certain very limited disorders, such as periodic paralysis, these effects may be profound. The concentration of electrolytes in cells and the extracellular water can influence other important biochemical processes, such as transport of amino acids across cell membranes and many intracellular metabolic processes. It is possible that any widespread abnormality of electrolytes could in themselves alter cellular excitability and produce further biochemical abnormalities. It is worth remembering this when considering the role of electrolytes in depression, as it must be remembered that there is increasing evidence of changes in amine metabolism as well as in electrolytes in the affective disorders.

Balance Studies

The study of water and electrolytes in affective disorders goes back for half a century,[1] and the earlier studies were of the balance type. They are reviewed by Gibbons.[22] Mostly they are confined to the rather rare type of patient who suffers from regularly recurring mania or depression. Most investigators have found that there are varying changes in water and salt excretion with mood, although these are not the same from patient to patient. These cases, although illuminating, are very uncommon, and it is uncertain what relationship they bear to the more usual type of depression of gradual onset which may last for weeks or months.

Russell[29] studied water, sodium and potassium balance in 15 depressed patients for several weeks during recovery from a depressive illness. Eleven of these patients recovered clinically during the period of study while they were treated by electroconvulsive therapy. It was found that there was no significant change in sodium, potassium or water balance during this time. The only significant finding was a transient retention of sodium and water on the day that electroconvulsive therapy was administered, and it was probable that this was related to an emotional reaction to ECT.

The Distribution of Electrolytes Measured by Isotope Dilution Studies

The balance studies have various limitations: it is difficult to measure the intake and excretion in mentally disturbed patients for days or weeks on end. Moreover, the balance studies give no information about the distribution of electrolytes between cells and the extracellular fluid, which, as we have seen, is of such fundamental biological importance.

The distribution of electrolytes is measured in man by techniques based on the principle of isotope dilution. This principle may be illustrated by considering the simple example of the measurement of total body water (TBW) by using tritiated water, that is, water labelled with the radioactive isotope of hydrogen. The subject drinks a carefully measured amount of tritiated water which is allowed to mix thoroughly with his body water (this is usually complete within 6 hours). The concentration of tritium is then measured in a sample of body water obtained from blood or urine. As the amount of administered isotope is known, it is easy to calculate the volume of body water in which it was diluted:

$$\text{TBW} = \frac{(\text{Administered dose}) - (\text{urine losses of tritiated water})}{\text{concentration of isotope in sample}}$$

It is not so easy to measure extracellular water (ECW) because this test requires a tracer substance that mixes rapidly and completely within the ECW, yet does not enter the cells. No substance is known which fulfils all these conditions. In the present investigations we have used radioactive bromine,[82]Br. This tracer has the advantage that it can be given by mouth, is easy to estimate and has been used extensively in estimating ECW,[34] but it is not exclusively extracellular in its distribution. Normally, however, it gives one of the most satisfactory measures of ECW.

When the amount of sodium in the body is to be measured an extension of the principle of isotope dilution is used. Instead of volumes of distribution the "exchangeable sodium" is measured. A radioactive isotope of sodium is given—either the short-lived isotope[24]Na or the long-lived isotope [22]Na, and the mass of sodium in the body with which the sodium mixes or "exchanges" in a given time is determined. It used to be thought that the isotope of sodium had mixed completely with the body sodium within 24 hours, but we were able to show that complete mixing took considerably longer than this.[15] Twenty-four hours is the usual time allowed and the results so obtained are referred to as the "twenty-four hour exchangeable sodium."

Body potassium can be estimated by the isotope dilution technique using the short life isotope of potassium, [42]K. However, in our work we were able to use a method of determining body potassium from the amount of the naturally occurring radioactive isotope of potassium, [40]K, in the subject. All potassium contains 0.012 per cent of this isotope, and radioactivity due to [40]K can be determined by means of a very sensitive body counter. By careful calibration of the body counter the total potassium in the body is calculated. It should be remembered that this method has the advantage that it measures total body potassium and not exchangeable potassium, as is the case of the isotope dilution techniques. We have described these techniques in detail elsewhere.[11,15]

The main fluid compartments of the body can be illustrated by considering those of a normal individual. TBW is made up of 16 litres of ECW and 19 litres of intracellular water (ICW). The bulk of the exchangeable sodium is in the ECW, where the concentration of this ion is about 10 times that of its concentration in the cells. If the volume of ECW is known and the concentration of sodium therein is measured, it is possible to estimate the mass of sodium in the ECW. When this mass of extracellular sodium is subtracted from the exchangeable sodium, the remaining mass of sodium is termed "residual sodium." This consists of intracellular sodium together with a small amount of exchangeable bone sodium. Similarly potassium, which is mainly an intracellular ion, can be divided into an extracellular and residual portion.

The first to apply the isotope dilution technique to measure exchangeable sodium and potassium in depression was Gibbons.[21] His investigation was prompted by the report by Schottstaedt et al.[31] that periods of depression in normal people were accompanied by a decreased urinary excretion of sodium. Gibbons measured the 24-hour exchangeable sodium and potassium in a group of 24 adult patients who showed the clinical picture of severe depression. Estimations were carried out initially just after admission when all the patients were depressed and later, after several weeks, when 16 of the patients had recovered; 8 of the patients who had failed to respond to treatment were also retested. 24-hour exchangeable sodium decreased, on the average by 10 per cent after recovery; the patients who did not recover showed no significant alteration in exchangeable sodium. Dietary factors were not thought to produce these results; patients suffering from malnutrition were not investigated in the series, and 10 of the patients, who were on a constant intake of sodium and potassium for balance studies, showed the same changes as the group as a whole. Exchangeable potassium showed no significant alteration with recovery.

These findings stimulated us to carry out an investigation into electrolyte distribution between cells and the extracellular fluid by means of the isotope dilution techniques and whole body counting of ^{40}K. First, the changes in body water. Altschule and Tillotson,[2] using the thiocyanate method for measuring extracellular space, found a significant increase on recovery from depression. Dawson et al.[16] found a reduction compared to their normal state in extracellular space in 4 patients during both depression and mania. Hullin et al.[24] found an increase in extracellular water and total body water following recovery from a depressive illness.

In our study,[11] using tritiated water and [82]Br, we found that the extracellular water significantly increased by 0.5 liter after recovery and total body water by 1.2 liter. The findings of other workers and ourselves therefore support the notion that there is a decrease in extracellular water and total body water during depression, and that clinical recovery is accompanied by an increase in both total body water and extracellular water.

The most striking abnormality we found during depression lay in "residual sodium," which is the sodium outside the extracellular space consisting mainly of intracellular sodium and a small amount of exchangeable bone sodium. Residual sodium was increased on average by about 50 per cent during the depressive illness and returned to normal after recovery. Total body potassium and intracellular potassium were low and did not change with clinical recovery. The average intracellular potassium concentration was about 135 mEq. per liter, which is considerably lower than the normal value found by this method of 165 mEq. per liter.[32] One limitation of this latter investigation was that data for normal subjects were obtained from other laboratories because of the restriction now imposed on the administration of radioactive isotopes to normal subjects. It should be noted that in depression there is no change in either extracellular potassium or sodium concentrations, which are normal both in plasma and in cerebrospinal fluid.[17]

These findings, it should be emphasized, are on the whole body, and it is not known whether similar changes take place in the central nervous system, although recent findings by Shaw et al.,[33] in this research unit, on the brains of depressives who died by suicide suggest that this may be so. Again it should be emphasized that the isotope dilution techniques provide only indirect evidence about intracellular electrolytes. For example, the measurement of extracellular water is fraught with difficulty because it is difficult to find a suitable marker for this space. However, if one takes these results as indicating alterations in intracellular electrolytes, then we have calculated that these could cause changes in both the resting and action potential of about 7 millivolts and that these changes would have considerable functional consequences.

These changes in intracellular electrolytes suggest there may be some deficiency in sodium transport mechanism across the cell membrane. Although the movement of sodium between cells and extracellular water is not easily studied in man, its rate of transfer from the blood to the cerebrospinal fluid can be studied. The rate of transfer of sodium from blood to cerebrospinal fluid was estimated, using ^{24}Na, in a series of 20 patients. In these patients the transfer rate was found to be half the normal rate when they were depressed, while after recovery the transfer rate of sodium was normal.

Anderson and Dawson[3,4] described a group of depressed patients who had high blood concentrations of acetyl-methyl carbinol. The depressed patients who showed this elevation were characterized by certain features of depression, such as retardation in speech and preoccupation with depressive ideas. These findings are of particular interest, since it is thought that a raised fasting blood concentration of acetyl-methyl carbinol is associated with increased intracellular sodium.

Magnesium and Calcium in Depression

There have been few studies of magnesium and calcium in depression. Flach[18] followed the urinary excretion of calcium in depressed patients maintained on a constant intake of calcium and phosphorus before and during recovery from their illness. He found that patients who recovered showed a significant decrease in the urinary excretion of calcium, but patients suffering from neurosis did not show such a change. In a more recent study, Flach,[19] using balance studies and the radioisotope ^{47}Ca, was able to calculate the body retention of the isotope and also to estimate the bone resorption rate. In a small series of 6 patients, Flach found a decrease in the bone resorption rate and an increased retention of ^{47}Ca on clinical recovery. However, Gour and Chaudrey[23] found plasma calcium normal in depression. Cade[8] reported significantly raised plasma magnesium concentrations in depressed patients, before and after recovery, and also in schizophrenia, but these observations are as yet unconfirmed. However, recent work in our Laboratory[20] found normal total and increased calcium and magnesium in depression.

Electrolytes in Mania

There are few investigations of electrolytes in mania. In a series of 22 patients we[13] measured the distribution of sodium and water by a technique similar to that we used in the investigation of depression. We found that residual sodium showed an average 200 per cent increase over normal when the patients were manic; some of the manic patients became depressed, and these patients then showed a 50 per cent increase in residual sodium—i.e. similar to the levels found in patients suffering from a depressive illness. After recovery the patients' residual sodium returned to normal. Manic patients, therefore, showed a similar but greater deviation from normal than depressive patients.

The Significance of Electrolyte Abnormalities

The etiological significance of these changes is at present obscure. In the remainder of this discussion I will assume that these findings represent changes in intracellular sodium and potassium and that these whole body changes include the brain, although none of these assumptions can be taken as entirely substantiated.

Very little is known about factors that can alter the distribution of electrolytes; obvious possibilities are steroid hormones such as cortisol, aldosterone or estrogens, and also the posterior pituitary hormones. However, the only hormone extensively studied is cortisol, and our conclusion is that although the secretion of this hormone is slightly increased in depression, its secretion shows little correlation with mental state. In mania, where the electrolyte changes are so marked, we found normal plasma cortisol.[6]

Are these changes in electrolytes causal or secondary to the changes in mood? It will only be possible to ascertain the role of electrolytes in depression when we can manipulate them and restore their normal distribution. There are, however, some reports indicating that changes in water and electrolyte distribution may alter mood. Büssow[7] gave water and vasopressin to patients suffering from mania or depression and found that both the manic and the depressive patients became very much worse. Karstens[25] repeated the same procedure on six normal subjects and produced some of the symptoms of a depressive illness.

It is of particular relevance in this context to consider the therapeutic actions of lithium, which has been shown to be effective in the treatment of mania[28] and to have a prophylactic action in patients prone to attacks of frequently recurring depression or mania.[5] The mechanism of action of lithium is being actively investigated. It is possible that its action is on monoamine metabolism,[30] but it may also affect water and sodium metabolism. The action of this salt has a very interesting and unique influence on sodium metabolism and sodium transport across biological membranes. Keynes and Swan (1959) have shown that during an action potential, when sodium normally enters the cell, lithium and sodium enter with equal facility, but lithium is removed from the cell at about one-tenth the rate of sodium. Coppen and Shaw[12] investigated the effects of lithium carbonate given in prophylactic doses over a week (on water and electrolyte distribution). They found an average increase of 1.5 liters in TBW and increases in both intracellular and extracellular water. Since we see that total body water, extracellular water and intracellular water increase with clinical recovery and since it is possible that lithium salts alter the physiological mechanisms responsible for these changes in water, this effect may be related to the therapeutic and prophylactic actions of lithium.

There is now much evidence accumulating that indoleamine metabolism is abnormal in depression:[10] the urinary excretion of tryptamine is low,[14] the concentration of 5-hydroxyindoleacetic acid is reduced in the cerebrospinal fluid (Ashcroft et al., 1966; Dencker et al., 1966), and there is a fall in 5-hydroxytryptamine concentration in the hind brains of depressed suicides.[33]

Now how are these changes in electrolytes related to the changes in amine metabolism? At this point it must be acknowledged that we enter the realm of pure speculation. However, it is possible that changes in electrolyte distribution could affect amino acid and amine metabolism. Intracellular potassium is known to be essential for many enzymatic processes within the cell.[6] A direct effect of potassium deficiency on protein synthesis has been demonstrated by Lubin and Ennis.[27] Changes in electrolyte distribution could also have important effects on the transport of amino acids into cells. Christensen et al.[9] and Vidaver[35] indicate that the sodium gradient between cells and their surrounding fluid is one of the determinants of the rate of transport of certain amino acids into cells.

The biochemistry of affective disorders is a rapidly expanding field of psychiatric research, and it is in this light that the changes in electrolytes must be reviewed. It is possible that electrolytes have only a secondary place in the etiology of depression and mania. I think we will not know until we are able to manipulate electrolytes and to examine the effects on mood of restoring them to normal. We need to know the endocrinological factors responsible for the changes in electrolyte distribution, and we also need to know the relationship between the changes in electrolytes and amine metabolism and possibly other biochemical changes responsible for depression as yet undescribed.

REFERENCES

1. Allers, R.: Z. Ges. Neurol. Psychiat. 9:585, 1914.
2. Altschule, M. D., and Tillotson, K. J.: Amer. J. Psychiat. 105:829, 1949.
3. Anderson, W. McC., and Dawson, J.: J. ment. Sci. 108:80, 1962.
4. Anderson, W. McC., and Dawson, J.: Brit. J. Psychiat. 109:225, 1963.
5. Baastrup, P. C., and Schou, M.: To be published, 1967.
6. Brooksbank, B. W. L., and Coppen, A.: Brit. J. Psychiat. 113:395, 1967.
7. Büssow, H.: Arch. Psychiat. Nervenkr. 184:357, 1950.
8. Cade, J. F. L.: Med. J. Australia 1:195, 1964.
9. Christensen, H.N., Inui, Y., Wheeler, K. P., and Eavenson, E.: Fed. Proc. 25:592, 1966.
10. Coppen, A.: In: Recent Advances in Pharmacology. In press, 1967.
11. Coppen, A., and Shaw, D. M.: Brit. Med. J. ii:1439, 1963.
12. Coppen, A., and Shaw, D. M.: Lancet ii:805, 1967.
13. Coppen, A., Shaw, D. M., Malleson, A., and Costain, R.: Brit. Med. J. i:71, 1966.
14. Coppen, A., Shaw, D. M., Malleson, A., Eccleston, E., and Gundy, G.: Brit. J. Psychiat. 111:993, 1965.
15. Coppen, A., Shaw, D. M., and Mangoni, A.: Brit. Med. J. ii: 295, 1962.
16. Dawson, J. Hullin, R. P., and Crocket, B. M.: J. Ment. Sci. 102:168, 1956.
17. Eichhorn, O.: Nervenarzt. 25:207, 1954.
18. Flach, F. F.: Brit. J. Psychiat. 110:588, 1964.
19. Flach, F. F.: Excerpta Medica. International Congress Series No. 117. IV World Congress of Psychiatry, 1966 p. 184.
20. Frizel, D., Coppen, A., and Marks, V.: To be published, 1968.
21. Gibbons, J. L.: Clin. Sci. 19:133, 1960.
22. Gibbons, J. L.: Postgrad. Med. J. 39:19, 1963.
23. Gour, K. N., and Chaudrey, H. M.: J. Ment. Sci. 103:275, 1957.
24. Hullin, R. F., Bailey, A. D., McDonald, R., Dransfield, G. A., and Milne, H. B.: Brit. J. Psychiat. 113:573, 1966.
25. Karstens, P.: Arch. Psychiat. Nervenkr. 186:231, 1951.
26. Kernan, R. P.: Cell K. London, 1965.
27. Lubin, M., and Ennis, H. L.: Biochem. Biophys. Acta. 81:614, 1964.
28. Maggs, R.: Brit. J. Psychiat. 109:56, 1963.
29. Russell, G. F. M.: Clin. Sci. 19:327, 1960.
30. Schildkraut, J. J., Schanberg, S. M., and Kopin, I. J.: Life Sci. 5:1479, 1966.
31. Schottstaedt, W. W., Grace, W. J., and Wolff, H. G.: J. Psychosom. Res. 1:287, 1956.
32. Shaw, D. M., and Coppen, A.: Brit. J. Psychiat. 112:269, 1966.
33. Shaw, D. M., Camps, F., and Eccleston, E.: Brit. J. Psychiat. (In press, 1967).
34. Staffurth, J. S., and Birchall, I.: Clin. Sci. 19:45, 1960.
35. Vidaver, G. A.: Biochemistry 3:803, 1964.

Discussion of Dr. Coppen's Paper

by JACK DURELL, M.D.

The Psychiatric Institute, Washington, D.C.

I AM VERY PLEASED to have the opportunity to discuss Dr. Coppen's masterly review of the field of electrolytes and mental illness. I myself have been interested in this field for a number of years and am presently engaged with several collaborators in further investigations in some of the areas discussed by Dr. Coppen. My own interest was largely stimulated by Dr. Coppen's body of imaginative and careful research. It was his work that led to the provocative hypothesis that subtle alterations in electrolyte gradients across cell membranes might be intimately related to the pathophysiology of affective disorders. Indeed, it has not seemed unreasonable to hypothesize that such changes in electrochemical gradients in specific areas of the nervous system might account for a good deal of the phenomenology of the affective disorders. There are several other observations that seem related and add to the interest in pursuing this hypothesis. The first is the now well-established clinical fact that lithium salts are remarkably effective and specific in the treatment of mania.[1] In addition, there is increasing evidence that they are prophylactic in recurrent depressions.[2] Lithium ion is a univalent cation closely related chemically to sodium and potassium; on a theoretical basis it might be expected to alter the efficiency of the sodium-potassium stimulated ATPase (the membrane "sodium pump"). There is some evidence to support this mode of action of lithium salts, which serves to focus our attention on the univalent electrolytes in affective disorders. Secondly, though uncorroborated, there is a report in the literature that certain schizophrenic patients show increased activity of the red cell membrane sodium-potassium stimulated ATPase.[3] Miss O'Brien has attempted to confirm some of these observations in our laboratory and, though the initial observations per se could not be confirmed, there is a suggestion that with the exacerbation of a schizophrenic syndrome there is a change in the activity of this ATPase. Even though these findings relate to schizophrenic patients and not patients with affective disorders, they increase our interest in the possible importance of electrolyte gradients.

406

Dr. Coppen's review has been thoughtful and he has taken great pains to point out certain methodological problems and difficulties of interpretation. I wish to limit my discussion to the studies bearing upon the metabolism and distribution of sodium ion and to emphasize the areas in which the methodological problems do lead to ambiguity in interpretation, and where I might suggest interpretations alternative to those proposed by Dr. Coppen.

In my opinion, the most definitively established finding in this entire area is the decrease in 24-hour exchangeable sodium upon recovery from depression. This has been most clearly demonstrated in the carefully controlled studies of Gibbons.[4] In Dr. Coppen's own studies there were changes in the same direction that were not statistically significant unless the results were corrected for changes in weights and total body water; corrected in that way, however, the results are almost identical with those of Gibbons. It is not as clear whether the decrease of 24-hour exchangeable sodium reflects a decrease in total body sodium or a redistribution of sodium. Studies undertaken by Russell and by Coppen failed to provide evidence for a decrease in total body sodium upon recovery from depression. They have by no means established, however, that such changes do not occur. Recently, in our laboratory, Dr. Leslie Baer, using total body counting, determined the sodium turnover rate on a constant sodium intake and found changes which are best interpreted as indicating a decrease in total body exchangeable sodium upon recovery from depression.[5]

Dr. Coppen's studies have led him to favor the interpretation that redistribution of sodium is associated with recovery from depression. The changes in residual sodium reported by Dr. Coppen, though small numerically, represent a large fraction of the residual sodium, are statistically significant, and lead directly to the hypothesis of an altered intracellular sodium. However, as Dr. Coppen himself stressed, the results depend heavily upon the validity of the measure of extracellular space, and he has utilized the radioactive bromide space. This measure, though as good as any other single method, like each of the others has its pitfalls. It is possible that the conclusions reached by the use of that method could be systematically biased, leading to the apparent change in residual sodium. One good candidate for a mechanism that could introduce a systematic error relates to the concentration of bromide in gastrointestinal fluids. It is known that the bromide/chloride ratio in gastric secretions may be about five times that in the plasma.[6] Increases of 100 to 200 cc. in the mean gastric fluid contents (or its equivalent in terms of chloride and bromide) of the gastrointestinal tract occurring upon recovery from depression might account for the apparent changes in residual sodium. Since changes in gastrointestinal function are known to occur in depression, and since it is possible that there is less gastric secretion in depression or that the bromide concentration in the gastric fluids is lower, it seems possible that this could result in a systematic error accounting for the observed differences in residual sodium. We are currently investigating this area, utilizing several measures of extracellular space including the early sodium space, a method that has been described previously and has been modified and utilized in our laboratory by Dr. Baer. It will be interesting to see whether the finding of an altered residual sodium in depression will be corroborated by independent methodology.

Dr. Coppen has reviewed the indirect evidence that leads him to the conclusion that the alterations in sodium metabolism associated with depression are not secondary to changes in adrenal cortical function. Dr. Baer's studies suggest the converse conclusion, in that each of the patients showing altered sodium turnover rate in depression also showed higher urinary excretion of 17-OHCS while depressed. The one patient who had a less severe neurotic depression and did not show significant changes in sodium turnover upon recovery also showed no significant changes in urinary 17-OHCS. It appears, therefore, that the matter of whether or not changes in sodium metabolism in depression are related to changes in adrenal cortical function remains an open and interesting question.

In considering mania, Dr. Coppen presents evidence that the alteration in sodium distribution is similar to that occurring in depression, but more marked—i.e., there is a higher residual sodium in mania than in depression. This is an interesting and provocative finding, but conclusions as to its validity and significance must be held in abeyance until confirmed independently. In those studies there is, as in the studies of depressed patients, the problem with the interpretation of the validity of the measurement of extracellular space. In addition, however, some of Dr. Coppen's manic patients have shown extraordinarily high values of 24-hour exchangeable sodium. The related studies in our laboratory are still in progress, but on the five manic patients studied to date we have not found particularly high values of 24-hour exchangeable sodium; nor have we been able to corroborate the occurrence of very large changes in residual sodium upon recovery from mania. These studies are not completed, however, and I mention them only in the interest of keeping the question open.

In conclusion, I wish to emphasize the very important hypotheses that have been generated in this field. Dr. Coppen's own work has been of major importance in focusing upon the potential importance of changes in electrolyte gradients in affective illness. There remain, however, serious methodological problems necessitating that conclusions as to the significance of the findings be held in abeyance.

REFERENCES

1. Schou, M.: J. Psychiat. Res. 6, 1968 (in press).
2. Baastrup, P. C., and Schou, M.: Arch. Gen. Psychiat. 16:162, 1967.
3. Seeman, P. M., and O'Brien, E.: Nature 200:263, 1963.
4. Gibbons, J. L.: Clin. Sci. 19:133, 1960.
5. Baer, L., Durell, J., Bunney, W. E., Levy, B. S., and Cardon, P. V.: Submitted to J. Psychiat. Res., 1968.
6. Gamble, J. L., Robertson, J. S., Hannigan, C. A., Foster, C. G., and Farr, L. E.: J. Clin. Invest. 32:483, 1953.

Membership of the
American Psychopathological Association*

Theodora M. Abel, Ph.D.
Palisades
Rockland County, N.Y. 10964

Nathan Ackerman, M.D.
149 East 78th Street
New York, N.Y. 10021

Alexandra Adler, M.D.
30 Park Avenue
New York, N.Y. 10016

Leo Alexander, M.D. (L)
433 Marlboro Street
Boston 15, Massachusetts

George S. Amsden, M.D. (L)
Acworth, New Hampshire

Leslie R. Angus, M.D. (L)
1120 East Market Street
Danville, Pennsylvania

Silvano Arieti, M.D.
103 East 75th Street
New York, N.Y. 10021

Irma Bache, M.D. (L)
1 East 356
Pentagon Building
Washington 25, D.C.

Janet Rioch Bard, M.D.
6 Meadow Road
Baltimore, Md. 21212

Lauretta Bender, M.D. (L)
44 Malone Avenue
Long Beach, New York

Herbert Birch, Ph.D.
Department of Pediatrics
Albert Einstein College of Med.
New York, N.Y. 10461

H. Waldo Bird, M.D.
St. Louis University
School of Medicine
1221 South Grand Boulevard
St. Louis, Mo. 63104

James Birren, Ph.D.
University of Southern California
Los Angeles, Calif. 90007

Eugene L. Bliss, M.D.
Salt Lake City General Hospital
156-168 Westminster Avenue
Salt Lake City, Utah 84115

Joseph M. Bobbitt, Ph.D.
Joint Commission on Mental Health
of Children, Inc.
5454 Wisconsin Avenue
Chevy Chase, Maryland 20203

Benjamin Boshes, M.D.
Department of Neurol. & Psychiat.
Northwestern University
303 East Chicago Avenue
Chicago, Illinois 60611

Wagner H. Bridger, M.D.
Department of Psychiatry
Albert Einstein School of Medicine
Bronx, N.Y. 10461

Henry Brill, M.D.
Box 202
West Brentwood, L.I., New York

Eugene Brody, M.D.
University of Maryland
School of Medicine
Baltimore, Maryland

Albert Browne-Mayers, M.D.
147 East 50th Street
New York, N.Y. 10022

Hilde Bruch, M.D.
1600 Holcombe Boulevard
Apt. 903
Houston, Texas 77025

*(L) = Life member. (H) = Honorary member.

A. Louise Brush, M.D. (L)
55 East 86th Street
New York, N.Y. 10029

Dexter M. Bullard, Sr., M.D. (L)
M.H.A.
500 W. Montgomery Avenue
Rockville, Maryland

Eugene I. Burdock, Ph.D.
Department of Psychiatry & Neurology
New York University Medical Center
550 First Avenue
New York, New York

Ernest W. Burgess, Ph.D.
University of Chicago
1225 East 60th Street
Chicago, Illinois 60637

Ewald W. Busse, M.D.
Department of Psychiatry
Duke University
Durham, North Carolina 27706

Enoch Callaway, M.D.
Langley Porter Neuropsychiatric
Institute
401 Parnassus Avenue
San Francisco, Calif. 94122

Douglas Campbell, M.D.
490 Post Street
San Francisco 2, California

Gerald Caplan, M.D.
58 Fenwood Road
Boston, Mass. 02115

Eric T. Carlson, M.D.
60 Sutton Place South
New York, N.Y. 10022

Edward J. Carroll, M.D. (L)
721 DuPont Plaza Center,
Miami, Florida 32131

James P. Cattell, M.D.
880 Fifth Avenue
New York, N.Y. 10021

Richard Allen Chase, M.D.
Neurocommunications Laboratory
Department of Psychiatry
The Johns Hopkins Hospital
Baltimore, Md. 21205

G. Brock Chisholm, M.D. (H)
Seawood, West Coast Road
R.R. 2, Victoria
British Columbia, Canada

Hollis E. Clow, M.D. (L)
121 Westchester Avenue
White Plains, New York

John A. Clausen, Ph.D.
1963 Yosemite Road
Berkeley 7, California

Dean J. Clyde, Ph.D.
Biometrics Laboratory
University of Miami
Coral Gables, Fla. 33124

Robert A. Cohen, M.D.
4514 Dorset Avenue
Chevy Chase, Md. 20015

Jonathan O. Cole, M.D.
78 Powell Street
Brookline, Mass. 02146

John H. Cumming, M.D.
Deputy Commissioner
N.Y.S. Dept. Mental Hygiene
44 Holland Avenue
Albany, N.Y. 12208

William Dement, M.D.
Department of Psychiatry
Stanford University Medical Ctr.
Stanford, Calif. 94304

Herman C. B. Denber, M.D.
Manhattan State Hospital
Ward's Island
New York, N.Y. 10035

Oskar Diethelm, M.D. (L)
New York Hospital
525 East 68th Street
New York, N.Y. 10021

Simon Dinitz, Ph.D.
Department of Sociology
Ohio State University
Columbus, Ohio 43210

Roy M. Dorcus, Ph.D.
Department of Psychology
University of California
405 Hilgard Avenue
Los Angeles, Calif. 90024

John M. Dorsey, M.D. (L)
Wayne St. University
Detroit 2, Michigan

Leon Eisenberg, M.D.
One Sparks Avenue
Cambridge, Mass. 02138

William V. Elgin, M.D. (L)
Sheppard & Enoch Pratt Hospital
Towson 4, Maryland

Joel Elkes, M.D.
Johns Hopkins Hospital
Baltimore, Md. 21205

George Engel, M.D.
Strong Memorial Hospital
Rochester, N.Y. 14620

David M. Engelhardt, M.D.
208 Marlborough Road
Brooklyn, N.Y. 11226

Milton H. Erickson, M.D. (L)
32 West Cypress Street
Phoenix, Arizona

Raymond Feldman, M.D.
205 Devon Place
Boulder, Colorado 80302

Max Fink, M.D.
39 Arleigh Road
Great Neck, L.I., N.Y. 11021

Barbara Fish, M.D.
New York University
550 First Avenue
New York, New York

Seymour Fisher, M.D.
Boston University
School of Medicine
Boston, Mass. 62118

Arthur N. Foxe, M.D. (L)
9 East 67th Street
New York, N.Y. 10021

Jerome D. Frank, M.D.
Department of Psychiatry
Johns Hopkins University
Baltimore, Md. 21205

Richard L. Frank, M.D. (L)
15 East 91st Street
New York, N.Y. 10028

Shervert H. Frazier, M.D.
N.Y.S. Psychiatric Institute
722 West 168th Street
New York, N.Y. 10032

Alfred M. Freedman, M.D.
161 West 86th Street
New York, N.Y. 10024

Daniel X. Freedman, M.D.
Department of Psychiatry
University of Chicago
950 East 59th Street
Chicago, Illinois 60637

Fritz A. Freyhan, M.D.
St. Vincent's Hospital & Medical
   Center
Cronin Research Building
153 West 11th Street
New York, N.Y. 10011

Arnold J. Friedhoff, M.D.
32-25 168th Street
Flushing, N.Y. 11358

John Frosch, M.D.
1 Gracie Terrace
New York, N.Y. 10028

Daniel H. Funkenstein, M.D.
74 Fenwood Road
Boston, Mass. 02115

W. Horsley Gantt, M.D. (L)
Johns Hopkins Hospital
Baltimore 5, Maryland

Norman Garmezy, Ph.D.
Department of Psychology
University of Minnesota
Minneapolis, Minnesota

Bernard Glueck, Sr., M.D. (L)
University of North Carolina
Box 1020
Chapel Hill, North Carolina

Bernard Glueck, Jr., M.D.
Box 2070
Hartford, Conn. 01602

Murray Glusman, M.D.
50 East 72nd Street
New York, N.Y. 10021

William Goldfarb, M.D.
1050 Fifth Avenue
New York, N.Y.

Sanford Goldstone, Ph.D.
Cornell University Medical College
21 Bloomingdale Road
White Plains, N.Y. 10605

Jacques Gottlieb, M.D.
Lafayette Clinic
951 Lafayette East
Detroit, Michigan 48207

Milton Greenblatt, M.D.
15 Ashburton Place
Boston, Mass. 02108

Samuel W. Greenhouse, Ph.D.
Chief, Epidemiology & Biometry
National Institute of Child Health
and Human Development
N. I. H.
Bethesda, Md. 20014

Roy R. Grinker, Sr., M.D.
Michael Reese Hospital
29th Street & Ellis Avenue
Chicago, Illinois 60616

Ernest M. Gruenberg, M.D.
722 West 168th Street
New York, N.Y. 10032

Samuel B. Guze, M.D.
Department of Psychiatry
Washington University
School of Medicine
St. Louis, Mo. 63110

A. Irving Hallowell, M.D. (L)
Box 14, Bennet Hall
University of Pennsylvania
Philadelphia, Pennsylvania

Ward C. Halstead, Ph.D.
5537 University Avenue
Chicago, Illinois 60637

David A. Hamburg, M.D.
Department of Psychiatry
Stanford University Medical School
Palo Alto, California

Donald M. Hamilton, M.D.
21 Bloomingdale Road
White Plains, New York

Morris Herman, M.D.
30 East 40th Street
New York, N.Y. 10016

Harold E. Himwich, M.D.
State Research Hospital
Galesburg, Illinois 61401

Hudson Hoagland, Ph.D.
Deerfoot Road
Southboro, Massachusetts

Leslie B. Hohman, M.D. (L)
Duke Medical School
Durham, North Carolina

Bernard Holland, M.D.
Emory University
Woodruff Building
Atlanta 22, Georgia

Joseph Hughes, M.D. (L)
111 North 49th Street
Philadelphia 39, Pennsylvania

Howard F. Hunt, Ph.D.
722 West 168th Street
New York, N.Y. 10032

William A. Hunt, Ph.D. (L)
Northwestern University
Evanston, Illinois

Paul E. Huston, M.D.
500 Newton Road
Iowa City, Iowa

Turan M. Itil, M.D.
Missouri Institute of Psychiatry
5400 Arsenal Street
St. Louis, Mo. 63139

Joseph Jaffe, M.D.
Columbia University
Department of Psychiatry
722 West 168th Street
New York, N.Y. 10032

Lissy Jarvik, M.D., Ph.D.
722 West 168th Street
New York, N.Y. 10032

Murray Jarvik, M.D.
Albert Einstein College of Medicine
Eastchester Road & Morris Park Ave.
Bronx, New York 10461

Karl Jaspers† (H)
Austrasse 126
4000 Basel, Switzerland

George A. Jervis, M.D., Ph.D. (L)
Letchworth Village
Research Department
Thiells, Rockland County, N.Y.

E. Roy John, Ph.D.
Brain Research Laboratory
New York Medical College
5th Avenue at 106th Street
New York, N.Y. 10029

Lothar B. Kalinowsky, M.D. (L)
115 East 82nd Street
New York, N.Y. 10028

Abram Kardiner, M.D. (L)
1100 Park Avenue
New York, New York

Martin M. Katz, Ph.D.
Chief, Special Studies Section
Psychopharmacology
Research Branch, N.I.M.H.
Chevy Chase, Maryland

Solomon Katzenelbogen, M.D. (L)
9305 Parkhill Terrace
Bethesda, Md. 20014

William Raymond Keeler, M.D.
484 Avenue Road
Apartment 102
Toronto 7, Ontario, Canada

Edward J. Kempf, M.D. (L)
Wading River
Long Island, New York

Isabelle V. Kendig, Ph.D. (L)
Sandy Spring, Maryland

Richard Kepner, M.D. (L)
P.O. Box 3119
Honolulu 2, Hawaii

Seymour S. Kety, M.D.
Department of Psychiatry
Massachusetts General Hospital
Boston, Mass. 02146

Elaine Kinder, Ph.D.
46 Kinney Street
Piermont, New York

H. E. King, Ph.D.
University of Pittsburgh
Medical School
3811 O'Hara Street
Pittsburgh, Penna. 15213

Gerald L. Klerman, M.D.
Connecticut Mental Health Center
34 Park Street
New Haven, Conn. 06508

Hilda Knobloch, M.D.
Mt. Sinai Hospital
Fifth Avenue at 100th Street
New York, N.Y. 10029

Lawrence Kolb, Sr., M.D. (L)
6645 32nd N.W.
Washington 15, D.C.

Lawrence C. Kolb, M.D.
722 West 168th Street
New York, N.Y. 10032

Vojtech Adalbert Kral, M.D.
4145 Blueridge Crescent
Montreal 25, Canada

Morton Kramer, Sc.D.
Room 13A23, Barlow Building
National Institute of Mental Health
5454 Wisconsin Avenue
Chevy Chase, Md. 20203

Rema Lapouse, M.D.
New York Medical College
Flower & Fifth Avenue Hospitals
Fifth Avenue at 106th Street
New York, N.Y. 10029

Emma Layman, Ph.D.
403 S. Walnut Street
Mt. Pleasant, Iowa 52641

Zigmond M. Lebensohn, M.D.
2431 K St. N.W.
Suite 215
Washington 37, D.C.

Heinz E. Lehmann, M.D.
6603 LaSalle Boulevard
Montreal, Quebec, Canada

Alexander H. Leighton, M.D.
Harvard School of Public Health
55 Shattuck Street
Boston, Massachusetts

Jerome Levine, M.D.
11101 Gainsborough Road
Potomac, Md. 20854

David M. Levy, M.D.
47 East 77th Street
New York, N.Y. 10021

Aubrey J. Lewis, M.D. (H)
The Maudsley Hospital
Denmark Hill, S.E. 5
London, England

Nolan D. C. Lewis, M.D. (H)
Route 5
Frederick, Md. 21701

William T. Lhamon, M.D.
Cornell University Medical College
525 East 68th Street
New York, N.Y. 10021

W. T. Liberson, M.D., Ph.D. (L)
Chief, Physical Education and
Rehabilitation Service
V. A. Hospital
P.O. Box 28
Hines, Illinois

Ogden R. Lindsley, Ph.D.
Educational Research
University of Kansas Medical Center
Kansas City, Kansas 66103

Louis Linn, M.D.
9 East 96th Street
New York, New York

Morris Lipton, M.D.
University of North Carolina
Memorial Hospital
Chapel Hill, North Carolina

Maurice Lorr, Ph.D.
1521 Erskine Street
Takoma Park, Md. 20012

Reginald S. Lourie, M.D. (L)
Children's Hospital
Washington 9, D.C.

Hans Lowenbach, M.D.
Duke University Medical Center
Durham, N.C. 27706

Donald J. MacPherson, M.D. (L)
1101 Beacon Street
Brookline 46, Massachusetts

Sidney Malitz, M.D.
722 West 168th Street
New York, N.Y. 10032

Robert Malmo, Ph.D.
1033 Pine Avenue, West
Montreal 2, Canada

Benjamin Malzberg, Ph.D. (L)
Research Foundation for Mental
Hygiene, Inc.
240 State Street
Albany 1, New York

Arnold J. Mandell, M.D.
School of Medicine
University of California
Irvine, California

Amedeo S. Marrazzi, M.D.
Department of Pharmacology
University of Minnesota
School of Medicine
Minneapolis, Minn. 55455

Edwin E. McNiel, M.D. (L)
3875 Wilshire Boulevard
Los Angeles 5, California

Sarnoff Mednick, Ph.D.
Department of Psychology
University of Michigan
Ann Arbor, Michigan

Ronald Melzack, Ph.D.
Department of Psychology
McGill University
Montreal, Canada

William C. Menninger, M.D.† (L)
Menninger Foundation
Topeka, Kansas

Alan Miller, M.D.
Commissioner of Mental Hygiene
State of New York
Albany, New York

James G. Miller, M.D.
Mental Health Research Institute
University of Michigan
Ann Arbor, Michigan

John Money, Ph.D.
Phipps 400
The Johns Hopkins Hospital
Baltimore, Md. 21205

Thomas Verner Moore, Ph.D., M.D. (H)
Ven. P.D. Pablo Maria Moore
O. Cart.
Cartuja de Miraflores
Apartado 43
Burgos, Spain

George Mora, M.D.
6 Walnut Hill Road
Poughkeepsie, New York 12603

Robert S. Morrow, Ph.D.
16 Pietro Place
Dobbs Ferry, New York

Leon Moses, M.D.
19 East 74th Street
New York, N.Y. 10021

Hobart Mowrer, Ph.D.
445 Gregory Hall
University of Illinois
Urbana, Illinois

Harry M. Murdock, M.D. (L)
Sheppard and Enoch Pratt Hospital
Towson 4, Maryland

Henry A. Murray, M.D. (L)
48 Mount Auburn Street
Cambridge, Massachusetts

J. Martin Myers, Jr., M.D.
Institute of Pennsylvania Hospital
111 North 49th Street
Philadelphia 39, Pennsylvania

Leo P. O'Donnell, M.D. (L)
36 Elm Street
Pawling, New York

Raymond L. Osborne, M.D. (L)
140 East 54th Street
New York, N.Y. 10022

Joseph B. Parker, Jr., M.D.
University of Kentucky
Medical Center
Lexington, Kentucky

Benjamin Pasamanick, M.D.
Associate Commissioner
Department of Mental Hygiene
15 Park Row
New York, New York 10038

Grosvenor B. Pearson, M.D. (L)
3101 W. DeBazan Avenue
St. Petersburg, Beach 6, Florida

Sygmunt A. Piotrowski, Ph.D. (L)
1025 Walnut Street
Philadelphia 7, Pennsylvania

Phillip Polatin, M.D. (L)
5281 Independence Avenue
Bronx, N.Y. 10471

Max Pollack, Ph.D.
Hillside Hospital
Glen Oaks
Long Island, New York

Karl Pribram, M.D.
Department of Psychiatry
Stanford University
School of Medicine
Palo Alto, Calif. 94304

Hyman L. Rachlin, M.D. (L)
35 Park Avenue
New York, N.Y. 10016

Sandor Rado, M.D. (L)
235 East 73rd Street
New York, N.Y. 10021

John Rainer, M.D.
9 Innisfree Place
Eastchester, New York

F. C. Redlich, M.D.
333 Cedar Street
New Haven 11, Connecticut

Julius B. Richmond, M.D.
Department of Pediatrics
State University of New York
Upstate Medical Center
766 Irving Avenue
Syracuse 10, New York

David McK. Rioch, M.D. (L)
4607 Dorset Avenue
Chevy Chase 15, Maryland

Margaret Rioch, Ph.D.
4607 Dorset Avenue
Chevy Chase 15, Maryland

Eli Robins, M.D.
Department of Psychiatry
Washington University
School of Medicine
St. Louis, Mo. 63110

Fred V. Rockwell, M.D. (L)
Grasslands Hospital
Valhalla, New York

Howard P. Roffwarg, M.D., Ph.D.
Montefiore Hospital
111 East 210th Street
Bronx, N.Y. 10467

Howard P. Rome, M.D.
Mayo Clinic
Rochester, Minnesota

David Rosenthal, Ph.D.
National Institute of Mental Health
Bethesda, Md. 20014

Saul Rosenzweig, Ph.D.
Box 1150, Main Campus
Department of Psychology
Washington University
St. Louis, Mo. 63130

Mathew Ross, M.D.
333 Commonwealth Avenue
Chestnut Hill, Mass. 02167

Theodore Rothman, M.D.
9201 Sunset Boulevard #616
Los Angeles, Calif. 90069

Eli A. Rubinstein, Ph.D.
Training & Manpower Resources
National Institute of Mental Health
Bethesda, Md., 20014

Melvin Sabshin, M.D.
912 South Wood Street
Chicago, Ill. 60612

William S. Sadler, M.D. (L)
533 Diversey Parkway
Chicago, Illinois

Kurt Salzinger, Ph.D.
722 West 168th Street
New York, N.Y. 10032

George S. Saslow, M.D.
University of Oregon
Medical School
Portland 1, Oregon

Isidore W. Scherer, Ph.D.
13511 Query Mill Road
Route 3
Gaithersburg, Md. 20760

G. Wilson Shaffer, Ph.D. (L)
The Johns Hopkins University
Baltimore 18, Maryland

Charles Shagass, M.D.
Eastern Pennsylvania Psychiatric
Institute
Henry Avenue & Abbottsford Road
Philadelphia, Pa. 19129

David Shakow, Ph.D. (L)
National Institute of Mental Health
Clinical Center
Bethesda, Md. 20014

Alexander Simon, M.D. (L)
Langley Porter Clinic
San Francisco, California

Bruce R. Sloane, M.D.
Department of Psychiatry
Temple Medical School
Philadelphia, Pennsylvania

John L. Smalldon, M.D. (L)
Denver Hospital & State School
Taunton, Massachusetts

George W. Smeltz, M.D. (L)
Marlborough-Blenheim Hotel
Atlantic City, New Jersey

Lauren H. Smith, M.D. (L)
111 North 49th Street
Philadelphia, Pennsylvania

Harry C. Solomon, M.D. (L)
15 Ashburton Place
Boston, Massachusetts

Rene A. Spitz, M.D. (L)
12 Rue Robert de Traz
Geneva, Switzerland

Robert Spitzer, M.D.
722 West 168th Street
New York, N.Y. 10032

Edward J. Stainbrook, M.D.
1277 Parkview Avenue
Pasadena, Calif. 91103

Albert J. Stunkard, M.D.
University of Pennsylvania Hospital
Philadelphia, Pa. 19104

Samuel Sutton, Ph.D.
722 West 168th Street
New York, N.Y. 10032

Joseph G. Sutton, M.D. (L)
5 Roosevelt Place
Montclair, New Jersey

Hans C. Syz, M.D. (L)
The Lifwynn Foundation
52 South Morningside Drive
Westport, Connecticut

George Tarjan, M.D.
The Neuropsychiatric Institute
760 Westwood Plaza
Los Angeles, Calif. 90024

William S. Taylor, Ph.D. (L)
27 Langworthy Road
Northampton, Massachusetts

Harry A. Teitelbaum, M.D. (L)
5605 Green Spring Avenue
Baltimore 9, Maryland

William B. Terhune, M.D. (L)
Silver Hill Foundation
Box 1114
New Canaan, Connecticut

Charles B. Thompson, M.D. (L)
The Lifwynn Foundation
52 South Morningside Drive
Westport, Conn. 06880

Kenneth J. Tillotson, M.D. (L)
1265 Beacon Street
Brookline, Massachusetts

James S. Tyhurst, M.D.
University of British Columbia
Vancouver 9, British Columbia,
Canada

Vladimir G. Urse, M.D. (L)
Cook County Hospital
Polk and Wood Streets
Chicago, Ill. 60612

Roy McL. Van Wart, M.D. (L)
10431 Bellogio Road
Los Angeles 24, California

Harold M. Visotsky, M.D.
160 N. LaSalle Street
Chicago, Ill. 60601

Raymond W. Waggoner, M.D. (L)
University Hospital
1313 East Ann Street
Ann Arbor, Michigan

James Hardin Wall, M.D. (L)
121 Westchester Avenue
White Plains, New York

David Wechsler, Ph.D. (L)
Bellevue Hospital
New York, New York

Edwin A. Weinstein, M.D.
7101 Pyle Road
Bethesda, Md. 20034

Livingston Welch, Ph.D.
Hunter College
695 Park Avenue
New York, N.Y. 10021

Frederick L. Weniger, M.D. (L)
108 Franklin Road
Pittsburgh 9, Pennsylvania

Louis J. West, M.D.
University of Oklahoma
Medical Center
800 N.E. 13th Street
Oklahoma City 4, Oklahoma

Robert W. White, Ph.D.
Department of Social Relations
Harvard University
Cambridge, Massachusetts

John C. Whitehorn, M.D. (L)
210 Northfield Place
Baltimore, Maryland

Abraham Wikler, M.D.
Department of Psychiatry
University of Kentucky College
of Medicine
1241 Summit Drive
Lexington, Kentucky 40502

George B. Wilbur, M.D. (L)
Cove Road
South Dennis, Massachusetts

William Preston Wilson, M.D.
Duke University Medical Center
Durham, North Carolina

George Winokur, M.D.
Renard Hospital
4940 Audubon Avenue
St. Louis, Missouri

Richard Wittenborn, M.D.
Department of Psychiatry
Rutgers University
New Brunswick, New Jersey

Cecil L. Wittson, M.D.
9651 North 20th Street
Omaha 12, Nebraska

Joseph Wolpe, M.D.
Department of Behavioral Science
Temple Medical Center
Henry Avenue & Abbottsford Road
Philadelphia, Pa. 19129

Joseph Wortis, M.D.
Maimonides Medical Center
Community Mental Health Center
4802 Tenth Avenue
Brooklyn, N.Y. 11219

Stanley Yolles, M.D.
5206 Locust Avenue
Bethesda, Md. 20014

Eugene Ziskind, M.D.
2010 Wilshire Boulevard
Los Angeles, California 90007

Joseph Zubin, Ph.D.
722 West 168th Street
New York, N.Y. 10032

Israel Zwerling, M.D.
161 West 86th Street
New York, N.Y. 10024

Presidents

1912	Adolf Meyer	1942	Roscoe W. Hall
1913	James T. Putnam	1943	Frederick L. Wells
1914	Alfred R. Allen	1944	Frederick L. Wells
1915	Alfred R. Allen	1945	Bernard Glueck
1916	Adolf Meyer	1946	Robert P. Knight
1917	Adolf Meyer	1947	Frederick L. Wells
1918	Smith Ely Jelliffe	1948	Donald J. MacPherson
1921	William A. White	1949	Paul Hoch
1922	John T. MacCurdy	1950	William B. Terhune
1923	L. Pierce Clark	1951	Lauren H. Smith
1924	L. Pierce Clark	1952	Joseph Zubin
1925	Albert M. Barrett	1953	Clarence P. Oberndorf
1927	Sanger Brown II	1954	David McK. Rioch
1928	Ross McC. Chapman	1955	Merrill Moore
1929	Ross McC. Chapman	1956	Oskar Diethelm
1930	William Healy	1957	Howard S. Liddell
1931	William Healy	1958	Leslie B. Hohman
1932	J. Ramsey Hunt	1959	Harry C. Solomon
1933	Edward J. Kempf	1960	David Wechsler
1934	Edward J. Kempf	1961	William Horsley Gantt
1935	Nolan D. C. Lewis	1962	Lauretta Bender
1936	Nolan D. C. Lewis	1963	D. Ewen Cameron
1937	Nolan D. C. Lewis	1964	Jerome D. Frank
1938	Samuel W. Hamilton	1965	Franz J. Kallmann
1939	Abraham Myerson	1966	Seymour S. Kety
1940	Douglas A. Thom	1967	Bernard C. Glueck, Jr.
1941	Roscoe W. Hall	1968	Joel Elkes

Vice-Presidents

1924	William Healy	1931	J. Ramsay Hunt
	George H. Kirby		Herman N. Adler
1925	J. Ramsey Hunt	1933	Albert M. Barrett
	Sidney L. Schwab		Trigant Burrow
1927	Ross McC. Chapman	1934	Albert M. Barrett
	Edward J. Kempf		Trigant Burrow
1928	Edward J. Kempf	1935	J. Ramsay Hunt
	E. Stanley Abbott		Smith Ely Jelliffe
1929	Edward J. Kempf	1936	J. Ramsay Hunt
	E. Stanley Abbott		Smith Ely Jelliffe
1930	J. Ramsay Hunt	1937	Samuel W. Hamilton
	Herman N. Adler		Ray G. Hoskins

Vice-Presidents

1938	Lydiard H. Horton	1951	Harry M. Murdock
	Hans Syz		Lauretta Bender
1939	Roscoe W. Hall	1952	William Horwitz
	Douglas A. Thom		S. Bernard Wortis
1940	George S. Sprague	1953	David McK. Rioch
	Bernard Glueck		Merrill Moore
1941	Frederick L. Wells		Howard S. Liddell
	Lowell S. Selling	1955	Oskar Diethelm
1943	Frederick L. Wells		Howard S. Liddell
	Lowell S. Selling	1956	Leslie R. Hohman
1944	Lowell S. Selling	1957	David Wechsler
	Flanders Dunbar	1958	David Wechsler
1945	Thomas V. Moore	1959	Clara Thompson
	Robert P. Knight	1960	Theodora M. Abel
1946	Paul H. Hoch	1961	Donald M. Hamilton
	Thos. A. C. Rennie	1962	D. Ewen Cameron
1947	William C. Menninger	1963	Jerome D. Frank
	Ruth Benedict	1964	Franz J. Kallmann
1948	Ruth Benedict	1965	Bernard C. Glueck, Jr.
	Lauren H. Smith	1966	Joel Elkes
1949	Arthur N. Foxe	1967	Benjamin Pasamanick
	Norman Cameron	1968	Milton Greenblatt
1950	Harry M. Murdock		
	William S. Taylor		

Secretaries

1921	H. W. Frink	1940-1948	Merrill Moore
1922-1926	Sanger Brown II	1944-1951	Samuel W. Hamilton
1927-1929	Martin W. Peck	1952-1960	Donald M. Hamilton
1930-1939	L. Eugene Emerson	1961-1967	Fritz A. Freyhan
		1968	Max Fink

Treasurers

1924-1942	William C. Garvin	1952-1964	Bernard C. Glueck, Jr.
1943-1951	Joseph Zubin	1965	Howard F. Hunt
		1966-1968	Murray Glusman

Index

423

DATE DUE

MAY 25 70			
GAYLORD			PRINTED IN U.S.A.